SMALL ARMS
VISUAL ENCYCLOPEDIA

SMALL ARMS
VISUAL ENCYCLOPEDIA

MORE THAN 800 ILLUSTRATIONS

MARTIN J. DOUGHERTY

amber
BOOKS

Reprinted in 2017, 2018, 2021, 2023

Published by
Amber Books Ltd
United House
North Road
London N7 9DP
United Kingdom
www.amberbooks.co.uk
Instagram: amberbooksltd
Facebook: amberbooks
Twitter: @amberbooks
Pinterest: amberbooksltd

ISBN: 978-1-78274-485-6

Project Editor: Michael Spilling
Picture Research: Terry Forshaw
Design: Andrew Easton

Printed in China

CONTENTS

INTRODUCTION

The invention of gunpowder, or 'black powder', caused some of the most profound changes in the history of human development. Black powder artillery made castles obsolete and changed the face of naval warfare. Lighter weapons – small arms – caused equally great upheavals in personal and military combat.

This did not, however, happen overnight; the armoured horseman was not instantly chased from the battlefield by a fusillade of bullets. Early black powder weapons were unreliable and not very effective, and it was entirely possible to construct armour that would stop or deflect a matchlock musket ball. Indeed, Renaissance armour usually has proving marks where it was tested at close range against a firearm. The main attractions of firearms were their ease of use and relative cheapness. It took years of training and immense expense to equip and field a force of armoured knights, but an equivalent (if very different) amount of fighting power could be assembled in a few days if firearms were available.

Having proven their worth in combat, firearms were subject to improvement and experimentation. At first, efforts concentrated on better and more reliable ways to ignite loose gunpowder, leading to the wheel-lock and the flintlock, and eventually to the percussion cap. The development of impact-initiated explosives did away with the need to strike sparks and hope they ignited loose powder in a pan on the side of the weapon.

Crew from a British fishing trawler practise how to use early model Lee Enfield rifles, 1939.

Full Metal Jacket

Separate caps gave way to unitary cartridges, and then to all-metal cartridges. These caused a revolution in weapons development. Rather than separate bits and pieces, or a soft and fragile cardboard or cloth cartridge, everything needed to send a bullet on its way was now available in a single robust unit. It became possible to carry ammunition more easily, and to subject it to a variety of mechanical operations. The modern firearm is built around the metal cartridge. It can be moved from magazine to breech, mechanically fired, and then reliably ejected without much possibility of malfunction. It can be carried in a speedloader, charging clip or belt and fed into the weapon without coming apart. The unitary cartridge is the single factor that makes all modern firearms possible.

Types and Roles

Experience had led designers to create a number of distinct weapon types, and most firearms fall clearly into one category or another. However, some do cross the boundaries, such as fully automatic pistols. Are these sub-machine guns or handguns? And what of a weapon marketed as a sub-machine gun but which fires rifle-calibre ammunition? Categorizing some weapons can be problematical.

However, what is more obvious is a weapon's role. Few people would choose to be armed only with a handgun in a major battle, but handguns are an excellent choice as backup weapons or to be carried when trouble is not expected, just in case. Conversely, a sub-machine gun is probably not a good choice for hunting small birds.

Successful weapon designs are normally aimed at a specific role, or a broader range of roles that require similar characteristics. It is possible for two very different weapons to meet the same tactical needs; meeting those needs well is far more important than the way in which they are met.

Thus improvement and innovation continue, with new concepts introduced and old ones revisited. Possibly, a new development as profound as the advent of black powder or the unitary cartridge is overdue, and the firearms of the future may be quite different to those of today.

Armed with an M107 (M82A1 Barrett) anti-materiel rifle, a US Army sniper team watch for enemy activity in Afghanistan, 2009.

EARLY FIREARMS

Gunpowder weapons were first developed in Ancient China. Experimentation showed that putting a few small stones in a tube helped form an effective flame jet, and this in turn led to the discovery that the pebbles were an effective weapon at greater range than the flames.

From the sixteenth century, firearms rapidly came to dominate the battlefields of Europe, and rather than supporting troops equipped with hand-to-hand weapons, they became the main armament of armies. However, these early firearms were not especially reliable and took a long time to reload.

Left: American militia take on Native American tribesmen in a scene from an early nineteenth-century illustration. The Native Americans proved to be expert shots with muskets.

Medieval Handguns

The earliest European small arms were 'hand-cannon' or 'handguns'; essentially a very short smoothbore tube mounted on a haft. The projectile was heavy enough to be lethal at short range, but extremely inaccurate. This was partially due to the fact that everything about the handgun was imprecise.

The projectile fitted loosely inside a short barrel which was unlikely to be finely made and might be significantly bent. A quantity of gunpowder was poured into the barrel before loading the ball, but the actual amount could vary considerably, as could the quality and thus its explosive force.

BARREL
The barrel was short and had no form of aiming device fitted; sights would have been meaningless on such a crude weapon.

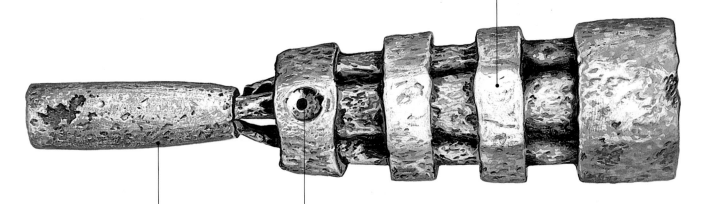

HAFT
The weapon was mounted on a simple pole, with no handgrip or shoulder stock.

VENT
Firing was accomplished by touching a slow-match to the vent, an unreliable process at best.

SPECIFICATIONS	
Country of Origin:	Kingdom of Hungary
Date:	1400
Calibre:	18mm (.71in)
Operation:	Gunpowder
Weight:	3.6kg (7.9lb)
Overall Length:	1.2m (48in)
Barrel Length:	600mm (24in)
Muzzle Velocity:	91m/sec (300ft/sec)
Feed/Magazine:	One shot
Range:	7m (23ft)

The weapon was aimed in the manner of pointing a stick, and a stick with a heavy weight on the end at that, and fired by touching a slow-match to a vent. This might be done by the man holding the weapon, in which case it had to be supported on a branch or other rest, or by another gunner. Neither approach was conducive to any sort of accuracy.

Various fairly basic designs were used, ranging from a simple iron tube mounted on a wooden handle (or tiller) to weapons recognizable as the forerunners of modern rifles. The hook under the barrel was used to steady the weapon for firing. It was rested on a fortification or supporting trestle and pulled back until the hook gripped the outer edge of the support. Handguns were more use in a siege than in open warfare, as they required significant time to reload, leaving the user vulnerable to enemy troops who might close and attack him.

SIMPLE HANDGUN

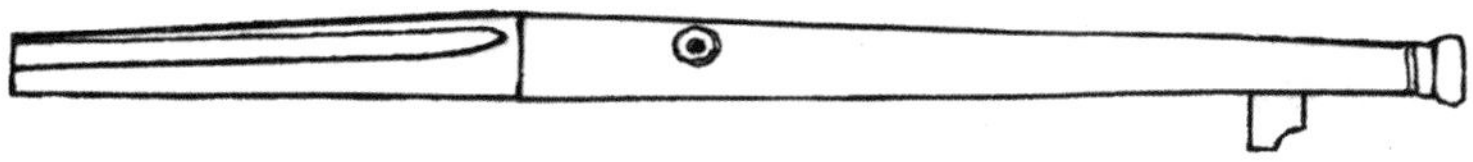

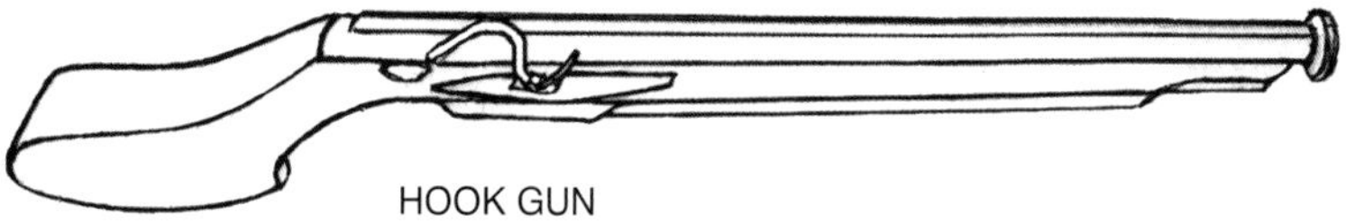

HOOK GUN

EARLY ARQUEBUS

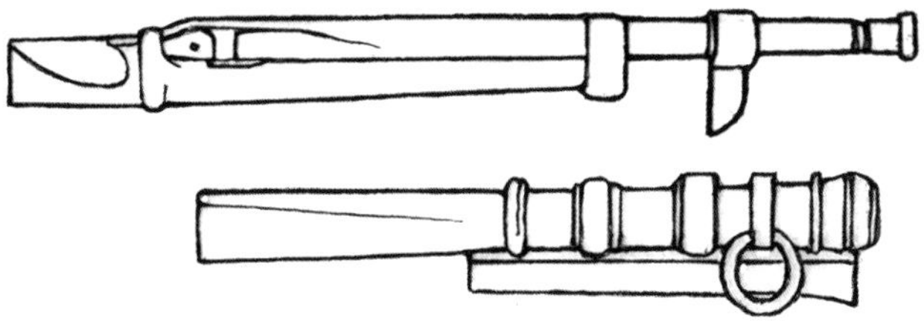

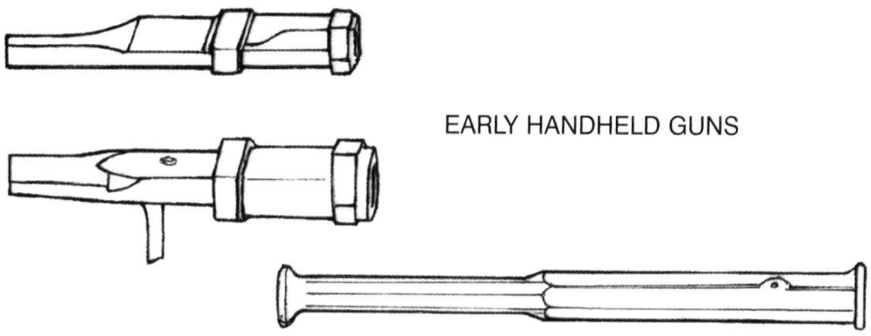

EARLY HANDHELD GUNS

This Hussite infantryman from 1420 is armed with a 'hand-gonne', one of the earliest of all firearms. This weapon consisted of a simple tube with a touch-hole near the closed end, mounted on a short wooden stave. It was loaded by pouring gunpowder into the bore and placing the projectile on top. The powder charge was ignited by a slow-match and the resulting explosion pushed the projectile out of the muzzle. Range was short and accuracy lamentable, and the time taken to reload was much longer than that required by an archer.

Early Black Powder Weapons

The main benefit of early gunpowder weapons was that they required little training to use. Thus a large army could be quickly raised at need, without having to maintain expensive training programmes or standing forces.

Early Matchlock

The matchlock was essentially a device to hold a slow-match and bring it to the firing vent. There was a significant delay while this happened, called 'lock time', which affected the accuracy of an already imprecise weapon.

SPECIFICATIONS	
Country of Origin:	Germany
Date:	1450
Calibre:	10.9mm (.42in)
Operation:	Matchlock – Serpentine mechanism
Weight:	4.1kg (9lb)
Overall Length:	1.2m (48in)
Barrel Length:	800mm (32in)
Muzzle Velocity:	137m/sec (450ft/sec)
Feed/Magazine:	Single shot
Range:	45.7m (150ft)

Serpentine Mechanism

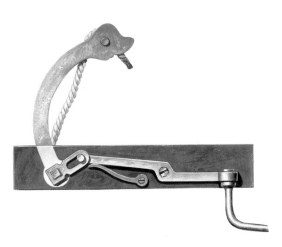

The 'serpentine' was a curved lever with a pivot on one end, which held the slow-match and moved it into contact with the firing vent. An incorrectly positioned slow-match would not ignite the powder.

SPECIFICATIONS	
Country of Origin:	Germany
Date:	1450
Calibre:	10.9mm (.42in)
Operation:	Matchlock – Serpentine mechanism
Weight:	4.1kg (9lb)
Overall Length:	1.2m (48in)
Barrel Length:	800mm (32in)
Muzzle Velocity:	137m/sec (450ft/sec)
Feed/Magazine:	Single shot
Range:	45.7m (150ft)

TIMELINE

 1450   1550

Wheel-lock

The wheel-lock did away with the cumbersome slow-match and instead ignited the weapon's gunpowder by means of a rotating wheel striking sparks against a piece of iron pyrites.

SPECIFICATIONS	
Country of Origin:	Italy
Date:	1550
Calibre:	10.9mm (.42in)
Operation:	Wheel-lock
Weight:	1.02kg (2.25lb)
Overall Length:	394mm (15.5in)
Barrel Length:	292mm (11.5in)
Muzzle Velocity:	122m/sec (400ft/sec)
Feed/Magazine:	Single shot
Range:	9.1m (30ft)

English Doglock

The doglock was an early form of flintlock, with a spring-loaded lever that snapped flint or iron pyrites against a plate called a 'frizzen' to create sparks. The 'dog' was a catch that held the weapon safely at half-cock.

SPECIFICATIONS	
Country of Origin:	England
Date:	1650
Calibre:	10.9mm (.42in)
Operation:	Flintlock
Weight:	1.02kg (2.25lb)
Overall Length:	394mm (15.5in)
Barrel Length:	292mm (11.5in)
Muzzle Velocity:	122m/sec (400ft/sec)
Feed/Magazine:	Single shot
Range:	9.1m (30ft)

Joseph Manton Model

Joseph Manton created a number of innovative weapons, though legal disputes and rival inventions, such as the percussion cap, eventually caused his firm to go bankrupt. His duelling pistols were of especially fine quality.

SPECIFICATIONS	
Country of Origin:	United Kingdom
Date:	1810
Calibre:	12.7mm (.5in)
Operation:	Flintlock
Weight:	1.13kg (2.5lb)
Overall Length:	375mm (14.75in)
Barrel Length:	254mm (10in)
Muzzle Velocity:	168m/sec (550ft/sec)
Feed/Magazine:	Single shot
Range:	9.1m (30ft)

1650

1810

Flintlock Pistols

The effective range of a flintlock pistol was extremely short and these weapons were not very reliable. However, despite these drawbacks they became popular as self-defence weapons or for use at close quarters by cavalry.

Dutch Snaphance

Early flintlock pistols were clumsy and inelegant, and somewhat difficult to carry about the user's person. They were useful weapons for cavalrymen, however, who might carry two, four or even more loaded pistols into action.

SPECIFICATIONS	
Country of Origin:	Netherlands
Date:	1650
Calibre:	17.1mm (.675in)
Operation:	Flintlock
Weight:	1.67kg (3.7lb)
Overall Length:	400mm (15.75in)
Barrel Length:	208mm (8.2in)
Muzzle Velocity:	137m/sec (450ft/sec)
Feed/Magazine:	Single shot
Range:	15m (49ft)

Improved Flintlocks

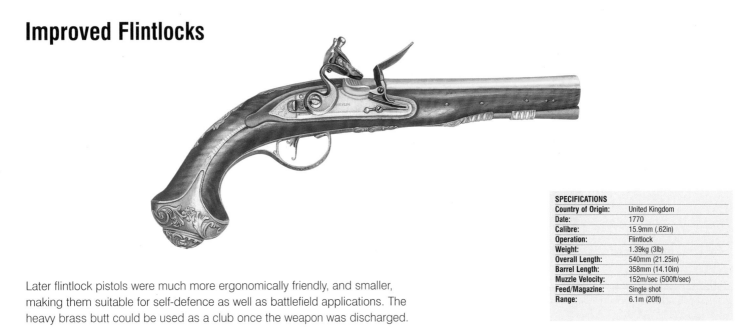

Later flintlock pistols were much more ergonomically friendly, and smaller, making them suitable for self-defence as well as battlefield applications. The heavy brass butt could be used as a club once the weapon was discharged.

SPECIFICATIONS	
Country of Origin:	United Kingdom
Date:	1770
Calibre:	15.9mm (.62in)
Operation:	Flintlock
Weight:	1.39kg (3lb)
Overall Length:	540mm (21.25in)
Barrel Length:	358mm (14.10in)
Muzzle Velocity:	152m/sec (500ft/sec)
Feed/Magazine:	Single shot
Range:	6.1m (20ft)

TIMELINE

1650

1770

Scottish All-Steel Pistol

Most pistols were primarily of wooden construction, with a metal barrel, lock and trigger mechanism. However, there was no reason why a weapon could not be made entirely of steel, a practice which became more common as time passed.

Long-Barrelled Pistols

Longer-barrelled pistols were favoured by cavalrymen, and also often for use at sea. The longer barrel gave a slight improvement in accuracy and range, but these weapons were never more than marginally effective.

SPECIFICATIONS	
Country of Origin:	United States
Date:	1805
Calibre:	15.9mm (.62in)
Operation:	Flintlock
Weight:	1.42kg (3.1lb)
Overall Length:	552mm (21.75in)
Barrel Length:	368mm (14.48in)
Muzzle Velocity:	152m/sec (500ft/sec)
Feed/Magazine:	Single shot
Range:	6.1m (20ft)

Kentucky Pistol

The 'Kentucky' pistol was a general type produced by American gunsmiths. Its reputation for accuracy owed as much to its users' hunting skills as to its own qualities.

SPECIFICATIONS	
Country of Origin:	United States
Date:	1805
Calibre:	15.9mm (.62in)
Operation:	Flintlock
Weight:	1.39kg (3lb)
Overall Length:	540mm (21.25in)
Barrel Length:	358mm (14.1in)
Muzzle Velocity:	152m/sec (500ft/sec)
Feed/Magazine:	Single shot
Range:	15m (49ft)

Specialist Flintlocks

A range of specialist designs were marketed to fit a variety of needs, from emergency self-defence to formal duelling. Not all of the experimental models were successful; many apparently workable concepts faded away as nothing more than novelties.

Flintlock Revolver

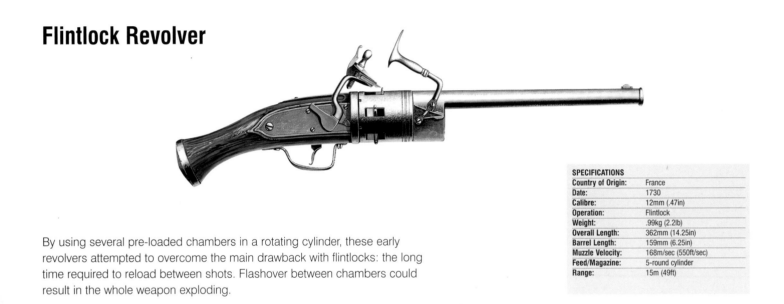

By using several pre-loaded chambers in a rotating cylinder, these early revolvers attempted to overcome the main drawback with flintlocks: the long time required to reload between shots. Flashover between chambers could result in the whole weapon exploding.

SPECIFICATIONS	
Country of Origin:	France
Date:	1730
Calibre:	12mm (.47in)
Operation:	Flintlock
Weight:	.99kg (2.2lb)
Overall Length:	362mm (14.25in)
Barrel Length:	159mm (6.25in)
Muzzle Velocity:	168m/sec (550ft/sec)
Feed/Magazine:	5-round cylinder
Range:	15m (49ft)

Queen Anne Pistol

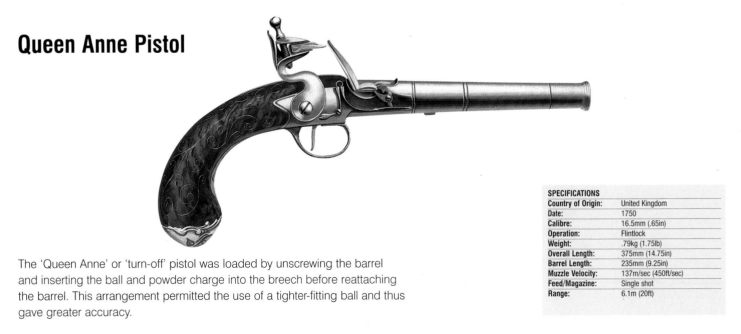

The 'Queen Anne' or 'turn-off' pistol was loaded by unscrewing the barrel and inserting the ball and powder charge into the breech before reattaching the barrel. This arrangement permitted the use of a tighter-fitting ball and thus gave greater accuracy.

SPECIFICATIONS	
Country of Origin:	United Kingdom
Date:	1750
Calibre:	16.5mm (.65in)
Operation:	Flintlock
Weight:	.79kg (1.75lb)
Overall Length:	375mm (14.75in)
Barrel Length:	235mm (9.25in)
Muzzle Velocity:	137m/sec (450ft/sec)
Feed/Magazine:	Single shot
Range:	6.1m (20ft)

TIMELINE   1730   1750   1760

Duelling Pistols

Although any weapon firing a loose-fitting ball from a smooth barrel is inherently imprecise, duelling pistols were capable of reasonable accuracy and were designed to be instinctively 'pointable', to enable a fast shot with a reasonable chance of a hit.

SPECIFICATIONS	
Country of Origin:	France
Date:	1760
Calibre:	15.9mm (.62in)
Operation:	Flintlock
Weight:	1.39kg (3lb)
Overall Length:	540mm (21.25in)
Barrel Length:	358mm (14.1in)
Muzzle Velocity:	152m/sec (500ft/sec)
Feed/Magazine:	Single shot
Range:	9.1m (30ft)

Blunderbuss Pistol

Wide-mouthed 'blunderbuss' firearms were designed to be quickly loaded with loose projectiles in the manner of a shotgun. The spread of shot increased the chance of a hit, making them effective close-range defensive weapons and also serving as a deterrent.

SPECIFICATIONS	
Country of Origin:	United Kingdom
Date:	1780
Calibre:	16.5mm (.65in)
Operation:	Flintlock
Weight:	1.3kg (2.9lb)
Overall Length:	444mm (17.49in)
Barrel Length:	229mm (9in)
Muzzle Velocity:	152m/sec (500ft/sec)
Feed/Magazine:	Buckshot
Range:	3m (10ft)

Pocket Pistol

Pocket pistols were simply small, short-barrelled weapons designed to be carried in a pocket for self-defence. The flintlock mechanism made such a weapon possible, as it could be carried ready to be quickly cocked and fired.

SPECIFICATIONS	
Country of Origin:	United States
Date:	1795
Calibre:	12.7mm (.5in)
Operation:	Flintlock
Weight:	.34kg (.75lb)
Overall Length:	168mm (6.62in)
Barrel Length:	76mm (3in)
Muzzle Velocity:	107m/sec (350ft/sec)
Feed/Magazine:	Single shot
Range:	1.5m (5ft)

1780

1795

Duck Foot Pistol

A loaded flintlock might serve as a deterrent to one or two people, if neither was willing to take the risk of being the first to attack and thus draw a shot. For someone facing a mob, such as a naval officer dealing with mutineers, a single shot might not be an adequate deterrent.

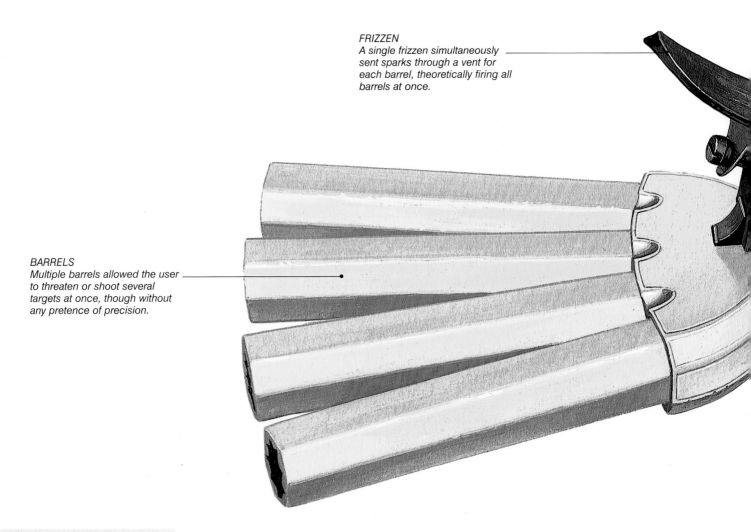

FRIZZEN
A single frizzen simultaneously sent sparks through a vent for each barrel, theoretically firing all barrels at once.

BARRELS
Multiple barrels allowed the user to threaten or shoot several targets at once, though without any pretence of precision.

SPECIFICATIONS	
Country of Origin:	United Kingdom
Date:	1800
Calibre:	15.9mm (.62in)
Operation:	Flintlock, four barrels
Weight:	1.2kg (2.6lb)
Overall Length:	254mm (10in)
Barrel Length:	127mm (5in)
Muzzle Velocity:	152m/sec (500ft/sec)
Feed/Magazine:	Single shot
Range:	6.1m (20ft)

The 'Duck Foot' pistol was obviously named for its splayed barrels, and could threaten several members of a mob at once. Assuming the weapon went off (which was never guaranteed with flintlocks), it was certain that some members of the mob would be hit, and difficult to predict exactly who.

As with other flintlocks, once it was discharged a 'Duck Foot' pistol was virtually useless, and it was unlikely to stop an entire crowd. Thus it was very much a deterrent rather than a serious combat weapon.

LOCK
The flintlock mechanism was notoriously unreliable, and it was not guaranteed that all (or indeed any) barrels would fire.

GRIP
While some pistols had a brass-reinforced butt for use as a club, the 'Duck Foot' pistol was too clumsy for use as a hand-to-hand weapon.

TRIGGER
Flintlock weapons always had a delay between pulling the trigger and firing (known as lock time). With multiple barrels, the delay might be different for each, creating an even more random spread of shot.

Black Powder Muskets

The flintlock musket became the standard infantry weapon for many decades, with several nations evolving roughly comparable designs. A musket shot had a reasonable chance of hitting a man-sized target at 80–100m (262–328ft), but virtually no chance at 200m (656ft).

Charleville Musket

The French Army adopted a slightly smaller calibre musket than the British, which progressed through a series of models from 1717 to the mid-1830s. The weapon's popular name derives from the Charleville armoury, one of several manufacturing sites.

SPECIFICATIONS	
Country of Origin:	France
Date:	1717
Calibre:	17mm (.67in) musket ball
Operation:	Flintlock
Weight:	4.5kg (10lb)
Overall Length:	1524mm (60in)
Barrel Length:	1168mm (46in)
Muzzle Velocity:	Variable
Feed/Magazine:	Single shot, muzzle loader
Range:	50–75m (164–246ft) effective; 100–200m (328–656ft) max

Long Land Pattern 'Brown Bess'

Nicknamed the 'Brown Bess', the Long Land Pattern musket was in service for most of the 1700s. A shorter version (the Short Land Pattern) supplemented but did not replace it.

SPECIFICATIONS	
Country of Origin:	United Kingdom
Date:	1722
Calibre:	18mm (.71in) lead ball
Operation:	Flintlock
Weight:	4.7kg (10.4lb)
Overall Length:	1590mm (62.5in)
Barrel Length:	1200mm (46in)
Muzzle Velocity:	Variable
Feed/Magazine:	Single shot, muzzle loader
Range:	Variable (50–100m/164–328ft)

TIMELINE

1717

1722

Model 1795 Musket

An American-made weapon derived from the French Charleville musket and firing the same 17mm (.67in) round, the Model 1795 was still available at the outbreak of the American Civil War and was issued to some troops.

SPECIFICATIONS	
Country of Origin:	United States
Date:	1795
Calibre:	17mm (.67in) musket ball
Operation:	Flintlock
Weight:	4.42kg (10lbs)
Overall Length:	1524mm (60in)
Barrel Length:	1066mm (42in)
Muzzle Velocity:	Variable
Feed/Magazine:	Single shot, muzzle loader
Range:	Variable (50–100m/164–328ft)

Jezail

Jezails were home-made flintlock weapons, usually but not always smoothbores, used by Afghan tribesmen. Many jezails used locks scavenged from the muskets of European casualties. On average the jezail had a longer accurate range than a musket.

SPECIFICATIONS	
Country of Origin:	Afghanistan
Date:	1797
Calibre:	Variable
Operation:	Flintlock
Weight:	5.4–6.4kg (12–14lb)
Overall Length:	Variable
Barrel Length:	Variable
Muzzle Velocity:	Variable
Feed/Magazine:	Single shot, muzzle loader
Range:	150m (492ft)

India Pattern Musket

At the end of the eighteenth century the British Army adopted the 'India Pattern' musket, which had been developed by the East India Company. Some light infantry and Guards units received the New Land Pattern musket instead.

SPECIFICATIONS	
Country of Origin:	United Kingdom
Date:	1797
Calibre:	18mm (.71in) lead ball
Operation:	Flintlock
Weight:	4.39kg (9.68lb)
Overall Length:	1403mm (55.25in)
Barrel Length:	990mm (39in)
Muzzle Velocity:	Variable
Feed/Magazine:	Single shot, muzzle loader
Range:	Variable (50–100m/164–328ft)

1795   1797

Nock Volley Gun

The Volley Gun was created for the Royal Navy as a means of delivering devastating firepower during a boarding action. It consisted of six outer barrels around a central one, with a single lock firing all seven at once.

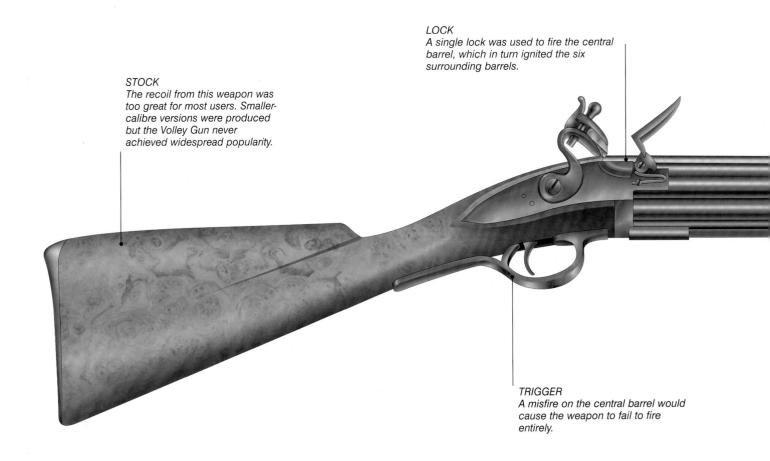

LOCK
A single lock was used to fire the central barrel, which in turn ignited the six surrounding barrels.

STOCK
The recoil from this weapon was too great for most users. Smaller-calibre versions were produced but the Volley Gun never achieved widespread popularity.

TRIGGER
A misfire on the central barrel would cause the weapon to fail to fire entirely.

SPECIFICATIONS	
Country of Origin:	United Kingdom
Date:	1779
Calibre:	13.2mm (.52in)
Operation:	Flintlock, seven barrels
Weight:	Not known
Overall Length:	Not known
Barrel Length:	510mm (20in)
Muzzle Velocity:	Variable
Feed/Magazine:	Single shot, muzzle loader
Rate of fire:	7 rounds per discharge, reloading rate variable
Range:	30m (95ft)

The Volley Gun was heavy and bulky, and was suitable only for use from a fixed position such as a warship's fighting top. Fired from here, its discharge posed a fire hazard to the ship's own rigging. It was used in action, notably during the Relief of Gibraltar in 1782, but never became popular.

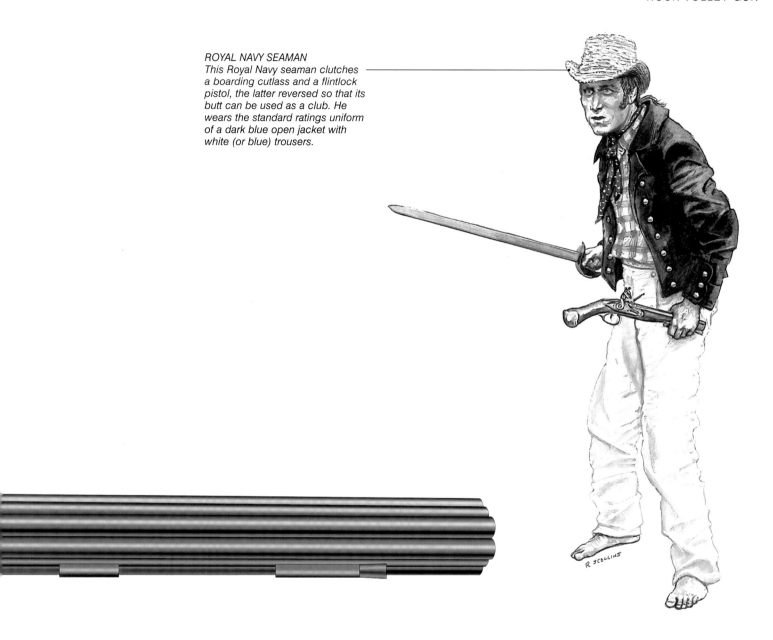

ROYAL NAVY SEAMAN
This Royal Navy seaman clutches a boarding cutlass and a flintlock pistol, the latter reversed so that its butt can be used as a club. He wears the standard ratings uniform of a dark blue open jacket with white (or blue) trousers.

The main problem with the Volley Gun was its immense recoil. The force of all seven barrels firing at once was too much for the user to cope with, and frequently caused injuries. A lighter variant was offered, but never achieved much success.

Black Powder Rifles

Although most black powder weapons (i.e. weapons that used loose gunpowder) were smoothbore pistols and muskets, some were rifled to increase range and accuracy. This also resulted in a longer loading time, so rifles were not standard issue to infantry.

Kentucky Rifle

The long Kentucky Rifle was primarily a hunting weapon, and proved well suited to skirmishing tactics in the hands of skilled marksmen. It took a long time to load, however, and was not an ideal weapon for massed infantry.

SPECIFICATIONS	
Country of Origin:	United States
Date:	1725
Calibre:	10mm (.4in)
Operation:	Flintlock
Weight:	3.3kg (7.2lb)
Overall Length:	1300mm (51in)
Barrel Length:	903mm (35.5in)
Muzzle Velocity:	350m/sec (1148ft/sec)
Feed/Magazine:	Single shot, muzzle loader
Range:	Variable (50–100m/164–328ft); 200m (656ft) by an experienced marksman

Ferguson Rifle

The Ferguson Rifle was an attempt to make rifles a viable weapon for 'line' infantry by reducing the loading time. These experimental breech-loading weapons proved useful in the colonial skirmishes of the 1760s and 1770s, but were not adopted for general issue.

SPECIFICATIONS	
Country of Origin:	United Kingdom
Date:	1776
Calibre:	16.5mm (.65in)
Operation:	Flintlock
Weight:	3.4kg (7.5lb)
Overall Length:	1270mm (50in)
Barrel Length:	Not known
Muzzle Velocity:	Not known
Feed/Magazine:	Single shot, breech loader
Range:	Variable; effective range 50–100m (164–328ft)

TIMELINE   1725   1776   1801

Baker Rifle

The Baker Rifle was shorter and of smaller calibre than the standard British Army musket, but more accurate and lethal, and much slower to load. It was issued to specialist troops, serving from 1800 to almost 1840.

SPECIFICATIONS	
Country of Origin:	United Kingdom
Date:	1801
Calibre:	15.88mm (.625in)
Operation:	Flintlock
Weight:	4.1kg (9lb)
Overall Length:	1156mm (45in)
Barrel Length:	762mm (30in)
Muzzle Velocity:	305m/sec (1000ft/sec)
Feed/Magazine:	Single shot
Range:	Variable (50–100m/164–328ft); reports of up to 600m (2000ft)

Brunswick Rifle

Developed in the 1830s, the Brunswick Rifle used black powder propellant which was ignited by a percussion cap containing fulminate of mercury. This detonated when struck by the hammer, and fired the weapon more reliably than a flintlock action.

SPECIFICATIONS	
Country of Origin:	United Kingdom
Date:	1836
Calibre:	17.88mm (.704in)
Operation:	Percussion
Weight:	4.1kg (9lb)
Overall Length:	1168mm (46in)
Barrel Length:	762mm (30in)
Muzzle Velocity:	305m/sec (1000ft/sec)
Feed/Magazine:	Single shot, muzzle loader
Range:	Variable; effective range 50–100m (164–328ft)

Enfield 1853

The Enfield 1853 Rifle-Musket was a percussion-fired muzzle loader of smaller calibre than the muskets it replaced. Its Minie-type bullet expanded under the pressure of firing, creating a seal in the barrel to allow much greater muzzle velocity than a smoothbore.

SPECIFICATIONS	
Country of Origin:	United Kingdom
Date:	1853
Calibre:	14.65mm (.577in)
Operation:	Percussion
Weight:	3.9kg (8.7lb)
Overall Length:	1397mm (55in)
Barrel Length:	991mm (39in)
Muzzle Velocity:	265m/sec (870ft/sec)
Feed/Magazine:	Single shot, muzzle loader
Range:	Variable; effective range 50–100m (164–328ft)

1836

1853

From Flintlock to Percussion: Springfield M1855 and M1863

The intermediate step between flintlock black powder weapons and unitary cartridge firearms was the introduction of percussion cap ignition. A percussion cap contained a small quantity of sufficiently unstable explosives that it would detonate when struck hard. The propellant for a percussion weapon was still the same black powder as before, usually poured loose into the barrel and topped with ball and wad as previously.

CAP
The M1855 used a tape primer system rather than individual percussion caps. The tape was automatically advanced to place an unfired cap over the vent each time the hammer was cocked.

HAMMER
The spring-loaded hammer mechanism was cocked and dropped in the same manner as a flintlock, the only real difference being that instead of scraping down a frizzen plate the hammer landed squarely on a percussion cap.

CHAMBER
The main charge was unchanged from the days of flintlock weapons, consisting of loose black powder held in place by the ball and a paper wad.

SPECIFICATIONS	
Country of Origin:	United States
Date:	1855
Calibre:	15mm (.58in)
Operation:	Percussion tape primer
Weight:	4.1kg (9lb)
Overall Length:	1400mm (56in)
Barrel Length:	1000mm (40in)
Muzzle Velocity:	300–370m/sec (1000–1200 ft/sec)
Feed/Magazine:	Single shot, muzzle loader
Range:	180–270m (590–886ft)

Rifle-muskets used a Minié bullet, a conical projectile with a hollow base which would temporarily expand under the pressure of propellant gases, making a tight seal in the barrel and enabling the weapon's rifling to spin the bullet for greater range and accuracy. However, many percussion weapons were still smoothbores firing a traditional loose ball.

The lock mechanism was easy to convert; instead of scraping a flint along a metal plate, the mechanism dropped a hammer to strike the nipple upon which a cap was placed. A vent under the nipple transmitted the cap's explosion into the main propellant, fulfilling the same function as priming powder in the pan but with far greater efficiency.

MUZZLE
Muzzle-loading still required powder to be poured in, then ball and wad to be rammed home. This normally required the shooter to be standing upright.

BARREL
Once the Minié ball was introduced, most percussion weapons were rifle-muskets rather than smoothbores.

This Confederate infantryman is armed with a Springfield M1855. Problems with uniform supply in the Confederate Army meant that soldiers wore whatever was available, and home-dyed 'butternut' jackets and trousers, as seen here, became characteristic items rather than traditional Confederate grey. The lack of standardization frequently caused confusion on the battlefield.

SPECIFICATIONS	
Country of Origin:	United States
Date:	1863
Calibre:	15mm (.58in)
Operation:	Percussion cap
Weight:	4.1kg (9lb)
Overall Length:	1400mm (56in)
Barrel Length:	1000mm (40in)
Muzzle Velocity:	300–370m/sec (1000–1200 ft/sec)
Feed/Magazine:	Muzzle-loaded
Range:	91–370m (100–400 yds)

The Model 1863 (above) was only a minor improvement over the Springfield Model 1861. The Model 1861, with all of its variants, was the most commonly used musket in the American Civil War, with over 700,000 manufactured. Due to its unreliability, the US Ordnance Department abandoned the Maynard tape primer, and the 1863 Model includes the standard percussion lock.

James Puckle Gun

Boarding actions were a common feature of naval combat in the 1700s, and much thought was given to how best to repel boarders. A combination of musket fire from the decks and sharpshooters in the rigging, along with a stout defence with cutlasses, axes and boarding pikes, was the usual method.

In 1718, James Puckle demonstrated a weapon intended to increase the firepower of a crew attempting to resist a boarding action. It was effectively a large black-powder revolver, fed by an 11-shot cylinder and firing through a single barrel. The Puckle Gun used standard ammunition or square bullets, which supposedly caused more serious wounds. The latter were reserved for use against non-Christian enemies.

The Puckle Gun was an interesting concept but suffered from overcomplexity. It was too difficult to manufacture and thus failed to attract sufficient investment or much market interest. A potentially revolutionary weapon had it overcome its technical difficulties, the Puckle Gun was an idea that was too far ahead of its time to be workable.

SPECIFICATIONS	
Country of Origin:	United Kingdom
Date:	1718
Calibre:	32mm (1.25in)
Operation:	Flintlock
Weight:	50kg (120lb)
Overall Length:	1168mm (46in)
Barrel Length:	910mm (35.8in)
Muzzle Velocity:	120m/sec (395ft/sec)
Feed/Magazine:	11-round revolving cylinder
Range:	120m (395ft)

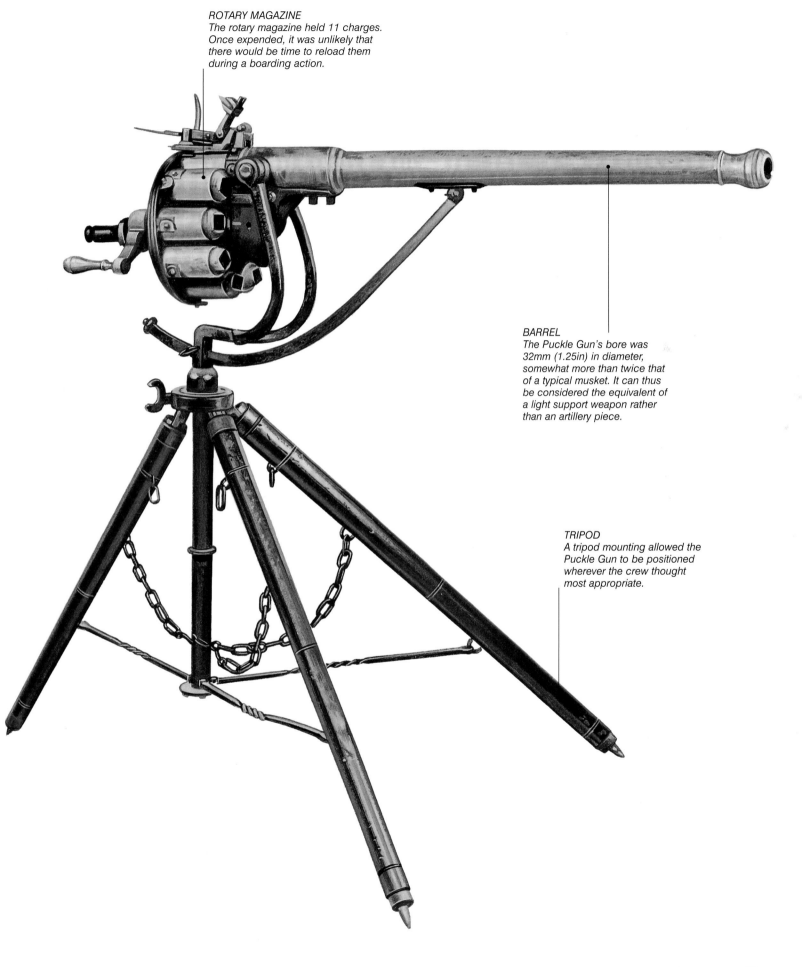

ROTARY MAGAZINE
The rotary magazine held 11 charges.
Once expended, it was unlikely that
there would be time to reload them
during a boarding action.

BARREL
The Puckle Gun's bore was
32mm (1.25in) in diameter,
somewhat more than twice that
of a typical musket. It can thus
be considered the equivalent of
a light support weapon rather
than an artillery piece.

TRIPOD
A tripod mounting allowed the
Puckle Gun to be positioned
wherever the crew thought
most appropriate.

THE RISE OF REPEATING FIREARMS

The ability to take more than one shot before reloading is an enormous asset in both self-defence and battlefield combat. Not every shot hits its target, and of those that do, some will not disable the enemy.

The answer was to create a weapon that could carry more than one projectile ready to fire, and revolver-type weapons became common. A revolver cylinder held each round in what was effectively its own breech, revolving to move each into position to be fired. Each chamber could be loaded with powder and a ball held fast with a paper wad; a percussion cap was placed on the rear of the chamber.

Left: Massed infantry exchange volleys at the Battle of Antietam, 17 September 1862. The American Civil War was the first time men were killed on an industrial scale using repeater weaponry.

Percussion Cap Pistol Designs

One key step along the way to effective repeating firearms was the creation of a reliable firing mechanism to replace the clumsy flintlocks of earlier weapons. The percussion cap was the invention that made this possible, though at first its potential was not entirely realized.

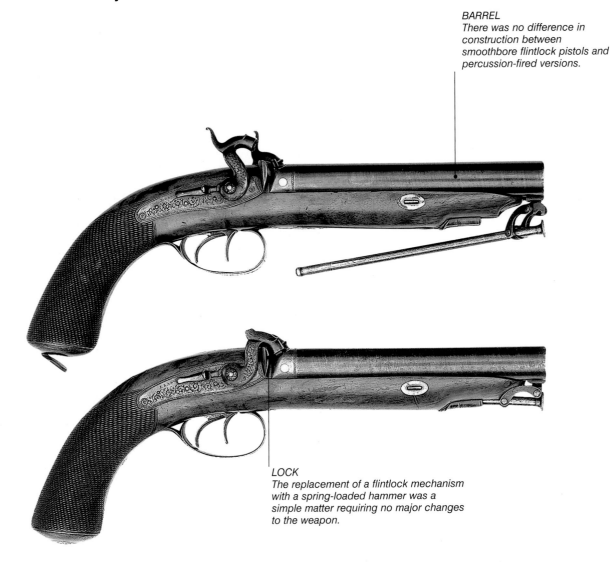

BARREL
There was no difference in construction between smoothbore flintlock pistols and percussion-fired versions.

LOCK
The replacement of a flintlock mechanism with a spring-loaded hammer was a simple matter requiring no major changes to the weapon.

SPECIFICATIONS	
Country of Origin:	United Kingdom
Date:	1820
Calibre:	12.7mm (.5in)
Operation:	Percussion cap
Weight:	1kg (2.2lb)
Overall Length:	Not known
Barrel Length:	177mm (7in)
Muzzle Velocity:	Not known
Feed/Magazine:	Single shot, muzzle loader
Range:	10m (32.8ft)

The first percussion weapons simply replaced the flintlock with a hammer which fell on a cap. The flash from the cap entered the weapon through the vent in exactly the same way as before, though now ignition was more reliable; there was less chance of a 'flash in the pan' where priming powder burned without igniting the main charge.

Many flintlocks were converted to percussion weapons and this did mark a real improvement. However, it was not until a method of presenting the powder charge and its associated percussion cap to the firing mechanism as a single unit that repeating guns became possible.

HAMMER
As on this four-barrelled turnover pistol, relocating the cap from its position on the vent allowed each barrel to be primed with its own cap, though this did increase the risk of a gang-fire.

BARRELS
The hammer mechanism was well suited to multiple barrel weapons (as on this over-and-under pistol), with a new barrel turned to present its associated cap to the hammer after each shot.

The First Repeaters

The earliest repeating handguns were for the most part clumsy affairs which were inconvenient to carry and prone to malfunction. However, repeat-fire capability was sufficiently attractive that experimentation continued despite the relatively poor results.

Lorenzoni Repeater

This ingenious weapon used gravity to self-reload. Rotating the breech-block brought it into line with a compartment containing powder, then one containing balls, which fell into the breech in turn. Realigning the breech block primed and cocked the pistol.

SPECIFICATIONS	
Country of Origin:	Italy
Date:	1680
Calibre:	12.7mm (.5in)
Operation:	Flintlock
Weight:	1.76kg (3.875lb)
Overall Length:	483mm (19in)
Barrel Length:	257mm (10.12in)
Muzzle Velocity:	152m/sec (500ft/sec)
Feed/Magazine:	7 rounds, gravity feed
Range:	10m (32.8ft)

Converted Flintlock

The replacement of the flintlock mechanism by the more reliable percussion cap system led to a gradual evolution in weapon design. However, external application of a small cap was a dangerously fiddly business in the middle of a fight.

SPECIFICATIONS	
Country of Origin:	United Kingdom
Date:	1825
Calibre:	Not known
Operation:	Percussion cap
Weight:	1kg (2.2lb)
Overall Length:	323mm (12.75in)
Barrel Length:	Not known
Muzzle Velocity:	Not known
Feed/Magazine:	Single shot, muzzle loader
Range:	10m (32.8ft)

TIMELINE

1680

1825

Percussion Pistol (John Manton Model)

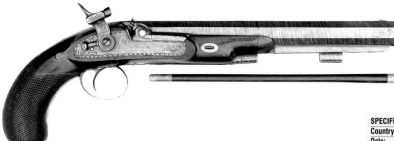

Single-shot percussion pistols demonstrated the usefulness of the percussion cap, and paved the way for a new generation of repeating weapons.

SPECIFICATIONS	
Country of Origin:	United Kingdom
Date:	1828
Calibre:	12.7mm (.5in)
Operation:	Percussion cap
Weight:	1kg (2.2lb)
Overall Length:	Not known
Barrel Length:	111mm (4.37in)
Muzzle Velocity:	Not known
Feed/Magazine:	Single shot, muzzle loader
Range:	10m (32.8ft)

Pepperbox Revolvers

'Pepperbox' revolvers were named for their resemblance to a pepper grinder. The whole multi-barrel assembly was rotated to bring a loaded barrel into line with the action. Each barrel contained powder, ball and wad, plus a percussion cap.

SPECIFICATIONS	
Country of Origin:	United States
Date:	1830
Calibre:	6mm (.23in)
Operation:	Percussion cap
Weight:	.42kg (.94lb)
Overall Length:	210mm (8.26in)
Barrel Length:	83mm (3.26in)
Muzzle Velocity:	152m/sec (500ft/sec)
Feed/Magazine:	1 shot per barrel
Range:	5m (16.4ft)

Practical Pepperboxes

Not all pepperbox pistols had an extreme number of barrels. Smaller versions could be carried in a pocket and kept ready for emergency self-defence. Most were smoothbores, which was acceptable for a weapon intended for very short-range combat.

SPECIFICATIONS	
Country of Origin:	United States
Date:	1840
Calibre:	10mm (.4in)
Operation:	Percussion cap
Weight:	.42kg (.94lb)
Overall Length:	279mm (11in)
Barrel Length:	127mm (5in)
Muzzle Velocity:	168m/sec (550ft/sec)
Feed/Magazine:	1 shot per barrel
Range:	12m (40ft)

1828

1830

1840

Percussion Revolvers

Although it took a significant time to load the cylinder of a 'cap-and-ball' revolver, being able to fire several shots in succession was a distinct advantage. The cylinder was rotated by the action of cocking the hammer.

Paterson Colt

Named for the location of Colt's factory, the 1836 Paterson Colt was a 5-shot weapon available with a variety of barrel lengths. The longest, all 305mm (12in) of it, was referred to as a 'Buntline'.

SPECIFICATIONS	
Country of Origin:	United States
Date:	1836
Calibre:	9.1mm (.36in)
Operation:	Revolver
Weight:	1.93kg (4.25lb)
Overall Length:	355mm (14in)
Barrel Length:	228mm (9in)
Muzzle Velocity:	259m/sec (850ft/sec)
Feed/Magazine:	5-round cylinder
Range:	20m (66ft)

Bentley

Joseph Bentley, whose guns were sold by the Webley brothers alongside their own, developed a self-cocking mechanism for his revolvers and a safety catch which locked the hammer in position.

SPECIFICATIONS	
Country of Origin:	United Kingdom
Date:	1853
Calibre:	11.2mm (.44in)
Operation:	Revolver
Weight:	.94kg (2.1lb)
Overall Length:	305mm (12in)
Barrel Length:	178mm (7in)
Muzzle Velocity:	183m/sec (600ft/sec)
Feed/Magazine:	5-round cylinder
Range:	12m (40ft)

TIMELINE 1836   1853   1860

Savage Model 1860

The Savage Model 1860 used a lever action to cock the hammer and rotate the cylinder. The lever below the trigger was pulled back then pushed forward again by the shooter's middle finger.

SPECIFICATIONS	
Country of Origin:	United States
Date:	1860
Calibre:	9.1mm (.36in)
Operation:	Revolver
Weight:	1.6kg (3.525lb)
Overall Length:	330mm (13in)
Barrel Length:	190mm (7.48in)
Muzzle Velocity:	213m/sec (700ft/sec)
Feed/Magazine:	6-round cylinder
Range:	20m (66ft)

Remington New Model Army 1863

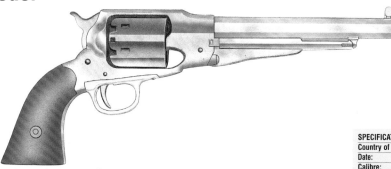

Remington produced a range of revolvers during the Civil War period which, while expensive, were rugged and accurate. An empty cylinder could be quickly swapped for a loaded one, greatly reducing reloading times.

SPECIFICATIONS	
Country of Origin:	United States
Date:	1863
Calibre:	11.2mm (.44in)
Operation:	Revolver
Weight:	1.25kg (2.75lb)
Overall Length:	349mm (13.74in)
Barrel Length:	203mm (8in)
Muzzle Velocity:	213m/sec (700ft/sec)
Feed/Magazine:	6-round cylinder
Range:	12m (40ft)

Kufahl Needle-Fire Revolver

To facilitate quicker reloading, the Kufahl revolver's cylinder was mounted on an easily removed pin. A needle pierced the cloth cartridge to initiate a primer located just behind the projectile.

SPECIFICATIONS	
Country of Origin:	Germany
Date:	1870
Calibre:	7.36mm (.29in)
Operation:	Revolver
Weight:	.62kg (1.375lb)
Overall Length:	244mm (9.6in)
Barrel Length:	81mm (3.18in)
Muzzle Velocity:	152m/sec (500ft/sec)
Feed/Magazine:	6-round cylinder
Range:	15m (49ft)

1863

1870

Early Colt Revolvers

Understanding the importance of the military market, Samuel Colt geared many of his products towards the needs of army and navy officers as well as cavalry troopers. The British and American armies were among his biggest customers.

Colt Whitneyville Walker Dragoon

After receiving a letter from Captain Walker of the Texas Rangers, which praised his Paterson revolver, Colt joined forces with Walker to develop a powerful 11.2mm (.44in) weapon optimized for mounted combat.

SPECIFICATIONS	
Country of Origin:	United States
Date:	1847
Calibre:	11.2mm (.44in)
Operation:	Revolver
Weight:	2.04kg (4.5lb)
Overall Length:	343mm (13.5in)
Barrel Length:	190mm (7.5in)
Muzzle Velocity:	259m/sec (850ft/sec)
Feed/Magazine:	6-round cylinder
Range:	20m (66ft)

Colt Whitneyville Hartford Dragoon

A developed version of the 'Walker', the Hartford Dragoon was the first gun produced at Colt's new Hartford factory. Only small numbers were made, but the Hartford Dragoon laid the groundwork for Colt's later revolvers.

SPECIFICATIONS	
Country of Origin:	United States
Date:	1847
Calibre:	11.2mm (.44in)
Operation:	Revolver
Weight:	1.87kg (4.125lb)
Overall Length:	305mm (12in)
Barrel Length:	190mm (7.5in)
Muzzle Velocity:	457m/sec (1500ft/sec)
Feed/Magazine:	6-round cylinder
Range:	20m (66ft)

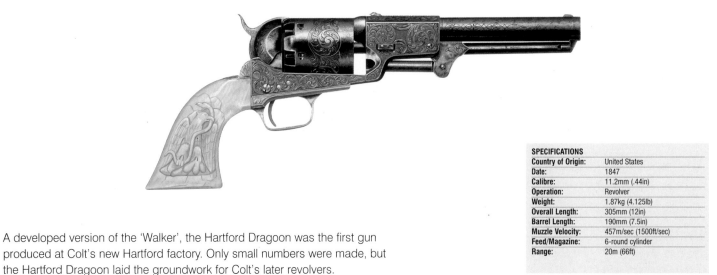

TIMELINE

1847

1860

M1860 'Army' Colt

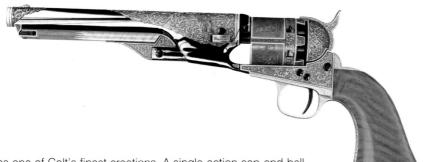

The M1860 was one of Colt's finest creations. A single-action cap-and-ball revolver, it was available in 11.2mm (.44in) as the 'Army' model and 9.1mm (.36in) as the 'Navy' model. In practice, both models served on land and at sea.

SPECIFICATIONS	
Country of Origin:	United States
Date:	1860
Calibre:	11.2mm (.44in)
Operation:	Revolver
Weight:	1.25kg (2.75lb)
Overall Length:	349mm (13.74in)
Barrel Length:	203mm (8in)
Muzzle Velocity:	213m/sec (700ft/sec)
Feed/Magazine:	6-round cylinder
Range:	20m (66ft)

M1861 'Navy' Colt

The 'Navy' Colt appealed to users who preferred a weapon with less recoil than the potent 11.2mm (.44in) 'Army' model. Among them were many cavalry troopers, especially within the army of the Confederacy.

SPECIFICATIONS	
Country of Origin:	United States
Date:	1861
Calibre:	9.1mm (.36in)
Operation:	Revolver
Weight:	1.02kg (2.25lb)
Overall Length:	328mm (12.91in)
Barrel Length:	190mm (7.5in)
Muzzle Velocity:	213m/sec (700ft/sec)
Feed/Magazine:	6-round cylinder
Range:	20m (66ft)

Colt Model 1862

Colt's Model 1862 was produced in two variants: 'Police' and 'Navy'. The 'Police' model had a smooth barrel, similar to the M1860 'Army'. The 'Navy' model had an octagonal barrel.

SPECIFICATIONS	
Country of Origin:	United States
Date:	1862
Calibre:	11.2mm (.44in)
Operation:	Revolver
Weight:	1.25kg (2.75lb)
Overall Length:	349mm (13.74in)
Barrel Length:	203mm (8in)
Muzzle Velocity:	213m/sec (700ft/sec)
Feed/Magazine:	6-round cylinder
Range:	12m (40ft)

1861

1862

Guns as Art Pieces: 'Navy' Colt

It was not uncommon for even workaday weapons to have some form of engraving or other decoration. For example the standard 'Navy' Colt often featured an engraving of a naval battle on the cylinder. However, some weapons took this a great deal further.

FRAME
Standard 'Navy' Colts were usually engraved with a naval battle scene on the cylinder, but decorative models generally had a theme covering the whole weapon.

MUZZLE
Although designated as a 'Navy Revolver', this was more a marketing identifier than an indication of role. More 'Navy' guns were bought to be used on land than for use at sea.

SPECIFICATIONS	
Country of Origin:	United States
Date:	1861
Calibre:	9.1mm (.36in)
Operation:	Revolver
Weight:	1.02kg (2.25lb)
Overall Length:	328mm (12.91in)
Barrel Length:	190mm (7.5in)
Muzzle Velocity:	213m/sec (700ft/sec)
Feed/Magazine:	6-round cylinder
Range:	20m (66ft)

Highly decorative weapons were often commissioned as presentation pieces, perhaps commemorating the retirement of a military or government officer, or as a mark of thanks for valued service. Others were simply offered for sale as 'prestige' versions of standard weapons, and commanded a correspondingly higher price.

As a general rule, however decorative a firearm was, it was still first and foremost a working gun which had to be able to fulfil its basic function as a weapon. Quality of manufacture was as important as decoration, and many of these weapons are today prized as both art pieces and also paragons of the gunmaker's art.

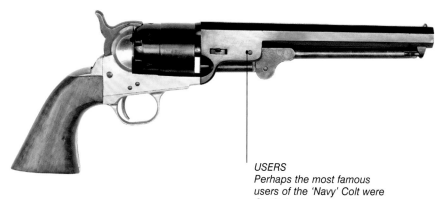

USERS
Perhaps the most famous users of the 'Navy' Colt were Confederate general Robert E. Lee and 'Wild Bill' Hickok.

CYLINDER
The 'Navy' designation came to be associated with small-calibre handguns, while 'Army' models of the same gun were often chambered for much larger calibres.

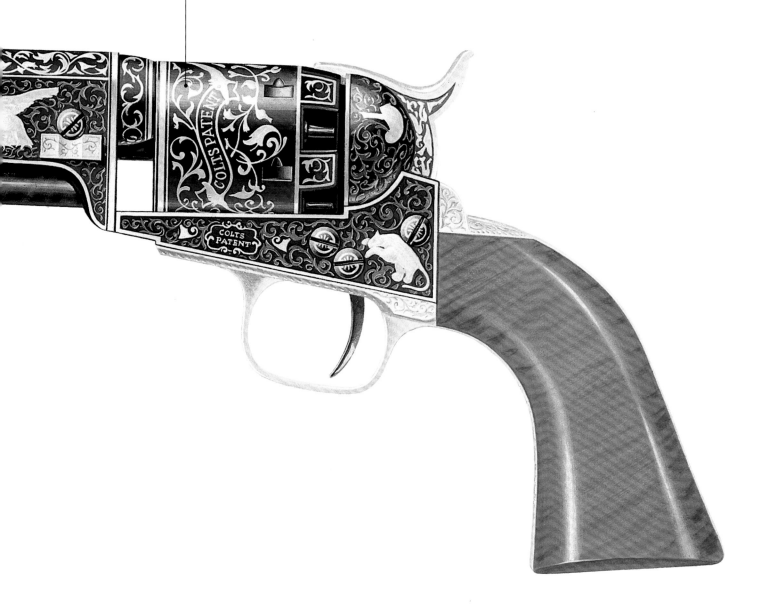

Experimental Revolvers

The nineteenth century was a time of experimentation, with many new technologies and ideas emerging. A range of interesting designs appeared in this period, some of which pushed firearm technology forward. Others turned out to be a blind alley.

Adams Self-Cocking Revolver

In 1851, as Samuel Colt was aggressively marketing his single-action guns, Robert Adams patented a weapon that was cocked and fired using only trigger action. This meant that there was no need for a hammer spur.

SPECIFICATIONS	
Country of Origin:	United Kingdom
Date:	1851
Calibre:	12.4mm (.49in)
Operation:	Revolver
Weight:	1.27kg (2.8lb)
Overall Length:	330mm (13in)
Barrel Length:	190mm (7.48in)
Muzzle Velocity:	213m/sec (700ft/sec)
Feed/Magazine:	6-round cylinder
Range:	12m (40ft)

Tranter Revolver

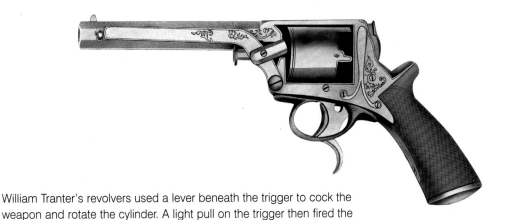

William Tranter's revolvers used a lever beneath the trigger to cock the weapon and rotate the cylinder. A light pull on the trigger then fired the weapon single-action. It was possible to pull trigger and lever together.

SPECIFICATIONS	
Country of Origin:	United Kingdom
Date:	1855
Calibre:	11.2mm (.44in)
Operation:	Revolver
Weight:	.88kg (1.9lb)
Overall Length:	292mm (11.5in)
Barrel Length:	165mm (6.5in)
Muzzle Velocity:	168m/sec (550ft/sec)
Feed/Magazine:	5-round cylinder
Range:	12m (40ft)

TIMELINE

1851   1855   1858

Le Mat

The Le Mat pistol had a single firing mechanism and hammer, which could be set to either of its barrels. The lower was a single-shot smoothbore firing buckshot; the upper was a 9.1mm (.36in) or 10.9mm (.42in) revolver.

SPECIFICATIONS	
Country of Origin:	France
Date:	1858
Calibre:	7.62mm (.3in)
Operation:	Revolver
Weight:	1.64kg (3.625lb)
Overall Length:	337mm (13.26in)
Barrel Length:	178mm (7in)
Muzzle Velocity:	183m/sec (600ft/sec)
Feed/Magazine:	9-round cylinder plus single shot
Range:	15m (49ft)

Lefaucheux

Casimir Lefaucheux was able to develop a workable self-contained cartridge, and built various handguns around it. His cartridge used cardboard to contain the powder charge, and was used as the basis for the world's first all-metal cartridges.

SPECIFICATIONS	
Country of Origin:	France
Date:	1861
Calibre:	9mm (.35in)
Operation:	Pinfire revolver
Weight:	0.56kg (1.2lb)
Overall Length:	213mm (8.4in)
Barrel Length:	102mm (4in)
Muzzle Velocity:	Not known
Feed/Magazine:	6-round cylinder
Range:	12m (40ft)

Beaumont-Adams

The Beaumont-Adams revolver was a true double-action weapon. It could be cocked and fired by trigger action only, or cocked using the spurred hammer and then fired single-action using a light trigger pull.

SPECIFICATIONS	
Country of Origin:	United Kingdom
Date:	1862
Calibre:	12.2mm (.479in)
Operation:	Double-action revolver
Weight:	1.1kg (2.4lb)
Overall Length:	286mm (11.25in)
Barrel Length:	Not known
Muzzle Velocity:	190m/sec (620ft/sec)
Feed/Magazine:	5-round cylinder
Range:	35m (115ft)

 1861 1862

Advancing Pistol Technology

Pistol technology advanced rapidly in the later nineteenth century, with improvements in firing mechanisms, weapon manufacturing techniques and other areas. Many designs of the era represented a transition rather than the end result of the design process.

Webley Longspur

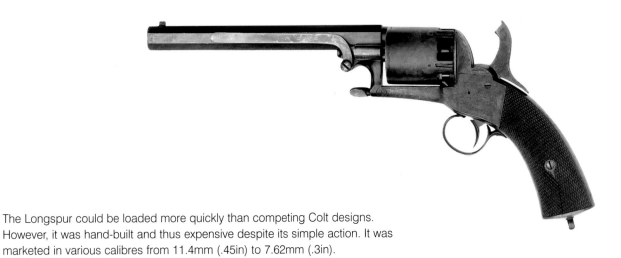

The Longspur could be loaded more quickly than competing Colt designs. However, it was hand-built and thus expensive despite its simple action. It was marketed in various calibres from 11.4mm (.45in) to 7.62mm (.3in).

The Longspur, a five-shot cap-and-ball revolver, was the first gun patented by the Webley brothers. Note the lanyard loop to prevent the weapon from being lost if dropped in action.

SPECIFICATIONS	
Country of Origin:	United Kingdom
Date:	1853
Calibre:	11.2mm (.44in)
Operation:	Revolver
Weight:	1.05kg (2.3lb)
Overall Length:	317mm (12.5in)
Barrel Length:	178mm (7in)
Muzzle Velocity:	213m/sec (700ft/sec)
Feed/Magazine:	5-round cylinder
Range:	20m (66ft)

TIMELINE

1853

1858

Pin Fire revolver

Early all-in-one cartridge weapons used a primer embedded within the cartridge and fired by a pin protruding from it. This was struck by the weapon's hammer, which acted vertically rather than horizontally as is the case with modern weapons.

SPECIFICATIONS	
Country of Origin:	France
Date:	1858
Calibre:	9mm (.35in)
Operation:	Revolver
Weight:	.56kg (1.25lb)
Overall Length:	213mm (8.38in)
Barrel Length:	102mm (4in)
Muzzle Velocity:	183m/sec (600ft/sec)
Feed/Magazine:	6-round cylinder
Range:	6m (20ft)

Starr Single-Action

Starr, the third-largest provider of handguns to the Union army, produced a double-action revolver in 1858. It was overcomplex and disliked by many of its users; the later (1863) Starr Single Action was much more popular.

SPECIFICATIONS	
Country of Origin:	United States
Date:	1863
Calibre:	11.2mm (.44in)
Operation:	Revolver
Weight:	1.36kg (3lb)
Overall Length:	343mm (13.5in)
Barrel Length:	198mm (7.8in)
Muzzle Velocity:	213m/sec (700ft/sec)
Feed/Magazine:	6-round cylinder
Range:	20m (66ft)

Lancaster 1882

Large-calibre two- or four-barrelled pistols were popular with hunters who used elephants for transport; they thus became known as 'howdah' pistols. Once revolvers that could be quickly reloaded became available, howdah pistols gradually fell out of fashion.

SPECIFICATIONS	
Country of Origin:	United Kingdom
Date:	1882
Calibre:	9.6mm (.38in)
Operation:	Percussion cap, revolving striker
Weight:	1.13kg (2.5lb)
Overall Length:	279mm (11in)
Barrel Length:	Not known
Muzzle Velocity:	Not known
Feed/Magazine:	Multi-barrel centrefire
Range:	15m (49ft)

1863

1882

Colt Single Action Army 'Peacemaker'

One of the most famous guns of all time, the Colt Single Action Army was adopted for service with the US Army in 1873. It was replaced by a double-action weapon in 1892. The Single Action Army was available with three barrel lengths: 191mm (7.5in), 140mm (5.5in), designated the 'gunfighter' model, and 114mm (4.5in), designated 'civilian'. It was popular with law enforcement officers, and perhaps for this reason gained the nickname 'Peacemaker'. A very long barrelled variant, known as the 'Buntline Special', was also offered.

EJECTOR
The ejector rod ran under the barrel. Pushing it back ejected cartridges through the open loading gate.

SPECIFICATIONS	
Country of Origin:	United States
Date:	1873–1892
Calibre:	11.2mm (.44in)
Operation:	Revolver
Weight:	1.08kg (2.4lb)
Overall Length:	330mm (13in)
Barrel Length:	190mm (7.5in)
Muzzle Velocity:	198m/sec (650ft/sec)
Feed/Magazine:	6-round cylinder
Range:	20m (66ft)

Confusingly, the M1873 is also sometimes known as the Colt Frontier. It was reloaded by placing the hammer at half-cock, which allowed the cylinder to be manually rotated. As each chamber was brought into alignment with the gate, spent rounds were ejected using the ejector rod, and the empty chambers then reloaded.

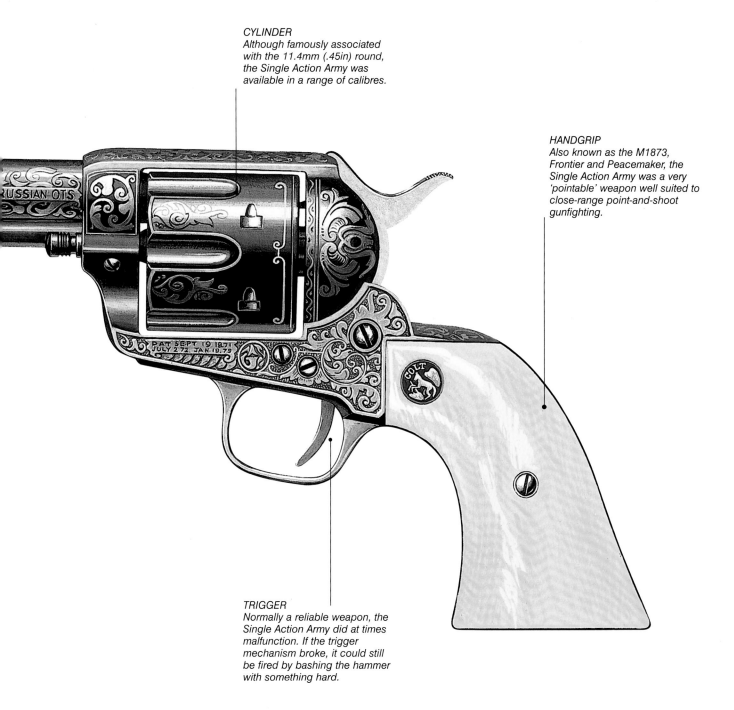

CYLINDER
Although famously associated with the 11.4mm (.45in) round, the Single Action Army was available in a range of calibres.

HANDGRIP
Also known as the M1873, Frontier and Peacemaker, the Single Action Army was a very 'pointable' weapon well suited to close-range point-and-shoot gunfighting.

TRIGGER
Normally a reliable weapon, the Single Action Army did at times malfunction. If the trigger mechanism broke, it could still be fired by bashing the hammer with something hard.

Late Nineteenth Century Combat Revolvers

By the last few years of the nineteenth century, revolvers of a modern appearance had begun to appear. However, many designers preferred break-open reloading to a swing-out cylinder. Other designs used a loading gate on the back of the cylinder.

Chamelot-Delvigne 1874

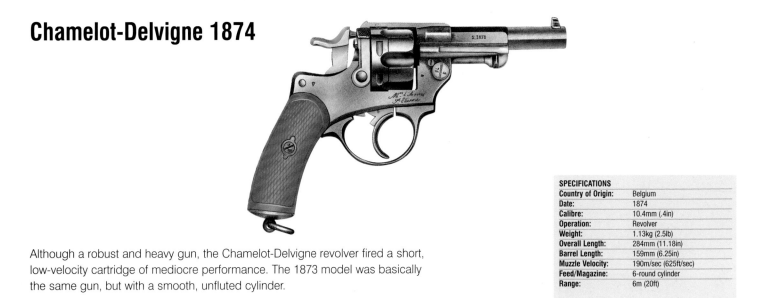

Although a robust and heavy gun, the Chamelot-Delvigne revolver fired a short, low-velocity cartridge of mediocre performance. The 1873 model was basically the same gun, but with a smooth, unfluted cylinder.

SPECIFICATIONS	
Country of Origin:	Belgium
Date:	1874
Calibre:	10.4mm (.4in)
Operation:	Revolver
Weight:	1.13kg (2.5lb)
Overall Length:	284mm (11.18in)
Barrel Length:	159mm (6.25in)
Muzzle Velocity:	190m/sec (625ft/sec)
Feed/Magazine:	6-round cylinder
Range:	6m (20ft)

Remington M1875

Designed as a competitor to the Colt .44 produced a year earlier, the Remington Model 1875 was offered in 11.2mm (.44in) and in 11.4mm (.45in) .45 Long Colt. A large order was supplied to the Egyptian Army.

SPECIFICATIONS	
Country of Origin:	United States
Date:	1875
Calibre:	11.2mm (.44in)
Operation:	Revolver
Weight:	1.2kg (2.6lb)
Overall Length:	330mm (13in)
Barrel Length:	190mm (7.2in)
Muzzle Velocity:	213m/sec (700ft/sec)
Feed/Magazine:	6-round cylinder
Range:	8m (25ft)

TIMELINE

1874   1875   1878

Mauser Zig-Zag

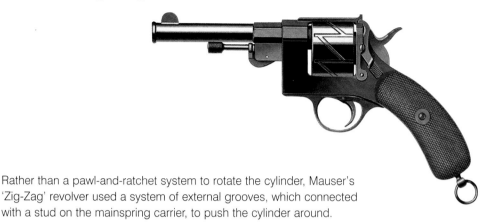

Rather than a pawl-and-ratchet system to rotate the cylinder, Mauser's 'Zig-Zag' revolver used a system of external grooves, which connected with a stud on the mainspring carrier, to push the cylinder around.

SPECIFICATIONS	
Country of Origin:	Germany
Date:	1878
Calibre:	10.9mm (.42in)
Operation:	Revolver
Weight:	1.19kg (2.625lb)
Overall Length:	298mm (11.75in)
Barrel Length:	165mm (6.5in)
Muzzle Velocity:	198m/sec (650ft/sec)
Feed/Magazine:	6-round cylinder
Range:	20m (66ft)

Bodeo Revolver

Developed from the Chamelot-Delvigne revolver, the Bodeo was intended to replace it in police and military service. Some versions had a folding trigger; others did not. Note the lack of a trigger guard.

SPECIFICATIONS	
Country of Origin:	Italy
Date:	1889
Calibre:	10.35mm (.4in)
Operation:	Revolver
Weight:	.91kg (2lb)
Overall Length:	235mm (9.25in)
Barrel Length:	114mm (4.48in)
Muzzle Velocity:	254.81m/sec (836ft/sec)
Feed/Magazine:	6-round cylinder
Range:	20m (66ft)

Nagant M1895

SPECIFICATIONS	
Country of Origin:	Russia
Date:	1895
Calibre:	7.62mm (.3in)
Operation:	Revolver
Weight:	.79kg (1.75lb)
Overall Length:	229mm (9in)
Barrel Length:	110mm (4.33in)
Muzzle Velocity:	178m/sec (584ft/sec)
Feed/Magazine:	7-round cylinder
Range:	20m (66ft)

When the M1895 was cocked, the cylinder moved forward to provide a better gas seal between chamber and barrel. This wasted less of the propellant gas and resulted in a higher muzzle velocity.

1889

1895

International Revolvers

Revolver development took slightly different paths in Europe, the United States, and elsewhere, and some weapons had a distinctly 'American' or 'European' flavour. However, even where features were not directly copied the influence of a successful design was felt worldwide.

Gasser Montenegrin

Austrian firm Gasser's 'Montenegrin' revolver used a star-shaped automatic ejector to push cartridges out of the cylinder when the barrel was tipped down for reloading. A smaller-calibre version was marketed outside Montenegro.

SPECIFICATIONS	
Country of Origin:	Austria-Hungary
Date:	1870
Calibre:	11.2mm (.44in)
Operation:	Revolver
Weight:	1.3kg (2.9lb)
Overall Length:	185mm (7.28in)
Barrel Length:	135mm (5.3in)
Muzzle Velocity:	168m/sec (550ft/sec)
Feed/Magazine:	5-round cylinder
Range:	20m (66ft)

Gasser Revolver

Gasser's earliest handguns were heavily influenced by Colt and Adams designs. Later models were copied by other makers in Europe and in some cases converted to break-open weapons.

SPECIFICATIONS	
Country of Origin:	Austria-Hungary
Date:	1870
Calibre:	11.2mm (.44in)
Operation:	Revolver
Weight:	1.30kg (2.9lb)
Overall Length:	325mm (12.6in)
Barrel Length:	185mm (7.28in), 115mm (4.53in)
Muzzle Velocity:	178m/sec (584ft/sec)
Feed/Magazine:	6-round cylinder
Range:	20m (66ft)

TIMELINE

1870

1893

Meiji Type 26

The Type 26 was named for the year of its introduction – the 26th year since the Meiji Restoration in Japan. It was a double-action-only top-break weapon, which suffered from a very heavy trigger pull.

SPECIFICATIONS	
Country of Origin:	Japan
Date:	1893
Calibre:	9mm (.35in)
Operation:	Revolver
Weight:	.91kg (2lb)
Overall Length:	235mm (9.25in)
Barrel Length:	119mm (4.7in)
Muzzle Velocity:	183m/sec (600ft/sec)
Feed/Magazine:	6-round cylinder
Range:	20m (66ft)

Iver Johnson (First Model)

Iver Johnson's top-break (or 'tip-down') revolvers used a transfer-bar safety device to prevent the weapon firing if the hammer was knocked. For this and their automatic cartridge ejector they were named 'safety automatics'.

SPECIFICATIONS	
Country of Origin:	United States
Date:	1894
Calibre:	8.1mm (.32in)
Operation:	Revolver
Weight:	.59kg (1.3lb)
Overall Length:	197mm (7.75in)
Barrel Length:	83mm (3.25in)
Muzzle Velocity:	168m/sec (550ft/sec)
Feed/Magazine:	6-round cylinder
Range:	20m (66ft)

Iver Johnson (Second Model)

Iver Johnson constructed a workable side-swinging cylinder revolver in 1896, but then reverted to top-break weapons. Note the prominent hinge in front of and below the cylinder.

SPECIFICATIONS	
Country of Origin:	United States
Date:	1896
Calibre:	8.1mm (.32in)
Operation:	Revolver
Weight:	.59kg (1.3lb)
Overall Length:	197mm (7.75in)
Barrel Length:	83mm (3.25in)
Muzzle Velocity:	168m/sec (550ft/sec)
Feed/Magazine:	6-round cylinder
Range:	20m (66ft)

1894

1896

Revolver Mechanisms: Webley & Scott Mk IV

The mechanism of a revolver rotates the cylinder to place the next round under the hammer at the same time as the hammer itself is cocked. Thus the chamber currently under the hammer is not the one that will be fired. This enabled early revolver users to carry the weapon with the hammer resting on an empty chamber if desired, thus keeping the weapon ready to fire but reducing the chance of an accidental discharge if the weapon were knocked.

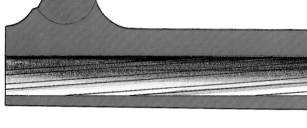

BARREL
Revolver barrels can theoretically be any length, with longer weapons offering more accuracy and a higher muzzle velocity. In practice, the need to keep the weapon at a convenient size to carry limits the barrel length.

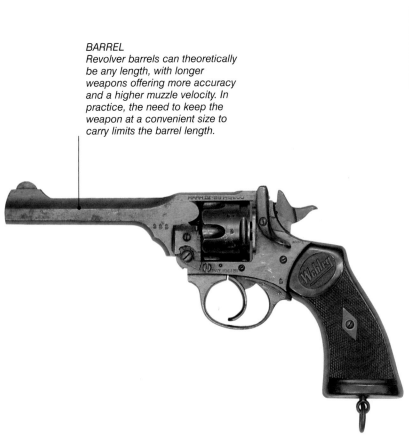

SPECIFICATIONS	
Country of Origin:	United Kingdom
Date:	1899
Calibre:	11.55mm (.455in)
Operation:	Revolver
Weight:	1.5kg (3.3lb)
Overall Length:	279mm (11in)
Barrel Length:	152mm (6in)
Muzzle Velocity:	198m/sec (650ft/sec)
Feed/Magazine:	6-round cylinder
Range:	20m (66ft)

Modern revolvers use a transfer bar to transmit force from the hammer to the primer, and this is only placed in position to do so when the trigger is pulled. Thus modern revolvers are entirely safe to carry with a fully loaded cylinder.

Some revolver users carry their weapon with an empty 'next' chamber, i.e. the one that will be brought under the hammer the first time the weapon is cocked. Thus they know that if their weapon it taken away from them, it will not fire on the first attempt. This may provide enough margin to attempt something desperate.

CYLINDER
The cocking mechanism also rotates the cylinder to place the next round under the hammer. In a double-action weapon this results in a fairly heavy trigger pull and consequent reduction in accuracy.

HAMMER
Cocking the hammer manually sets the weapon ready to fire on a very light trigger pull, which assists accurate shooting.

LOCKWORK
The internal lockwork of the revolver transmits force from the cocking mechanism to a pawl-and-ratchet system, which moves the cylinder into position and locks it there.

Specialist Pistols

There has always been a market for specialist weapons that give a particular set of users exactly what they want. Some such weapons become 'mainstream'; others remain obscure for lack of a big enough market to justify mass production.

Remington Derringer

The name 'derringer' refers to a type of weapon rather than a specific model. Most derringers were simple break-open weapons with one or two barrels, firing a fairly large-calibre bullet. Their primary use was last-ditch self-defence.

SPECIFICATIONS	
Country of Origin:	United States
Date:	1850
Calibre:	10.4mm (.4in)
Operation:	Breech-loading cartridge
Weight:	.34kg (.75lb)
Overall Length:	121mm (4.76in)
Barrel Length:	76mm (3in)
Muzzle Velocity:	137m/sec (450ft/sec)
Feed/Magazine:	Single shot in each barrel
Range:	3m (10ft)

Volcanic Pistol

The Volcanic pistol was neither a revolver nor a semi-automatic, but used lever action to load rounds from an under-barrel tubular magazine. This system was widely used on rifles and carbines, but was not successful in the handgun marketplace.

SPECIFICATIONS	
Country of Origin:	United States
Date:	1855
Calibre:	11.2mm (.44in)
Operation:	Lever action
Weight:	.8kg (1.75lb)
Overall Length:	279mm (11in)
Barrel Length:	178mm (7in)
Muzzle Velocity:	150m/sec (492ft/sec)
Feed/Magazine:	6-round tubular magazine
Range:	15m (49ft)

TIMELINE			
	 1850	 1855	1869

Apache Pistol

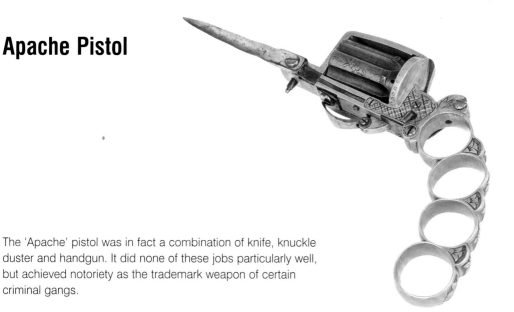

The 'Apache' pistol was in fact a combination of knife, knuckle duster and handgun. It did none of these jobs particularly well, but achieved notoriety as the trademark weapon of certain criminal gangs.

SPECIFICATIONS	
Country of Origin:	France
Date:	1869
Calibre:	7mm (.275in)
Operation:	Revolver
Weight:	.362kg (.8lb)
Overall Length:	105mm (4.3in) folded; 200mm (7.8in) unfolded
Barrel Length:	N/A
Muzzle Velocity:	N/A
Feed/Magazine:	Detachable cylinder
Range:	3m (10ft)

Modèle 1892 (Lebel Revolver)

The Modèle 1892, a double-action revolver with a swing-out cylinder, was developed as a sidearm for French officers. However, it used the low-powered 8mm (.314in) Lebel cartridge and thus lacked stopping power.

SPECIFICATIONS	
Country of Origin:	France
Date:	1892
Calibre:	8mm (.314in)
Operation:	Double-action revolver
Weight:	.94kg (2.1lb)
Overall Length:	240mm (9.44in)
Barrel Length:	117mm (4.60in)
Muzzle Velocity:	213m/sec (698ft/sec)
Feed/Magazine:	6-round cylinder
Range:	20m (66ft)

Galand Velo Dog

SPECIFICATIONS	
Country of Origin:	France
Date:	1894
Calibre:	5.75mm (.22in)
Operation:	Double-action revolver
Weight:	Not known
Overall Length:	Not known
Barrel Length:	38.1mm (1.5in)
Muzzle Velocity:	342.9m/sec (1125ft/sec)
Feed/Magazine:	6-round cylinder
Range:	15m (49ft)

Among the increasing number of pocket pistols intended for the self-defence market was the Velo Dog. This extremely small revolver was intended for use by cyclists who needed to protect themselves from dog attacks.

1892

1894

From Rifle-Musket to Rifle

The percussion musket was only slightly more effective than any other smoothbore weapon, but the advent of the Minié bullet permitted quick-firing accurate rifle-muskets to become general issue to infantry.

M1841 Mississippi Rifle

The first percussion rifle to enter US Army service, the M1841 gained its 'Mississippi' nickname from a volunteer unit (from Mississippi) which used it to great effect during the US-Mexican War.

SPECIFICATIONS	
Country of Origin:	United States
Date:	1841
Calibre:	13.7mm (.54in), 15mm (0.58in)
Operation:	Percussion cap
Weight:	4.2kg (9.25lb)
Overall Length:	1230mm (48.5in)
Barrel Length:	840mm (33in)
Muzzle Velocity:	335m/sec (1100ft/sec)
Feed/Magazine:	Single shot, muzzle-loader
Range:	1000m (3280ft) maximum

Sharps Rifle

The Sharps rifle was a breech loader, with the mechanism operated by lever action using the trigger guard. It was available with either a conventional percussion cap system or a tape primer, and later with an automatic cap positioning system.

SPECIFICATIONS	
Country of Origin:	United States
Date:	1850
Calibre:	14.65mm (.577in)
Operation:	Percussion lock
Weight:	4.2kg (9.25lb)
Overall Length:	1230mm (48.5in)
Barrel Length:	840mm (33in)
Muzzle Velocity:	335m/sec (1100ft/sec)
Feed/Magazine:	Single shot, breech-loader
Range:	460m (1509ft)

TIMELINE
 1841
 1850
 1854

Whitworth Rifle

The Whitworth rifle used a hexagonal bore rather than more conventional rifling. It was highly accurate out to 1000m (3280ft) or possibly even more, and was used by Confederate sharpshooters during the American Civil War.

SPECIFICATIONS	
Country of Origin:	United Kingdom
Date:	1854
Calibre:	11.4mm (.45in)
Operation:	Percussion cap
Weight:	3.4kg (7.4lb)
Overall Length:	1230mm (48.5in)
Barrel Length:	840mm (33in)
Muzzle Velocity:	335m/sec (1100ft/sec)
Feed/Magazine:	Single shot, muzzle-loader
Range:	1400m (4593ft)

Werndl Model 1867 Infantry Rifle

The principal feature of the M1867 was its drum breech, which, while sturdy and secure, compromised extraction. The rifle had a one-piece stock with a straight wrist, a back-action lock and an external hammer.

SPECIFICATIONS	
Country of Origin:	Austria-Hungary
Date:	1867
Calibre:	11mm (.433in) rimmed
Operation:	Rotary-block breech, with an external hammer
Weight:	4.1kg (9lb)
Overall Length:	1278mm (50.3in)
Barrel Length:	855mm (33.7in)
Muzzle Velocity:	436m/sec (1430ft/sec)
Feed/Magazine:	Single cartridge, breech-loader
Range:	1400m (4593ft)

Berdan Rifle

Hiram Berdan was a strong advocate of sharpshooting during the Civil War period, and afterwards developed a single-shot rifle which was adopted by the Russian Army. Accurate and reliable, the Berdan was produced in vast numbers.

SPECIFICATIONS	
Country of Origin:	United States/Russia
Date:	1869
Calibre:	10.75mm (.42in)
Operation:	Berdan I: 'Trapdoor'; Berdan II: 'Bolt'
Weight:	4.2kg (9.25lb)
Overall Length:	1300mm (51.18in)
Barrel Length:	830mm (32.67in)
Muzzle Velocity:	Not known
Feed/Magazine:	Single shot, breech-loader
Range:	280m (919ft)

1867

1869

Early Cartridge Rifles

The earliest unitary cartridge rifles were single-shot weapons, but still offered huge advantages over percussion rifles. One key advantage was that troops equipped with breech loaders could reload while prone, whereas a muzzle loader required the user to remain exposed whilst loading.

Dreyse Needle Rifle

The Dreyse rifle was a single-shot bolt-action weapon, which used a needle to pierce the cartridge and ignite the primer. This was located at the front of the cartridge, behind the bullet.

SPECIFICATIONS	
Country of Origin:	Germany
Date:	1836
Calibre:	15.43mm (.6in)
Operation:	Bolt action
Weight:	4.1kg (9lb)
Overall Length:	1422mm (56in)
Barrel Length:	964mm (38in)
Muzzle Velocity:	290m/sec (950ft/sec)
Feed/Magazine:	Single shot, breech-loaded
Range:	600m (1968ft)

Fusil Modèle 1866 (Chassepot)

The Chassepot rifle entered service with the French Army in 1866, serving through the Franco-Prussian War where it outranged the Dreyse rifles in Prussian service. Conversion to all-metallic cartridges began in 1874, creating what became known as the Gras rifle.

SPECIFICATIONS	
Country of Origin:	France
Date:	1866
Calibre:	11mm (.433in)
Operation:	Bolt action
Weight:	3.7kg (8.125lb)
Overall Length:	1314mm (51.80in)
Barrel Length:	795mm (31.3in)
Muzzle Velocity:	396m/sec (1300ft/sec)
Feed/Magazine:	Single shot, breech-loaded
Range:	1200m (3937ft)

TIMELINE
1836
1866
1867

Snider-Enfield

The Snider-Enfield was a conversion of the British Army's Enfield 1853 muzzle-loading rifle. Cartridge ejection was manual, sometimes by means of turning the rifle upside down and shaking it.

SPECIFICATIONS	
Country of Origin:	United Kingdom
Date:	1867
Calibre:	14.65mm (.577in)
Operation:	Hinged breech percussion
Weight:	3.7kg (8.125lb)
Overall Length:	1219mm (48in)
Barrel Length:	838mm (33in)
Muzzle Velocity:	335m/sec (1100ft/sec)
Feed/Magazine:	Single shot, breech-loaded
Range:	550m (1804ft)

Martini-Henry

Firing a powerful 11.4mm (.45in) bullet, the single-shot Martini-Henry rifle was a potent force during Britain's late-nineteenth-century colonial campaigns. It used a falling-block mechanism; the breech block was moved down by a lever, to expose the chamber and permit reloading.

SPECIFICATIONS	
Country of Origin:	United Kingdom
Date:	1871
Calibre:	11.4mm (.45in)
Operation:	Falling block
Weight:	3.9kg (8.625lb)
Overall Length:	1129mm (48in)
Barrel Length:	851mm (33.5in)
Muzzle Velocity:	411m/sec (1350ft/sec)
Feed/Magazine:	Single shot, breech-loaded
Range:	370m (1213ft)

Model 1873 Trapdoor Springfield

The Model 1873 Trapdoor Springfield was the first standard-issue breech-loading rifle adopted by the United States Army. Initially, the 'Trapdoor' was a conversion of existing rifles to breech-loading operation. Production of new guns to this design followed.

SPECIFICATIONS	
Country of Origin:	United States
Date:	1873
Calibre:	11.4mm (.45in)
Operation:	Hinged breech-block
Weight:	3.7kg (8.125lb)
Overall Length:	1295mm (51in)
Barrel Length:	825mm (32.5in)
Muzzle Velocity:	411m/sec (1359ft/sec)
Feed/Magazine:	Single shot, breech-loaded
Range:	550m (1804ft)

1871

1873

Repeating Rifles

A repeating rifle offered the user a very significant firepower advantage over an opponent armed with a single-shot weapon. Most repeaters used bolt action, though lever-action weapons became popular in America and for many are associated with the 'Wild West'.

Henry Rifle

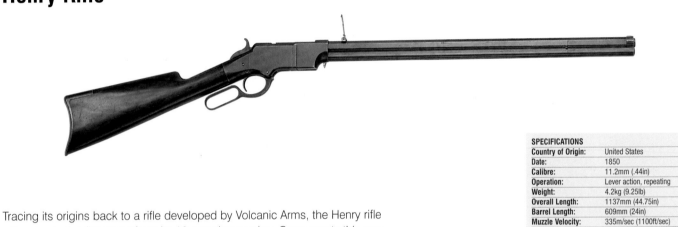

Tracing its origins back to a rifle developed by Volcanic Arms, the Henry rifle offered massive firepower from its 16-round magazine. Once empty this was reloaded via a clumsy muzzle-end process, which could be a drawback.

SPECIFICATIONS	
Country of Origin:	United States
Date:	1850
Calibre:	11.2mm (.44in)
Operation:	Lever action, repeating
Weight:	4.2kg (9.25lb)
Overall Length:	1137mm (44.75in)
Barrel Length:	609mm (24in)
Muzzle Velocity:	335m/sec (1100ft/sec)
Feed/Magazine:	16-round tubular magazine
Range:	400m (1312ft)

Lebel M1886

Developed from the Gras rifle, which was itself a converted Chassepot, the M1886 used a new 8 x 50mm (.314 x 1.97in) cartridge and smokeless powder propellant, creating a higher muzzle velocity. Its eight-round magazine was a big advantage over previous single-shot weapons.

SPECIFICATIONS	
Country of Origin:	France
Date:	1886
Calibre:	8mm (.314in)
Operation:	Bolt action
Weight:	4.24kg (9.375lb)
Overall Length:	1303mm (51.33in)
Barrel Length:	798mm (31.4in)
Muzzle Velocity:	725m/sec (2379ft/sec)
Feed/Magazine:	8-round tubular magazine
Range:	400m (1312ft)

TIMELINE

1850
1886

1888

Lee-Metford

The Lee-Metford rifle might have had a longer service career with the British Army, but it entered service at a time when black powder was being replaced with smokeless propellants. It was thus soon replaced by the Lee-Enfield.

SPECIFICATIONS	
Country of Origin:	United Kingdom
Date:	1888
Calibre:	7.7mm (.303in)
Operation:	Bolt action
Weight:	4.1kg (9.04lb)
Overall Length:	1257mm (49.5in)
Barrel Length:	767mm (30.2in)
Muzzle Velocity:	622m/sec (2040ft/sec)
Feed/Magazine:	8- or 10-round magazine
Range:	730m (2395ft)

FN-Mauser Infantry Rifle Model 1889

Produced by Fabrique Nationale in Belgium, using a Mauser action, the Model 1889 featured a five-round vertical magazine rather than a tubular magazine. This was loaded through the weapon's open action using a charger.

SPECIFICATIONS	
Country of Origin:	Belgium
Date:	1889
Calibre:	7.65mm (.301in)
Operation:	Bolt action
Weight:	4.1kg (8.8lb)
Overall Length:	1295mm (51in)
Barrel Length:	780mm (30.6in)
Muzzle Velocity:	610m/sec (2000ft/sec)
Feed/Magazine:	5-round box magazine
Range:	1000m (3280ft)

Mannlicher-Carcano 1891

Designed by Salvatore Carcano using elements of Mauser and Mannlicher designs, the Modello 1891 was used as the basis of several variant weapons. It was adopted for service with the Imperial Japanese Navy, chambered for the 6.5mm (.256in) Arisaka round.

SPECIFICATIONS	
Country of Origin:	Italy
Date:	1891
Calibre:	6.5mm (.256in)
Operation:	Bolt action
Weight:	3.8kg (8.375lb)
Overall Length:	1291mm (50.79in)
Barrel Length:	780mm (30.6in)
Muzzle Velocity:	730m/sec (2400ft/sec)
Feed/Magazine:	6-round integral box magazine
Range:	1000m (3280ft)

1889

1891

Winchester Repeating Rifles

First appearing in 1866, the Winchester rifle used a tubular magazine under the barrel, reloading with a lever action of the trigger guard. The original front-loading operation was replaced by a loading gate on the side of the receiver.

Model 1866

The initial Winchester model offered huge firepower advantages over the single-shot carbines which were standard cavalry armament in the United States.

SPECIFICATIONS	
Country of Origin:	United States
Date:	1866
Calibre:	11.2mm (.44in)
Operation:	Lever-action, repeating
Weight:	4.3kg (9.5lb)
Overall Length:	1252mm (49.29in)
Barrel Length:	619mm (24.37in)
Muzzle Velocity:	335m/sec (1100ft/sec)
Feed/Magazine:	15-round tubular magazine
Range:	250m (820ft)

Model 1873

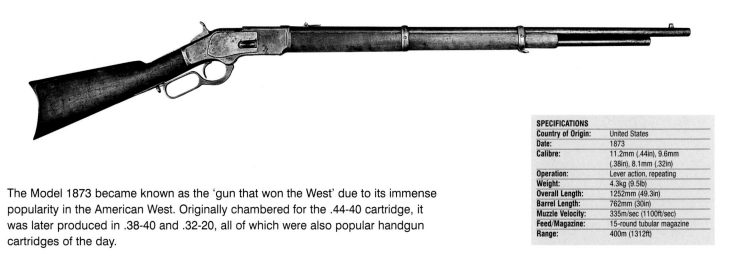

The Model 1873 became known as the 'gun that won the West' due to its immense popularity in the American West. Originally chambered for the .44-40 cartridge, it was later produced in .38-40 and .32-20, all of which were also popular handgun cartridges of the day.

SPECIFICATIONS	
Country of Origin:	United States
Date:	1873
Calibre:	11.2mm (.44in), 9.6mm (.38in), 8.1mm (.32in)
Operation:	Lever action, repeating
Weight:	4.3kg (9.5lb)
Overall Length:	1252mm (49.3in)
Barrel Length:	762mm (30in)
Muzzle Velocity:	335m/sec (1100ft/sec)
Feed/Magazine:	15-round tubular magazine
Range:	400m (1312ft)

TIMELINE 1866   1873   1886

Model 1886

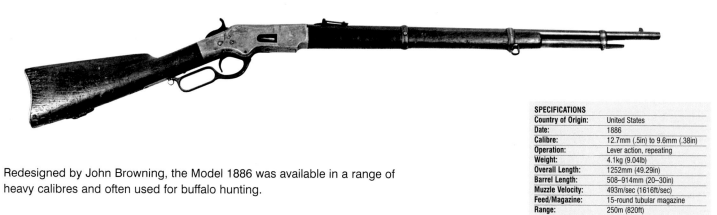

Redesigned by John Browning, the Model 1886 was available in a range of heavy calibres and often used for buffalo hunting.

SPECIFICATIONS	
Country of Origin:	United States
Date:	1886
Calibre:	12.7mm (.5in) to 9.6mm (.38in)
Operation:	Lever action, repeating
Weight:	4.1kg (9.04lb)
Overall Length:	1252mm (49.29in)
Barrel Length:	508–914mm (20–30in)
Muzzle Velocity:	493m/sec (1616ft/sec)
Feed/Magazine:	15-round tubular magazine
Range:	250m (820ft)

Model 1892

Generally chambered for handgun calibres, the Model 1892 allowed a user to carry one type of ammunition to fit both pistol and rifle.

SPECIFICATIONS	
Country of Origin:	United States
Date:	1892
Calibre:	11.2mm (.44in), 9.6mm (.38in), 8.1mm (.32in), 6.35mm (.25in), 5.53mm (.218in)
Operation:	Lever action, repeating
Weight:	3.8kg (8.375lb)
Overall Length:	960mm (37.8in)
Barrel Length:	508mm (20in)
Muzzle Velocity:	759m/sec (2490ft/sec)
Feed/Magazine:	15-round tubular magazine
Range:	183m (590ft)

Model 1894

Built around new smokeless propellants, the Model 1894 remained a popular hunting rifle until production ceased over a century later.

SPECIFICATIONS	
Country of Origin:	United States
Date:	1894
Calibre:	9.6mm (.38in), 8.1mm (.32in), 7.62mm (.3in), 6.35mm (.25in)
Operation:	Lever action, repeating
Weight:	3.1kg (6.8lb)
Overall Length:	960mm (37.8in)
Barrel Length:	508mm (20in)
Muzzle Velocity:	759m/sec (2490ft/sec)
Feed/Magazine:	6- or 7-round tubular magazine
Range:	180m (590ft)

1892

1894

Winchester Model 1895

The Model 1895 was the first of Winchester's rifles to use a box magazine rather than the traditional under-barrel tubular design. Capacity was rather low, however, at four rounds plus one in the breech. This was also the last lever-action rifle to be designed by John Browning.

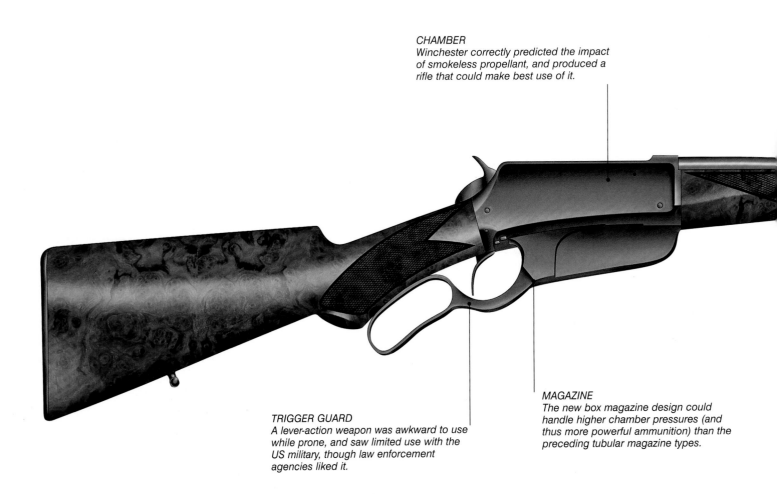

CHAMBER
Winchester correctly predicted the impact of smokeless propellant, and produced a rifle that could make best use of it.

TRIGGER GUARD
A lever-action weapon was awkward to use while prone, and saw limited use with the US military, though law enforcement agencies liked it.

MAGAZINE
The new box magazine design could handle higher chamber pressures (and thus more powerful ammunition) than the preceding tubular magazine types.

SPECIFICATIONS	
Country of Origin:	United States
Date:	1895
Calibre:	10.29mm (.405in) to 7.62mm (.3in)
Operation:	Lever action, repeating
Weight:	4.1kg (9lb)
Overall Length:	1067mm (42in)
Barrel Length:	711mm (28in)
Muzzle Velocity:	818m/sec (2680ft/sec)
Feed/Magazine:	5-round or 4-round internal magazine
Range:	180m (590ft)

The Model 1895 achieved considerable success at home and abroad, with large numbers bought under military contracts. It was also a popular hunting weapon, with some big-game hunters favouring the weapon chambered in rounds up to 10.29mm/.405in (.405 Winchester) calibre.

Among the famous users of the Model 1895 was Theodore Roosevelt, who carried one while fighting with the 'Roughriders' and on big-game hunting expeditions in Africa.

RECEIVER
The first 5000–6000 Model 1895s to leave the factory had flat-sided receivers and are today collector's items.

BARREL
The standard barrel length varied from 609–711mm (24–28 inches), depending on chambering and configuration.

Cartridge Carbines

Shorter rifles were easier to shoot and reload on horseback, and so tended to be issued to cavalry. Carbines were also issued to artillery crews, who might need to defend themselves but were not expected to engage in infantry fighting.

Tarpley Carbine

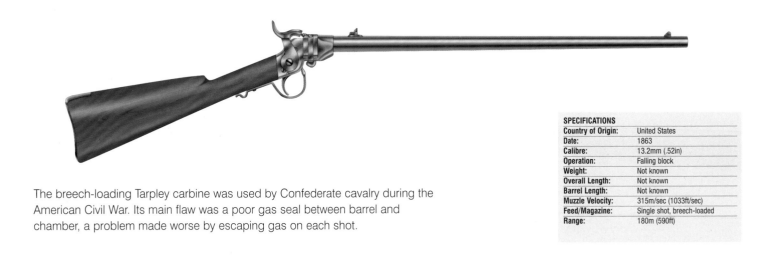

The breech-loading Tarpley carbine was used by Confederate cavalry during the American Civil War. Its main flaw was a poor gas seal between barrel and chamber, a problem made worse by escaping gas on each shot.

SPECIFICATIONS	
Country of Origin:	United States
Date:	1863
Calibre:	13.2mm (.52in)
Operation:	Falling block
Weight:	Not known
Overall Length:	Not known
Barrel Length:	Not known
Muzzle Velocity:	315m/sec (1033ft/sec)
Feed/Magazine:	Single shot, breech-loaded
Range:	180m (590ft)

Spencer Carbine

The Spencer carbine used lever action to chamber each round from the internal magazine. It was manually cocked; the lever did not set the hammer. A charger was available, capable of refilling the magazine with seven rounds at once.

SPECIFICATIONS	
Country of Origin:	United States
Date:	1863
Calibre:	12.7mm (.5in)
Operation:	Lever action, repeating
Weight:	4.1kg (9.04lb)
Overall Length:	760mm (29.92in)
Barrel Length:	560mm (22.05in)
Muzzle Velocity:	315m/sec (1033ft/sec)
Feed/Magazine:	6–13 round tubular magazine
Range:	180m (590ft)

TIMELINE

1863

1866

Chassepot Carbine

A smaller version of the Fusil Mle 1866 Chassepot rifle, the Chassepot carbine used a centre-fire mechanism to initiate its all-metallic cartridge. The primer was located at the rear of the cartridge, as in modern centre-fire weapons.

SPECIFICATIONS	
Country of Origin:	France
Date:	1866
Calibre:	11mm (.433in)
Operation:	Bolt action
Weight:	Not known
Overall Length:	Not known
Barrel Length:	Not known
Muzzle Velocity:	450m/sec (1476ft/sec)
Feed/Magazine:	Single shot, breech-loaded
Range:	600m (1968ft)

Moschetto 1891 Per Cavalleria

A carbine version of the Fucile Modello 91, this weapon was intended, as the name suggests, for use by mounted troops. It incorporated a folding bayonet for use when dismounted.

SPECIFICATIONS	
Country of Origin:	Italy
Date:	1891
Calibre:	6.5mm (.256in)
Operation:	Bolt action
Weight:	3kg (6.6lb)
Overall Length:	920mm (36.2in)
Barrel Length:	610mm (24in)
Muzzle Velocity:	700m/sec (2275ft/sec)
Feed/Magazine:	6-round integral box magazine
Range:	600m (1968ft)

Berthier Artillery Musketoon Mle 1892

The term 'musketoon' is a traditional one, referring to a short musket used by cavalry, and was applied to various carbines, such as the short version of the Berthier rifle, long after it had ceased to be, strictly speaking, appropriate.

SPECIFICATIONS	
Country of Origin:	France
Date:	1892
Calibre:	8mm (.314in)
Operation:	Bolt action
Weight:	3.1kg (6.8lb)
Overall Length:	940mm (37in)
Barrel Length:	445mm (17.5in)
Muzzle Velocity:	610m/sec (2000ft/sec)
Feed/Magazine:	3-round integral box magazine, clip-loaded
Range:	500m (1640ft)

1891

1892

Early Support Weapons

Improving weapons technology made possible a range of support weapons which eventually led to the machine gun. The interim step was a range of multi-barrel weapons firing a rifle-calibre round either in a volley or sequentially.

Montigny Mitrailleuse

The Mitrailleuse consisted of 37 rifle-calibre barrels, loaded simultaneously by a plate cartridge holder and fired in a single volley. It underperformed in the Franco-Prussian War mainly due to a lack of understanding of its capabilities.

SPECIFICATIONS	
Country of Origin:	Belgium
Date:	1866
Calibre:	11mm (.433in) Chassepot
Operation:	Crank-operated
Weight:	140kg (308lb)
Overall Length:	1370mm (54in)
Barrel Length:	1050mm (41.3in)
Muzzle Velocity:	410m/sec (1345ft/sec)
Feed/Magazine:	Volley gun, breech-loaded
Cyclic Rate:	c.300rpm
Range:	400m (1312ft)

Gatling Model 1868

The Gatling was also a mechanical repeater, though a more complex one than the Gardner Gun. Each chamber was loaded in turn from the top-mounted drum, then moved into position to be fired by turning the crank.

SPECIFICATIONS	
Country of Origin:	United States
Date:	1868
Calibre:	12.7mm (.5in)
Operation:	Mechanical multi-barrel revolver
Weight:	64kg (140lb)
Overall Length:	1220mm (48in)
Barrel Length:	626mm (26in)
Muzzle Velocity:	400m/sec (1320ft/sec)
Feed/Magazine:	Drum magazine
Cyclic Rate:	c.300rpm
Range:	400m (1312ft)

TIMELINE

1866

1868

1874

Gardner 5-barrelled Gun

Gardner's 5-barrelled gun was not a machine gun in the true sense; it was a mechanically-operated repeater. Multiple barrels increased the effective rate of fire, with cartridges gravity-fed into the breech.

SPECIFICATIONS	
Country of Origin:	United States/United Kingdom
Date:	1874
Calibre:	11.4mm (.45in) Gatling-Gardner
Operation:	Mechanical repeater
Weight:	24kg (53lb) gun only
Overall Length:	915mm (36in)
Barrel Length:	626mm (26in)
Muzzle Velocity:	400m/sec (1320ft/sec)
Feed/Magazine:	Multi-barrel, breech-loaded
Cyclic Rate:	800rpm
Range:	400m (1312ft)

Nordenfelt Gun

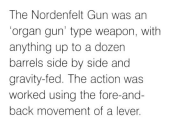

The Nordenfelt Gun was an 'organ gun' type weapon, with anything up to a dozen barrels side by side and gravity-fed. The action was worked using the fore-and-back movement of a lever.

SPECIFICATIONS	
Country of Origin:	United Kingdom
Date:	1880
Calibre:	25.4mm (1in)
Operation:	Lever-operated
Weight:	203kg (447lb)
Overall Length:	Not known
Barrel Length:	901mm (35.48in)
Muzzle Velocity:	446m/sec (1464ft/sec)
Feed/Magazine:	Multi-barrel, gravity-fed
Cyclic Rate:	N/A
Range:	400m (1312ft)

Gatling Model 1893 'Bulldog'

The 'Bulldog' Gatling Gun perhaps derived its name from the snub-nosed 'Bulldog' revolvers that were popular at the time. It was a smaller version of the Gatling Gun, firing rifle-calibre ammunition.

SPECIFICATIONS	
Country of Origin:	United States
Date:	1893
Calibre:	11.2mm (.44in)
Operation:	Mechanical multi-barrel revolver
Weight:	20kg (44lb)
Overall Length:	610mm (24in)
Barrel Length:	457mm (18in)
Muzzle Velocity:	400m/sec (1310ft/sec)
Feed/Magazine:	Drum magazine
Cyclic Rate:	c.300rpm
Range:	400m (1312ft)

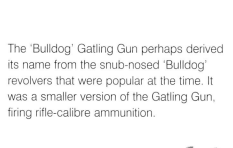

1880

1893

Mobile Support Weapons: Gatling Model 1878

The two main problems facing support weapon users are keeping the weapon adequately supplied with ammunition and making it mobile enough to be where it is needed. One ingenious solution to the latter problem was attempted by the British Army during the colonial campaigns of the late nineteenth century.

While the camel is one of the few animals strong enough to carry the weight of a Gatling Gun and its operator, it is not the most docile of beasts. Camels tend to be unpredictable at the best of times, and the noise of a gun battle (not to mention the Gatling itself firing just behind the beast's head) was virtually guaranteed to upset the animal.

Expedients of this sort were attempted for lack of anything better, but the advent of motorized transport did away with the need and this experiment has not been repeated since.

FIELD OF FIRE
Placing the gun high up on camelback gave good mobility and field of fire, but also made the user a rather prominent target.

RELOADING
It is debatable whether anyone ever tried to fire a Gatling Gun from the back of camel. Reloading would certainly have been virtually impossible, so a single volley would have had to be effective.

CAMEL
The operator had to control his camel and aim his weapon, both at the same time.

TRANSPORT
Camels are not known for their docile nature when upset. A spooked animal might flee the scene, taking with it the fire support capability for a mobile force.

SPECIFICATIONS	
Country of Origin:	United States
Calibre:	11.4mm (.45in)
Operation:	Mechanical multi-barrel revolver
Weight:	34kg (75lb)
Overall Length:	1220mm (48in)
Barrel Length:	610mm (24in)
Muzzle Velocity:	400m/sec (1320ft/sec)
Feed/Magazine:	Drum magazine
Cyclic Rate:	c.300rpm
Range:	500m (1640ft)

The First Machine Guns

A true 'machine gun' is reloaded and made ready to shoot by the action of firing the previous round, and will go on firing until the trigger is released. Once practical weapons of this sort appeared, multi-barrel support weapons rapidly disappeared.

Maxim Mk 1

Hiram Maxim patented his machine gun in 1884, but struggled to find a buyer for his new weapon. Many prospective users considered it wasteful of ammunition, and it was some years before the Maxim Gun attracted serious interest.

SPECIFICATIONS	
Country of Origin:	United Kingdom
Date:	1884
Calibre:	7.7mm (.303in)
Operation:	Recoil, water-cooled
Weight:	18.2kg (40lb) gun only
Overall Length:	1180mm (46.5in)
Barrel Length:	720mm (28.25in)
Muzzle Velocity:	600m/sec (1970ft/sec)
Feed/Magazine:	Belt-fed
Cyclic Rate:	c.600rpm
Range:	2000m (6560ft)

Maxim Pom Pom

The 'Pom Pom' was a 37mm (1.45in) gun that fell somewhere between quick-firing artillery and an infantry support weapon. It saw action in the Boer War and was deployed as an anti-aircraft gun during World War I.

SPECIFICATIONS	
Country of Origin:	United Kingdom
Date:	1895
Calibre:	37mm (1.45in)
Operation:	Recoil, water-cooled
Weight:	186kg (410lb) gun only
Overall Length:	2130mm (84in) gun only
Barrel Length:	876mm (34.5in)
Muzzle Velocity:	850m/sec (230ft/sec)
Feed/Magazine:	Belt-fed
Cyclic Rate:	c.200rpm
Range:	1000m (3280ft) +

TIMELINE

1884

1895

Colt Browning Model 1895

The M1895 demonstrated a workable gas-operation system but was not as effective or reliable as had been hoped for. Development work led to the water-cooled M1917, which became the progenitor of one of the most successful machine gun families of all time.

SPECIFICATIONS	
Country of Origin:	United States
Date:	1895
Calibre:	7.62mm (.3in), 6mm (.23in)
Operation:	Gas-operated
Weight:	16kg (35.25lb)
Overall Length:	1040mm (40.94in)
Barrel Length:	711mm (28in)
Muzzle Velocity:	732m/sec (2400ft/sec)
Feed/Magazine:	Belt-fed
Cyclic Rate:	400rpm
Range:	2740m (8990ft)

Madsen Let Maschingevaer

The Madsen machine gun was the first light machine gun. It was light enough to move with infantry rather than needing an artillery-type carriage or heavy tripod. Although complex it gave good service and remained in use into the 1940s.

SPECIFICATIONS	
Country of Origin:	Denmark
Date:	1903
Calibre:	8mm (.314in) M89
Operation:	Recoil, air-cooled
Weight:	9kg (20lb)
Overall Length:	1145mm (45in)
Barrel Length:	585mm (23in)
Muzzle Velocity:	715m/sec (2350ft/sec)
Feed/Magazine:	25, 30 or 40 box magazine
Cyclic Rate:	450rpm
Range:	1000m (3280ft)

Saint-Etienne M1907

The M1907 was overcomplex, largely because its designers reinvented the wheel to get around existing patents on machine gun gas mechanisms. The gas piston moved forwards rather than back, requiring an additional mechanical system to work the bolt.

SPECIFICATIONS	
Country of Origin:	France
Date:	1907
Calibre:	8mm (.314in)
Operation:	Gas-operated
Weight:	26kg (57.3lb)
Overall Length:	1180mm (46.45in)
Barrel Length:	710mm (27.95in)
Muzzle Velocity:	724m/sec (2375ft/sec)
Feed/Magazine:	25-round metal strips or 300-round fabric belt
Cyclic Rate:	8–650rpm adjustable
Range:	Not known

1903

1907

WORLD WAR I

World War I represented the coming of age of modern firearms. It was the first major war in which repeating and automatic weapons were the mainstay of infantry firepower. The majority of infantrymen were armed with a bolt-action rifle fed from an internal magazine, allowing rapid aimed firepower.

The tactical balance very much favoured the defender in this period. Not only was rifle fire deadly over long distances but the machine gun made traditional close-order advances a suicidal prospect. Heavily shell-cratered ground and barbed wire further slowed the attacker, granting additional time for the defenders' firepower to do its work.

Left: The first contingent of US servicemen to arrive in England in 1917 for deployment to the Western Front stand at ease, their Springfield 1903 rifles arranged in front of them.

Smith & Wesson Revolvers

Smith & Wesson became a household name with both government contracts and sales to the private market. These weapons evolved through a series of stages into effective modern firearms which proved their worth in close combat.

Smith & Wesson Model 1

First introduced in 1857, the No 1 fired a 5.6mm (.22in) short round of very limited stopping power. Although not especially effective, this round has endured; it is the oldest calibre of ammunition still in use today.

SPECIFICATIONS	
Country of Origin:	United States
Date:	1857
Calibre:	5.6mm (.22in)
Operation:	Single-action revolver
Weight:	.33kg (.72lb)
Overall Length:	178mm (7in)
Barrel Length:	81mm (3.2in)
Muzzle Velocity:	Not known
Feed/Magazine:	7-round cylinder
Range:	10m (33ft)

Smith & Wesson No 2 'Old Army' Revolver

A scaled-up version of the No 1, firing an 8.1mm (.32in) round, this weapon was later modified into the S&W No 2, or 'Old Army' revolver. The latter was never officially adopted by the US military, but was a popular private purchase.

SPECIFICATIONS	
Country of Origin:	United States
Date:	1866
Calibre:	8.1mm (.32in)
Operation:	Single-action revolver
Weight:	.33kg (.72lb)
Overall Length:	178mm (7in)
Barrel Length:	81mm (3.2in)
Muzzle Velocity:	Not known
Feed/Magazine:	7-round cylinder
Range:	10m (33ft)

TIMELINE

1857

1866

Smith & Wesson No 3

Developed in the 1880s, the No 3 was a double-action revolver chambered for 9.6mm (.38in) ammunition. It remained popular for many decades, until break-open revolvers passed out of fashion.

SPECIFICATIONS	
Country of Origin:	United States
Date:	1870
Calibre:	9.6mm (.38in)
Operation:	Revolver
Weight:	2.27kg (5lb)
Overall Length:	838mm (33in)
Barrel Length:	406mm (16in)
Muzzle Velocity:	250m/sec (820ft/sec)
Feed/Magazine:	6-round cylinder
Range:	100m (328ft)

Smith & Wesson Russian Model

A version of the No 3 was manufactured in large numbers for the Russian government. There were three main batches, each incorporating upgrades requested by the client.

SPECIFICATIONS	
Country of Origin:	United States
Date:	1870
Calibre:	11.2mm (.44in)
Operation:	Revolver
Weight:	1.02kg (2.25lb)
Overall Length:	317mm (12.5in)
Barrel Length:	203mm (8in)
Muzzle Velocity:	214m/sec (700ft/sec)
Feed/Magazine:	6-round cylinder
Range:	20m (66ft)

Smith & Wesson M1917 'Hand Ejector'

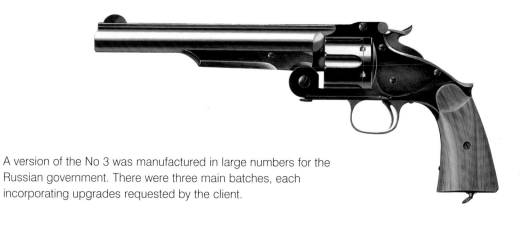

Pushed into service to remedy the US Army's handgun shortage, the M1917 was loaded using two three-round 'half moon' clips, without which the ejector could not grip its rimless 11.4mm (.45in) rounds.

SPECIFICATIONS	
Country of Origin:	United States
Date:	1917
Calibre:	11.4mm (.45in)
Operation:	Revolver
Weight:	1.08kg (2.4lb)
Overall Length:	298mm (11.75in)
Barrel Length:	185mm (7.3in)
Muzzle Velocity:	198m/sec (650ft/sec)
Feed/Magazine:	6-round cylinder
Range:	20m (66ft)

1870

1917

Smith & Wesson Model 10

In 1899, Smith & Wesson built a double-action revolver around their new .38 Special ammunition. This round was essentially a version of the previous .38 Long Colt, with a slightly heavier bullet and more propellant. The combination of these two factors resulted in higher muzzle energy and consequently better knockdown performance. Indeed, the .38 Special round offered a sufficiently impressive balance of ballistic performance against recoil that it remains in use today.

The original weapon in the series that became known as the Model 10 was the Smith & Wesson Military and Police, and was developed as a version of the 'Hand Ejector' revolver chambered for .38 Special. At various times in its long career it has been designated Model 1905 and, during World War II, the Victory Model. Arguably, the Model 10 is the most successful handgun of all time, with over six million examples manufactured.

SPECIFICATIONS	
Country of Origin:	United States
Date:	1899
Calibre:	9.6mm (.38in)
Operation:	Double action revolver
Weight:	.51kg (1.1lb)
Overall Length:	190mm (7.5in)
Barrel Length:	83mm (3.27in)
Muzzle Velocity:	190m/sec (625ft/sec)
Feed/Magazine:	5-round cylinder
Range:	20m (66ft)

BUTT
Swapping handgrips is a relatively simple matter on most handguns, but can make a considerable difference to accuracy and comfort.

Large numbers of Model 10s were used by US, British and Canadian troops in World War II, with most British models chambered for the weaker British .38/200 round. Victory Model .38s were issued to US aviators as sidearms and served in a security role at sensitive installations within the United States. Some remained in service as late as 1990.

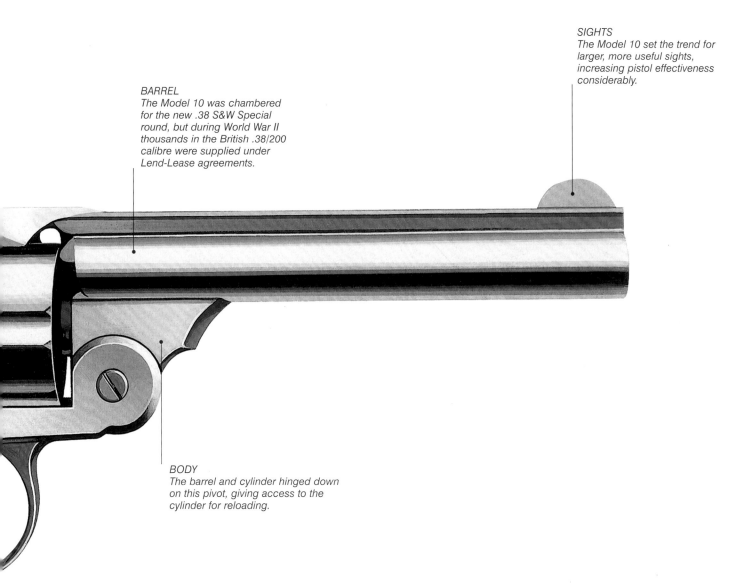

SIGHTS
The Model 10 set the trend for larger, more useful sights, increasing pistol effectiveness considerably.

BARREL
The Model 10 was chambered for the new .38 S&W Special round, but during World War II thousands in the British .38/200 calibre were supplied under Lend-Lease agreements.

BODY
The barrel and cylinder hinged down on this pivot, giving access to the cylinder for reloading.

From its introduction, the Model 10 was a double-action revolver, allowing the user to manually cock the hammer for an accurate shot, or to use the trigger action to cock the weapon before firing, trading accuracy for rapid fire. The various models incorporated improvements over time, including a 1915 upgrade to the weapon's sights. This was so successful that most other service revolver designs followed suit, gaining enlarged sights. The lockwork was also simplified early in the weapon's career.

British Revolvers

The Webley revolver first saw action in the colonial campaigns of the late nineteenth century, and remained in British service through two world wars. Webley revolvers were the standard British service revolvers until the mid-1960s.

Webley-Pryse

One of the finest revolvers available during the 'Colonial Wars' era, the Webley-Pryse served in the Boer and Zulu wars, and heavily influenced the development of later Webley handguns.

SPECIFICATIONS	
Country of Origin:	United Kingdom
Date:	1876
Calibre:	12.09mm (.476in)
Operation:	Double-action revolver
Weight:	.7kg (1.5lb)
Overall Length:	215mm (8.5in)
Barrel Length:	139.7mm (5.5in)
Muzzle Velocity:	198m/sec (650ft/sec)
Feed/Magazine:	5-round cylinder
Range:	20m (66ft)

Webley Bulldog

Available in various calibres, the Bulldog was a cheap but very robust revolver. Its five-shot capacity was a drawback, and its very short barrel limited effective range to about 15m (49ft). Despite this it was popular and widely copied.

SPECIFICATIONS	
Country of Origin:	United Kingdom
Date:	1878
Calibre:	8.1mm (.32in)
Operation:	Revolver
Weight:	.31kg (.7lb)
Overall Length:	140mm (5.5in)
Barrel Length:	53mm (2.1in)
Muzzle Velocity:	190m/sec (625ft/sec)
Feed/Magazine:	5-round cylinder
Range:	15m (49ft)

TIMELINE 1876 1878 1901

Webley-Fosbery Automatic Revolver

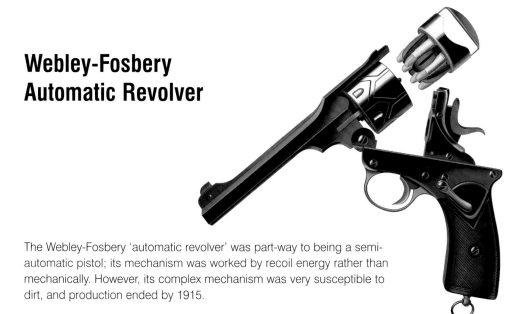

The Webley-Fosbery 'automatic revolver' was part-way to being a semi-automatic pistol; its mechanism was worked by recoil energy rather than mechanically. However, its complex mechanism was very susceptible to dirt, and production ended by 1915.

SPECIFICATIONS	
Country of Origin:	United Kingdom
Date:	1901
Calibre:	11.55mm (.455in)
Operation:	Revolver
Weight:	1.08kg (2.4lb)
Overall Length:	292mm (11.5in)
Barrel Length:	190mm (7.5in)
Muzzle Velocity:	198m/sec (650ft/sec)
Feed/Magazine:	6-round cylinder
Range:	20m (66ft)

Webley & Scott Mk VI

Webley & Scott produced a series of robust, accurate and reliable revolvers, culminating in the definitive Mk VI model. Introduced in 1915, it fired a powerful 11.55mm (.455in) cartridge with excellent stopping power. A bayonet was available, but saw little use.

SPECIFICATIONS	
Country of Origin:	United Kingdom
Date:	1915
Calibre:	11.55mm (.455in)
Operation:	Double-action revolver
Weight:	1.1kg (2.425lb)
Overall Length:	279mm (11in)
Barrel Length:	152mm (6in)
Muzzle Velocity:	198m/sec (650ft/sec)
Feed/Magazine:	6-round cylinder
Range:	20m (66ft)

Enfield .38

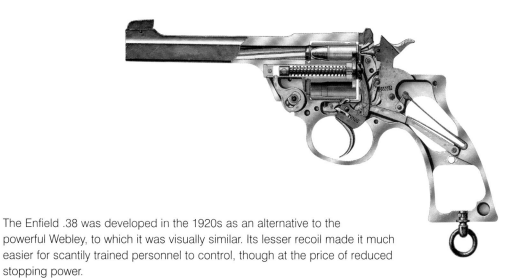

The Enfield .38 was developed in the 1920s as an alternative to the powerful Webley, to which it was visually similar. Its lesser recoil made it much easier for scantily trained personnel to control, though at the price of reduced stopping power.

SPECIFICATIONS	
Country of Origin:	United Kingdom
Date:	1920
Calibre:	9.6mm (.38in)
Operation:	Revolver
Weight:	.82kg (1.8lb)
Overall Length:	254mm (10in)
Barrel Length:	127mm (5in)
Muzzle Velocity:	213m/sec (700ft/sec)
Feed/Magazine:	6-round cylinder
Range:	20m (66ft)

1915   1920

Early Self-Loading Pistols

Towards the end of the nineteenth century, handgun designers began to create weapons that used recoil energy to automatically reload the chamber. These early attempts were little, if any, improvement on a revolver, but they paved the way for more efficient designs.

Laumann 1892

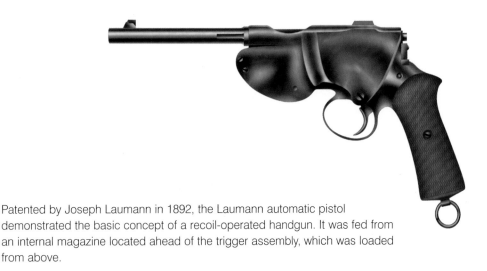

Patented by Joseph Laumann in 1892, the Laumann automatic pistol demonstrated the basic concept of a recoil-operated handgun. It was fed from an internal magazine located ahead of the trigger assembly, which was loaded from above.

SPECIFICATIONS	
Country of Origin:	Germany
Date:	1892
Calibre:	7.8mm (.307in)
Operation:	Recoil operated
Weight:	1.13kg (2.5lb)
Overall Length:	254mm (10in)
Barrel Length:	102mm (4in)
Muzzle Velocity:	300m/sec (1200ft/sec)
Feed/Magazine:	5-round fixed magazine
Range:	30m (98ft)

Schönberger

Patented soon after the Laumann, the Schönberger was based on similar principles. Although it achieved the distinction of being the earliest semi-automatic handgun to go into commercial production, it was not a success in the marketplace.

SPECIFICATIONS	
Country of Origin:	Germany
Date:	1892
Calibre:	8mm (.314in)
Operation:	Recoil operated
Weight:	Not known
Overall Length:	Not known
Barrel Length:	Not known
Muzzle Velocity:	300m/sec (1200ft/sec)
Feed/Magazine:	5-round fixed magazine
Range:	30m (98ft)

TIMELINE

1892

1893

Borchardt C93

Borchardt's pistol used the toggle-locking system developed for the Maxim machine gun, which gave it a distinctive appearance. It also demonstrated the practicality of a detachable box magazine for rapid reloading.

SPECIFICATIONS

Country of Origin:	Germany
Date:	1893
Calibre:	7.65mm (.301in)
Operation:	Toggle-lock
Weight:	1.13kg (2.5lb)
Overall Length:	355mm (14in)
Barrel Length:	184mm (7.24in)
Muzzle Velocity:	355m/sec (1164.7ft/sec)
Feed/Magazine:	8-round magazine
Range:	30m (98ft)

Bergmann Mars Pistol

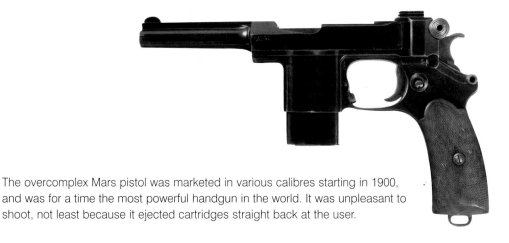

The overcomplex Mars pistol was marketed in various calibres starting in 1900, and was for a time the most powerful handgun in the world. It was unpleasant to shoot, not least because it ejected cartridges straight back at the user.

SPECIFICATIONS

Country of Origin:	Belgium/Germany
Date:	1897
Calibre:	9mm (.35in)
Operation:	Locked-breech
Weight:	.94kg (2.1lb)
Overall Length:	254mm (10in)
Barrel Length:	101mm (3.97in)
Muzzle Velocity:	300m/sec (1200ft/sec)
Feed/Magazine:	8-round magazine
Range:	30m (98ft)

Mannlicher M1901/M1903

The M1901 operated on a delayed-blowback principle, using a spring-and-cam system to restrain the slide during its rearward travel. The original design used 8mm (.314in) ammunition; a series of developed models chambered for 7.63mm (.3in) and 7.65mm (.301in) followed.

SPECIFICATIONS

Country of Origin:	Austria
Date:	1901
Calibre:	7.63mm (.3in)
Operation:	Blowback
Weight:	.94kg (2.1lb)
Overall Length:	239mm (9.4in)
Barrel Length:	165mm (6.5in)
Muzzle Velocity:	312m/sec (1025ft/sec)
Feed/Magazine:	8-round magazine
Range:	30m (98ft)

1897

1901

Front-Loading Semi-Automatics

Many early semi-automatic pistols held their ammunition in an internal magazine located in front of the trigger assembly. This was an inefficient layout which contributed to an excessively long, though elegant, weapon.

Bergmann 1896

Bergmann's 1896 pistol did away with the previous model's extraction system, which bounced the spent case off the next ready round, in favour of a less hazardous method. This design survived well into the twentieth century.

SPECIFICATIONS	
Country of Origin:	Germany
Date:	1896
Calibre:	7.63mm (.3in)
Operation:	Blowback
Weight:	1.13kg (2.5lb)
Overall Length:	254mm (10in)
Barrel Length:	102mm (4in)
Muzzle Velocity:	380m/sec (1250ft/sec)
Feed/Magazine:	5-round magazine
Range:	30m (98ft)

Mauser C96

Chambered for a high-velocity 7.63 x 23mm (.3 x .9in) round, the Mauser 'Broomhandle' was manufactured in huge numbers and proved popular with military and private users worldwide. Unlicensed copies were also made in China.

SPECIFICATIONS	
Country of Origin:	Germany
Date:	1896
Calibre:	7.63mm (.3in)
Operation:	Short recoil
Weight:	1.045kg (2.3lb)
Overall Length:	295mm (11.6in)
Barrel Length:	140mm (5.51in)
Muzzle Velocity:	305m/sec (1000ft/sec)
Feed/Magazine:	6 or 10-round integral or detachable magazine
Range:	100m (328ft)

TIMELINE

1896

1897

Bergmann Simplex

Theodore Bergmann developed his 1896 model pistol into the Bergmann Simplex, using ideas from the Mars pistol. Chambered for a specially developed 8mm (.314in) round, the Bergmann Simplex was manufactured under licence in Belgium.

SPECIFICATIONS	
Country of Origin:	Germany
Date:	1897
Calibre:	8mm (.314in)
Operation:	Blowback
Weight:	.59kg (1.3lb)
Overall Length:	190mm (7.5in)
Barrel Length:	70mm (2.75in)
Muzzle Velocity:	198m/sec (650ft/sec)
Feed/Magazine:	6- or 8-round detachable box magazine
Range:	30m (98ft)

Bergmann-Bayard M1910

Visually similar to the Mauser C96, the M1910 was a reliable short-recoil-operated weapon taken into service with the Spanish, Greek and Danish armed forces. After experimentation with various calibres, 9 x 23mm (.35 x .9in) was settled upon as standard.

SPECIFICATIONS	
Country of Origin:	Germany
Date:	1910
Calibre:	9mm (.35in)
Operation:	Locked-breech
Weight:	1.01kg (2.2lb)
Overall Length:	251mm (9.9in)
Barrel Length:	102mm (4in)
Muzzle Velocity:	305m/sec (1000ft/sec)
Feed/Magazine:	6-round box magazine
Range:	30m (98ft)

Mauser M1912

The C12 or M1912 model was the definitive military version of the C96. Later models were chambered for 9mm (.35in) Parabellum rather than 7.63 x 25mm (.3 x .98in). It was available with a six, 10 or 20-round magazine.

SPECIFICATIONS	
Country of Origin:	Germany
Date:	1912
Calibre:	7.63mm (.3in)
Operation:	Short recoil
Weight:	1.25kg (2.75lb)
Overall Length:	295mm (11.6in)
Barrel Length:	140mm (5.51in)
Muzzle Velocity:	427m/sec (1400ft/sec)
Feed/Magazine:	6, 10 or 20-round integral or detachable magazine
Range:	100m (328ft)

1910

1912

Pistole Parabellum 1908

Modern self-loading (or semi-automatic) handguns offer a number of advantages to the user. These include a slimmer frame for easier carry, faster reloading via a detachable magazine, and usually a higher ammunition capacity than a revolver of the same calibre. Recoil-operated reloading also offers a higher rate of fire than a mechanical repeater such as a revolver can manage.

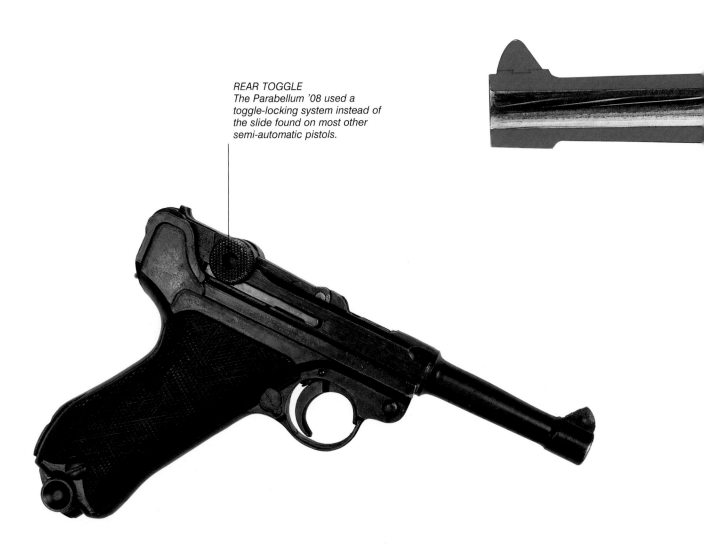

REAR TOGGLE
The Parabellum '08 used a
toggle-locking system instead of
the slide found on most other
semi-automatic pistols.

SPECIFICATIONS	
Country of Origin:	Germany
Date:	1908
Calibre:	9mm (.35in)
Operation:	Toggle-locked, short recoil
Weight:	.96kg (2.125lb)
Overall Length:	222mm (8.8in)
Barrel Length:	127mm (5in)
Muzzle Velocity:	351m/sec (1150ft/sec)
Feed/Magazine:	8-round detachable box magazine
Range:	30m (98ft)

The advantages that modern pistols have were not all present in early semi-automatics. Most were bulky and often held little more ammunition than a revolver. Reloading an internal magazine, even with a stripper clip, was no faster than placing rounds in a revolver's cylinder. Early semi-automatics were often unreliable and prone to malfunction under dirty conditions.

Despite initially being viewed with suspicion in some quarters, the semi-automatic handgun quickly came of age. The Parabellum 1908 (or Luger) offered reliable operation, accuracy and rapid reloading, and quickly became a popular military sidearm. Copies of this weapon are still bought today for target shooting and as 'fun guns'.

ROUND
The Parabellum '08 pistol was instrumental in popularizing the 9mm (.35in) Parabellum round, which became standard load for semi-automatic pistols.

MAGAZINE
Locating the magazine in the handgrip allowed for a shorter overall weapon than placing it in front of the trigger group.

MAGAZINE SPRING
As the action ran backwards after firing, the magazine spring pushed a round into the chamber.

Combat Semi-Automatics

In the early years of the twentieth century, various manufacturers developed semi-automatic pistols for the law enforcement and military markets. Some were highly effective; others deeply flawed.

Type A Model 1902 'Grandpa Nambu'

Chambered for the underpowered 8 x 22mm (.314 x .86in) Nambu round, the Type A Model 1902 also suffered from weak magazine springs that frequently caused stoppages. It was nevertheless adopted as an officer's sidearm by the Japanese Army.

SPECIFICATIONS	
Country of Origin:	Japan
Date:	1902
Calibre:	8mm (.314in)
Operation:	Recoil-spring
Weight:	.9kg (1.98lb)
Overall Length:	230mm (9.06in)
Barrel Length:	117mm (4.61in)
Muzzle Velocity:	289.6m/sec (950ft/sec)
Feed/Magazine:	8-round box magazine
Range:	50m (164ft)

Type A Model 1902 Modified 'Baby Nambu'

The 'Baby Nambu' is broadly similar to the 'Grandpa Nambu', but had a swivelling lanyard ring and aluminum magazine base. The sights, grip, safety and magazine finger pad were also different. This was the most common variant of the Type A with about 10,300 manufactured.

SPECIFICATIONS	
Country of Origin:	Japan
Date:	1902
Calibre:	7mm (.275in)
Operation:	Recoil-spring
Weight:	.9kg (1.98lb)
Overall Length:	230mm (9.06in)
Barrel Length:	117mm (4.61in)
Muzzle Velocity:	289.6m/sec (950ft/sec)
Feed/Magazine:	8-round box magazine
Range:	50m (164ft)

TIMELINE

1902

Savage 1907

The Savage 1907 model achieved modest military sales despite being aimed mainly at the civilian user. Small enough to fit in a pocket it offered respectable firepower from its 10-round magazine.

SPECIFICATIONS	
Country of Origin:	United States
Date:	1907
Calibre:	8.1mm (.32in)
Operation:	Blowback
Weight:	.57kg (1.25lb)
Overall Length:	165mm (6.5in)
Barrel Length:	95mm (3.75in)
Muzzle Velocity:	244m/sec (800ft/sec)
Feed/Magazine:	10-round magazine
Range:	30m (98ft)

Glisenti Modelo 1910

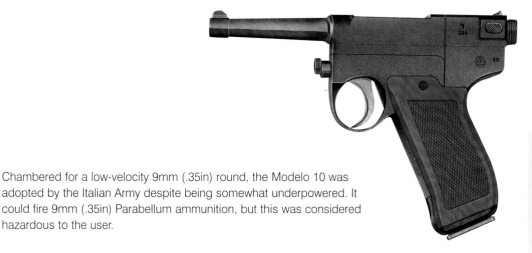

Chambered for a low-velocity 9mm (.35in) round, the Modelo 10 was adopted by the Italian Army despite being somewhat underpowered. It could fire 9mm (.35in) Parabellum ammunition, but this was considered hazardous to the user.

SPECIFICATIONS	
Country of Origin:	Italy
Date:	1910
Calibre:	9mm (.35in)
Operation:	Short recoil, locked-breech
Weight:	.82kg (1.8lb)
Overall Length:	210mm (8.25in)
Barrel Length:	99mm (3.9in)
Muzzle Velocity:	305m/sec (1000ft/sec)
Feed/Magazine:	7-round magazine
Range:	20m (66ft)

Savage 1915

The Savage 1915 was essentially a 'hammerless' version of the 1907; that is, it had a shrouded hammer that could not snag on clothing during a draw. It proved less popular than its predecessor, however.

SPECIFICATIONS	
Country of Origin:	United States
Date:	1915
Calibre:	8.1mm (.32in)
Operation:	Blowback
Weight:	.57kg (1.25lb)
Overall Length:	165mm (6.5in)
Barrel Length:	95mm (3.75in)
Muzzle Velocity:	244m/sec (800ft/sec)
Feed/Magazine:	10-round magazine
Range:	30m (98ft)

1907

1910

1915

Service Pistols of the Central Powers

Although the Parabellum P08 (Luger) is the most famous of the handguns used by the Central Powers, a number of other pistols were used by German and Austrian troops during the Great War period.

Roth-Steyr 1907

The very first semi-automatic sidearm adopted by any army was the Roth-Steyr 1907, which served with Austrian cavalry units from 1909 until the 1940s. Its ammunition was unique to this one weapon.

SPECIFICATIONS	
Country of Origin:	Austria-Hungary
Date:	1907
Calibre:	8mm (.314in)
Operation:	Short recoil
Weight:	1.03kg (2.25lb)
Overall Length:	233mm (9in)
Barrel Length:	131mm (5in)
Muzzle Velocity:	332m/sec (1089ft/sec)
Feed/Magazine:	10-round magazine
Range:	30m (98ft)

Dreyse M1907

The Dreyse M1907 was influenced by early Browning pistols. It was used by Austrian and German officers, and later by Volkssturm troops towards the end of World War II.

SPECIFICATIONS	
Country of Origin:	Germany
Date:	1907
Calibre:	7.65mm (.301in)
Operation:	Blowback
Weight:	.71kg (1.6lb)
Overall Length:	160mm (6.3in)
Barrel Length:	92mm (3.6in)
Muzzle Velocity:	300m/sec (984ft/sec)
Feed/Magazine:	7-round detachable single-stack magazine
Range:	50m (164ft)

TIMELINE

1907

1911

Steyr M1911/1912

The M1911 and M1912 models were virtually identical but for a redesigned foresight. The weapon was adopted by the Austrian Army at the outbreak of war. Some examples were converted to fully automatic fire.

SPECIFICATIONS	
Country of Origin:	Austria-Hungary
Date:	1911
Calibre:	9mm (.35in)
Operation:	Short recoil
Weight:	1.02kg (2.25lb)
Overall Length:	216mm (8.5in)
Barrel Length:	128mm (5.1in)
Muzzle Velocity:	340m/sec (1115ft/sec)
Feed/Magazine:	8-round magazine
Range:	30m (98ft)

Mauser M1912 (Austrian Model)

The Great War created an enormous demand for handguns to arm officers and cavalry troopers. In 1916 the Austrian Army ordered thousands of 7.65mm (.301in) M1912s to meet this requirement.

SPECIFICATIONS	
Country of Origin:	Austria-Hungary
Date:	1912
Calibre:	7.65mm (.301in), 9mm (.35in)
Operation:	Short recoil
Weight:	1.25kg (2.75lb)
Overall Length:	295mm (11.6in)
Barrel Length:	140mm (5.51in)
Muzzle Velocity:	433m/sec (1421ft/sec)
Feed/Magazine:	8–10-round box magazine
Range:	100m (328ft)

Langenham

Around 50,000 Langenham pistols were manufactured for the German Army during the war years. A small 'pocket pistol' version was also made for the private market.

SPECIFICATIONS	
Country of Origin:	Germany
Date:	1914
Calibre:	7.65mm (.301in)
Operation:	Blowback
Weight:	.77kg (1.7lb)
Overall Length:	165mm (6.5in)
Barrel Length:	101.5mm (4in)
Muzzle Velocity:	282m/sec (925ft/sec)
Feed/Magazine:	8-round box magazine
Range:	30m (98ft)

1912

1914

Colt Revolvers

Colt marketed a number of new revolver designs in the early years of the twentieth century. Many of these made use of the powerful new 11.4mm (.45in) ammunition used in army service pistols.

Colt Police Positive

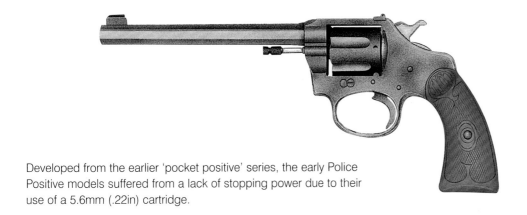

Developed from the earlier 'pocket positive' series, the early Police Positive models suffered from a lack of stopping power due to their use of a 5.6mm (.22in) cartridge.

SPECIFICATIONS	
Country of Origin:	United States
Date:	1907
Calibre:	5.6mm (.22in)
Operation:	Revolver
Weight:	.68kg (1.5lb)
Overall Length:	260mm (10.25in)
Barrel Length:	152mm (6in)
Muzzle Velocity:	213m/sec (700ft/sec)
Feed/Magazine:	6-round cylinder
Range:	20m (66ft)

Colt Police Positive Special

An upgraded Police Positive, the Special was available in .32 or more commonly .38 Special chamberings. As intended by the designers, the Police Positive series was very popular with law enforcement agencies.

SPECIFICATIONS	
Country of Origin:	United States
Date:	1908
Calibre:	9.6mm (.38in)
Operation:	Revolver
Weight:	.68kg (1.5lb)
Overall Length:	260mm (10.25in)
Barrel Length:	152mm (6in)
Muzzle Velocity:	213m/sec (700ft/sec)
Feed/Magazine:	6-round cylinder
Range:	20m (66ft)

TIMELINE

1907

1908

1909

Colt New Service

The Colt New Service was introduced in 1909, replacing previous 9.6mm (.38in) revolvers with one chambered for rimless 11.4mm (.45in) ammunition. The New Service was later developed into the M1917 Army Model.

SPECIFICATIONS	
Country of Origin:	United States
Date:	1909
Calibre:	11.43mm (.45in)
Operation:	Revolver
Weight:	1.3kg (2.9lb)
Overall Length:	273mm (10.75in)
Barrel Length:	140mm (5.5in)
Muzzle Velocity:	198m/sec (650ft/sec)
Feed/Magazine:	6-round cylinder
Range:	20m (66ft)

Colt New Service (snub-nosed)

A snub-nosed (i.e. short-barrelled) version of the Colt New Service was also introduced, making the weapon easier to carry and draw at the price of reduced range and accuracy.

SPECIFICATIONS	
Country of Origin:	United States
Date:	1909
Calibre:	11.43mm (.45in)
Operation:	Revolver
Weight:	1kg (2.2lb)
Overall Length:	180mm (7in)
Barrel Length:	40mm (1.6in)
Muzzle Velocity:	198m/sec (650ft/sec)
Feed/Magazine:	6-round cylinder
Range:	10m (33ft)

Colt .45 Army Model (M1917)

A shortage of handguns caused the US Army to adopt an improved Colt New Service, designated M1917, until sufficient M1911 semi-automatics could be made available. This was the last US military revolver.

SPECIFICATIONS	
Country of Origin:	United States
Date:	1917
Calibre:	11.43mm (.45in)
Operation:	Revolver
Weight:	1.13kg (2.5lb)
Overall Length:	273mm (10.75in)
Barrel Length:	140mm (5.5in)
Muzzle Velocity:	198m/sec (650ft/sec)
Feed/Magazine:	6-round cylinder
Range:	20m (66ft)

1909

1917

John Browning's Early Pistols

John Moses Browning developed a range of weapons including machine guns and shotguns, but it was in the field of semi-automatic handguns that he was perhaps most influential. Many modern handguns are based upon Browning's designs of the early twentieth century.

Browning Model 1900

In conjunction with Fabrique Nationale d'Armes de Guerre (FN), Browning developed several highly influential handguns. The first was the Model 1900, which introduced the concept of a recoil spring above the barrel, which also acted as the firing-pin spring.

SPECIFICATIONS	
Country of Origin:	Belgium
Date:	1900
Calibre:	7.65mm (.301in)
Operation:	Blowback
Weight:	.62kg (1.375lb)
Overall Length:	163mm (6.4in)
Barrel Length:	102mm (4in)
Muzzle Velocity:	259m/sec (850ft/sec)
Feed/Magazine:	7-round magazine
Range:	30m (98ft)

Browning Model 1903

Chambered for 9 x 20mm (.35 x .78in) or 7.65 x 17mm (.301 x .67in) ammunition, the Browning 1903 (also known as FN Model 1903) was adopted by several national police forces. It did not achieve much success in the military market, however.

SPECIFICATIONS	
Country of Origin:	Belgium/United States
Date:	1903
Calibre:	9mm (.35in), 7.65mm (.301in)
Operation:	Blowback
Weight:	.9kg (2.1lb)
Overall Length:	205mm (8in)
Barrel Length:	127mm (5in)
Muzzle Velocity:	259m/sec (850ft/sec)
Feed/Magazine:	7–8 round box magazine
Range:	50m (164ft)

TIMELINE

1900

1910

Browning Model 1910

Also designated FN Model 1910, this pistol influenced the design of later weapons such as the Makarov and the Walther PPK. It achieved notoriety as the weapon used to assassinate Archduke Franz Ferdinand, providing the flashpoint for the Great War.

SPECIFICATIONS	
Country of Origin:	Belgium
Date:	1910
Calibre:	7.65mm (.301in), 9mm (0.35in)
Operation:	Blowback
Weight:	.57kg (1.25lb)
Overall Length:	154mm (6in)
Barrel Length:	88.5mm (3.5in)
Muzzle Velocity:	299m/sec (981ft/sec)
Feed/Magazine:	7-round magazine
Range:	30m (98ft)

Colt M1911 Ace

Designed by John Browning, the M1911 used a swinging-link short-recoil system to produce a reliable, powerful handgun. It was adopted by the US armed forces after exhaustive tests, and remained in mainstream service (as the M1911A1) until the 1980s.

SPECIFICATIONS	
Country of Origin:	United States
Date:	1911
Calibre:	11.4mm (.45in)
Operation:	Short recoil
Weight:	1.1kg (2.425lb)
Overall Length:	216mm (8.5in)
Barrel Length:	127mm (5in)
Muzzle Velocity:	262m/sec (860ft/sec)
Feed/Magazine:	7-round magazine
Range:	30m (98ft)

Colt M1911A1

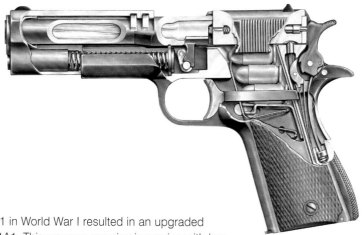

Experience with the M1911 in World War I resulted in an upgraded version designated M1911A1. This weapon remains in service with law enforcement agencies and is a popular civilian handgun. It is also widely used by special operations units.

SPECIFICATIONS	
Country of Origin:	United States
Date:	1924
Calibre:	11.4mm (.45in)
Operation:	Short recoil
Weight:	1.1kg (2.425lb)
Overall Length:	216mm (8.5in)
Barrel Length:	127mm (5in)
Muzzle Velocity:	262m/sec (860ft/sec)
Feed/Magazine:	7-round magazine
Range:	50m (164ft)

1910

1911

1924

Colt M1911

Despite its venerable age, the M1911 is recognizably a 'modern' semi-automatic pistol. Its reliability and the stopping power of its .45 ACP (Automatic Colt Pistol) cartridge ensured generations of satisfied users.

The M1911 does lack a number of modern features, for good or ill. Its single-stack magazine contains only seven rounds, limiting firepower when compared to double-stacked magazines in smaller calibres. On the plus side, this does make for a slimmer weapon which is easier to conceal and better suited to users with small hands than a more 'chunky' weapon.

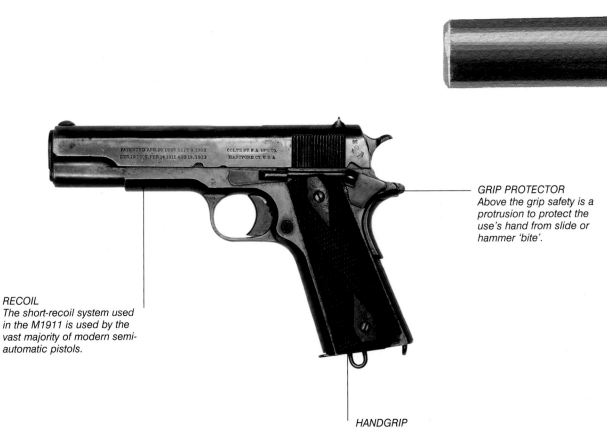

GRIP PROTECTOR
Above the grip safety is a protrusion to protect the use's hand from slide or hammer 'bite'.

RECOIL
The short-recoil system used in the M1911 is used by the vast majority of modern semi-automatic pistols.

HANDGRIP
One way to tell an M1911 from the later M1911A1 is to look for the distinctive diamonds on the grip. They are absent on the M1911A1.

SPECIFICATIONS

Country of Origin:	United States
Date:	1911
Calibre:	11.4mm (.45in)
Operation:	Short recoil
Weight:	1.1kg (2.425lb)
Overall Length:	216mm (8.5in)
Barrel Length:	127mm (5in)
Muzzle Velocity:	262m/sec (860ft/sec)
Feed/Magazine:	7-round magazine
Range:	50m (164ft)

The US military and some private concerns have also experimented with a modernized M1911, retaining the basic functionality of the weapon but adding modern features and advanced materials. Many of the users of these updated M1911s are elite formations – FBI hostage rescue units, US Marine Recon and the LAPD's SWAT teams all favour them.

The sheer number of users, licence-built versions, variants and outright copies of the M1911 is staggering. Even today, a century after its introduction, identical weapons to the M1911 are bought with confidence, often selected over more modern semi-automatics by many users.

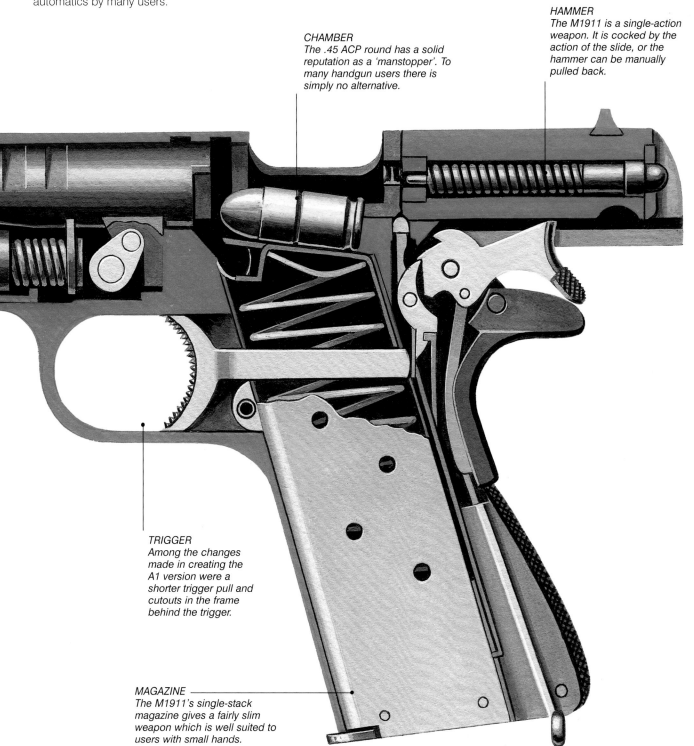

CHAMBER
The .45 ACP round has a solid reputation as a 'manstopper'. To many handgun users there is simply no alternative.

HAMMER
The M1911 is a single-action weapon. It is cocked by the action of the slide, or the hammer can be manually pulled back.

TRIGGER
Among the changes made in creating the A1 version were a shorter trigger pull and cutouts in the frame behind the trigger.

MAGAZINE
The M1911's single-stack magazine gives a fairly slim weapon which is well suited to users with small hands.

Developing Semi-Automatics

The early years of the twentieth century saw the semi-automatic handgun go from an interesting novelty to a serious combat weapon. Not every design was a success, however; many blind alleys had to be explored before the concept came of age.

Frommer Model 1910

Rudolf Frommer's Model 1910 used a long-recoil system in which the barrel and bolt recoiled for a distance greater than the entire length of the cartridge. Later Frommer designs used a more suitable Browning-derived short-recoil system.

SPECIFICATIONS	
Country of Origin:	Austria-Hungary
Date:	1910
Calibre:	7.65mm (.301in)
Operation:	Blowback
Weight:	.59kg (1.3lb)
Overall Length:	184mm (7.25in)
Barrel Length:	108mm (4.25in)
Muzzle Velocity:	335m/sec (1100ft/sec)
Feed/Magazine:	7-round magazine
Range:	20m (66ft)

Webley & Scott Pistol Self-Loading .455 1912

Built around an immensely potent 11.55mm (.455in) round (which was not compatible with 11.55mm/.455in revolvers as it could burst the cylinder when fired), Webley & Scott's self-loader was issued to the Royal Flying Corps and the horse artillery, among other users.

SPECIFICATIONS	
Country of Origin:	United Kingdom
Date:	1912
Calibre:	11.55mm (.455in)
Operation:	Self-loader
Weight:	.68kg (1.5lb)
Overall Length:	216mm (8.5in)
Barrel Length:	127mm (5in)
Muzzle Velocity:	220m/sec (720ft/sec)
Feed/Magazine:	6-round magazine
Range:	20m (66ft)

TIMELINE

1910

1912

Webley & Scott Pistol Self-Loading .455 Mark I Navy

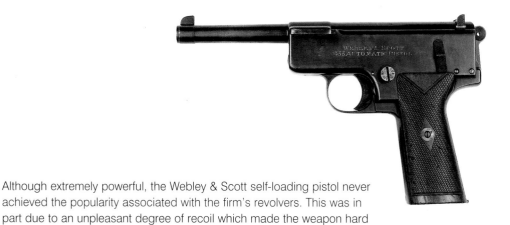

SPECIFICATIONS	
Country of Origin:	United Kingdom
Date:	1912
Calibre:	11.55mm (.455in)
Operation:	Self-loader
Weight:	.68kg (1.5lb)
Overall Length:	216mm (8.5in)
Barrel Length:	127mm (5in)
Muzzle Velocity:	220m/sec (720ft/sec)
Feed/Magazine:	6-round magazine
Range:	20m (66ft)

Although extremely powerful, the Webley & Scott self-loading pistol never achieved the popularity associated with the firm's revolvers. This was in part due to an unpleasant degree of recoil which made the weapon hard to control, and its awkward shape.

Beretta Model 1915

SPECIFICATIONS	
Country of Origin:	Italy
Date:	1915
Calibre:	7.65mm (.301in), 9mm (.35in) Glisenti
Operation:	Blowback
Weight:	.57kg (1.25lb)
Overall Length:	149mm (5.87in)
Barrel Length:	84mm (3.31in)
Muzzle Velocity:	266m/sec (873ft/sec)
Feed/Magazine:	7-round box
Range:	30m (98ft)

Beretta's first entry into the military semi-automatic marketplace was a small 7.65mm (.301in) or 9mm (.35in) weapon fed from a seven-round magazine. It was not a commercial success and only 16,000 were made.

Steyr Model 1917

SPECIFICATIONS	
Country of Origin:	Austria-Hungary
Date:	1917
Calibre:	9mm (.35in)
Operation:	Blowback
Weight:	.99kg (2.18lb)
Overall Length:	216mm (8.5in)
Barrel Length:	128mm (5.03in)
Muzzle Velocity:	335m/sec (1100ft/sec)
Feed/Magazine:	8-round fixed magazine
Range:	30m (98ft)

Developed from the M1912, the Model 1917 was adopted by the Austro-Hungarian armed forces and used until 1945. It was reloaded using a charger inserted down into the fixed internal magazine, a slow process compared with changing a detachable magazine.

1915

1917

Handgun Carbines: Artillery Luger

The Parabellum P08, also known as the Luger after its designer, Georg Luger, was one of several handguns capable of functioning as a carbine. A long-barrelled (artillery) model was developed, which could be adapted as a carbine by fixing a wooden shoulder stock to the base of the handgrip. Other than having slightly modified sights, this weapon was functionally no different to the handgun variant.

The concept behind the weapon was reasonable enough: artillery crews, airmen and engineering troops needed a weapon that was lighter and less bulky than an infantry rifle but more effective than a pistol.

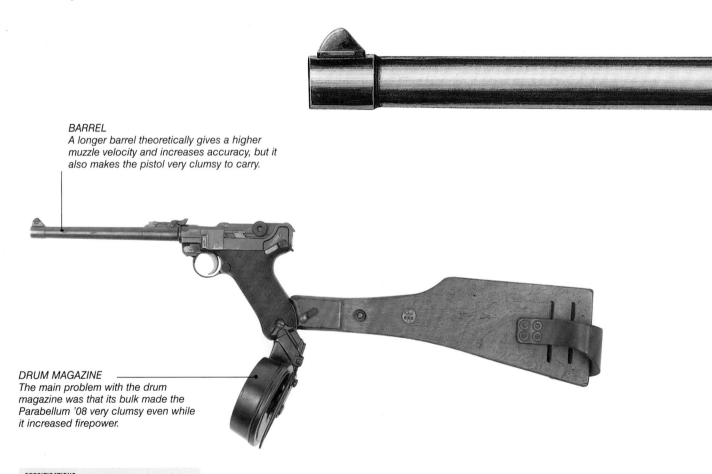

BARREL
A longer barrel theoretically gives a higher muzzle velocity and increases accuracy, but it also makes the pistol very clumsy to carry.

DRUM MAGAZINE
The main problem with the drum magazine was that its bulk made the Parabellum '08 very clumsy even while it increased firepower.

SPECIFICATIONS	
Country of Origin:	Germany
Date:	1913
Calibre:	9mm (.35in)
Operation:	Toggle-locked, short recoil
Weight:	.96kg (2.125lb)
Overall Length:	222mm (8.8in)
Barrel Length:	203mm (8in)
Muzzle Velocity:	351m/sec (1150ft/sec)
Feed/Magazine:	8- or 32-round magazine
Range:	80m (260ft) +

In practice the Luger carbine was never as effective or as popular as the designers hoped, even though it could use standard pistol magazines or a high-capacity 'snail' drum magazine, which theoretically enhanced the user's firepower. The handgun carbine was not a big success, though the option was available for several weapons including the Mauser 1912.

The handgun carbine concept quietly died away in the early years of the twentieth century, but recently there has been something of a revival of interest in such weapons. Some handguns can be converted to full-automatic fire and be fitted with a stock to make a small sub-machine gun, and an increasing number of small 'personal defence weapon' sub-machine guns are reaching the marketplace. It may be that the handgun carbine, or something very much like it, may yet make a resurgence.

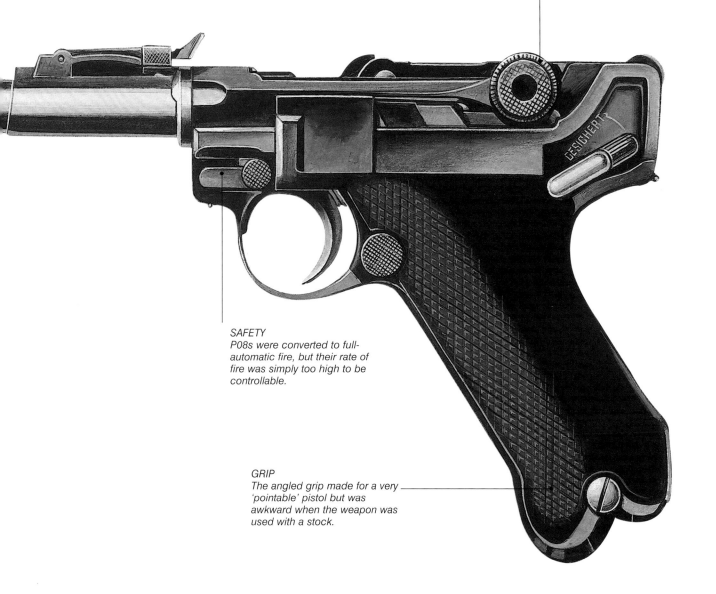

TOP TOGGLE
The Parabellum '08's toggle-locking system interfered with use of the sights when the weapon was used from the shoulder.

SAFETY
P08s were converted to full-automatic fire, but their rate of fire was simply too high to be controllable.

GRIP
The angled grip made for a very 'pointable' pistol but was awkward when the weapon was used with a stock.

European Bolt-Action Rifles

By the beginning of the twentieth century, the bolt-action rifle was the standard infantry weapon. Most carried 5–10 rounds in an internal magazine which was manually loaded, sometimes using a stripper clip. Once a design was proven it tended to remain in service for many years.

Fusil Lebel Mle 1886

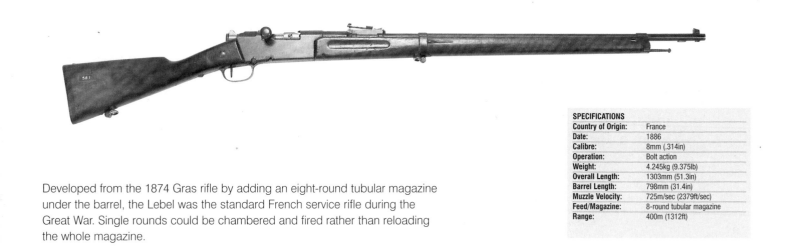

Developed from the 1874 Gras rifle by adding an eight-round tubular magazine under the barrel, the Lebel was the standard French service rifle during the Great War. Single rounds could be chambered and fired rather than reloading the whole magazine.

SPECIFICATIONS	
Country of Origin:	France
Date:	1886
Calibre:	8mm (.314in)
Operation:	Bolt action
Weight:	4.245kg (9.375lb)
Overall Length:	1303mm (51.3in)
Barrel Length:	798mm (31.4in)
Muzzle Velocity:	725m/sec (2379ft/sec)
Feed/Magazine:	8-round tubular magazine
Range:	400m (1312ft)

Fusil FN-Mauser Mle 1889

Produced by Belgian arms manufacturer Fabrique Nationale, the bolt-action mechanism was a copy of the German Mauser. The barrel was encased in a metal jacket to separate it from the woodwork, which stopped the barrel becoming distorted as it heated up.

SPECIFICATIONS	
Country of Origin:	Belgium
Date:	1889
Calibre:	7.63mm (.3in)
Operation:	Bolt action
Weight:	4.01kg (8.8lb)
Overall Length:	1270mm (50in)
Barrel Length:	780mm (30.6in)
Muzzle Velocity:	610m/sec (2001ft/sec)
Feed/Magazine:	5-round magazine
Range:	400m (1312ft)

TIMELINE 1886 1889 1895

Mannlicher Modell 1895

Although eclipsed by the later K98, the Mannlicher Modell 1895 was a highly effective battle rifle which was sold to several national armies. It was favoured by the Boers, whose long-range marksmanship got the best from this model.

SPECIFICATIONS	
Country of Origin:	Austria-Hungary
Date:	1895
Calibre:	8mm (.314in)
Operation:	Bolt action
Weight:	3.78kg (8.3lb)
Overall Length:	1270mm (50in)
Barrel Length:	765mm (30.1in)
Muzzle Velocity:	619m/sec (2031ft/sec)
Feed/Magazine:	5-round box
Range:	500m (1640ft)

Lebel Berthier Mle 1907/15 carbine

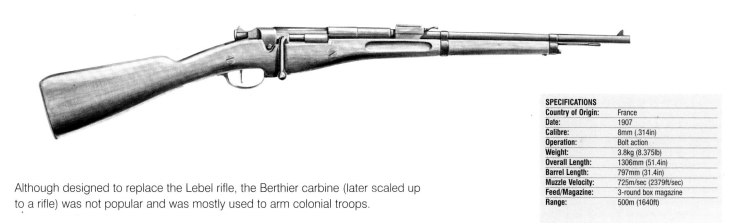

Although designed to replace the Lebel rifle, the Berthier carbine (later scaled up to a rifle) was not popular and was mostly used to arm colonial troops.

SPECIFICATIONS	
Country of Origin:	France
Date:	1907
Calibre:	8mm (.314in)
Operation:	Bolt action
Weight:	3.8kg (8.375lb)
Overall Length:	1306mm (51.4in)
Barrel Length:	797mm (31.4in)
Muzzle Velocity:	725m/sec (2379ft/sec)
Feed/Magazine:	3-round box magazine
Range:	500m (1640ft)

Fusil Berthier Mle 1907/15

In 1915, the French Army began to phase out the Lebel rifle in favour of the Berthier mle 1907/15. It was based specifically on the Senegal rifle from 1907 used by colonial troops. It had a limited three-round magazine.

SPECIFICATIONS	
Country of Origin:	France
Date:	1915
Calibre:	8mm (.314in)
Operation:	Bolt action
Weight:	3.8kg (8.4lb)
Overall Length:	1306mm (51.4in)
Barrel Length:	797mm (31in)
Muzzle Velocity:	640m/sec (2100ft/sec)
Feed/Magazine:	3-round box magazine
Range:	500m (1640ft)

1907   1915

Infantry Weapons and Tactics: Mauser Gewehr 98

It is axiomatic that armed forces are always preparing to fight the last war. Certainly the armies that fought World War I were shaped by the experiences of the late nineteenth century.

Innovations such as the machine gun had not yet had time to be fully appreciated, and the influence of railways on military mobility and logistics was as yet improperly understood. The lesson that had been learned from previous conflicts was that infantry were capable of delivering heavy firepower at long range.

To do this, infantrymen needed a long, powerful rifle which was accurate out to several hundred metres, and they needed good marksmanship training. An internal magazine and rapid bolt-action reloading allowed cavalry and infantry attacks to be broken up before they could make contact, so infantrymen (and their rifles) had to be capable of fast, accurate fire.

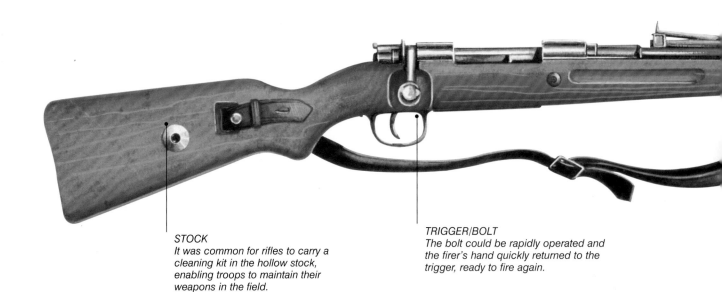

STOCK
It was common for rifles to carry a cleaning kit in the hollow stock, enabling troops to maintain their weapons in the field.

TRIGGER/BOLT
The bolt could be rapidly operated and the firer's hand quickly returned to the trigger, ready to fire again.

SPECIFICATIONS	
Country of Origin:	Germany
Date:	1898
Calibre:	7.92mm (.312in)
Operation:	Bolt action
Weight:	4.2kg (9.25lb)
Overall Length:	1250mm (49.2in)
Barrel Length:	740mm (29.1in)
Muzzle Velocity:	640m/sec (2100ft/sec)
Feed/Magazine:	5-round box magazine
Range:	500m (1640ft)

Long rifles such as the Mauser Gewehr 98 which armed the German infantry were not ideally suited to close-quarters fighting in a trench assault, though they served admirably in a defensive role. The same weapon, albeit in a shortened 'carbine' format, was the standard German infantry rifle at the outbreak of World War II.

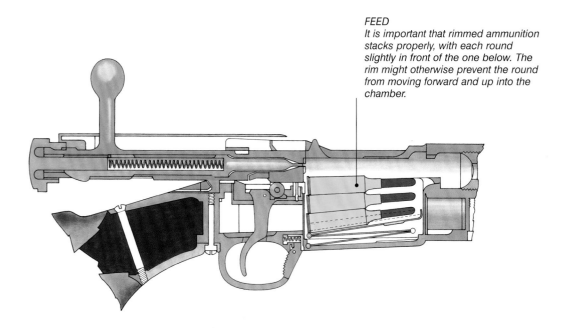

FEED
It is important that rimmed ammunition stacks properly, with each round slightly in front of the one below. The rim might otherwise prevent the round from moving forward and up into the chamber.

Throughout the twentieth century the trend was for combat ranges to become shorter, for weapons to become shorter and lighter, and for infantry to operate in ever more dispersed formations to avoid becoming an easy target. The long bolt-action rifles of 1914 gave way to shorter semi-automatic and finally automatic weapons, representing an exponential growth in the combat power of the infantryman even as enemy firepower pushed him ever further from his comrades.

FOREARM
The weapon was supported with the firer's left hand while the bolt was operated, allowing at least general aim to be maintained.

SLING
A sling was essential to carry the weapon on the march, but one that attached at an unsuitable point could make the rifle very awkward to use.

BAYONET LUG
Although the bayonet was rarely used, the act of fixing bayonets had a profound psychological effect.

Western Bolt-Action Rifles

It was not uncommon in the early twentieth century for a weapon to start its life in one nation and enter service in another. Many weapon designs crossed the Atlantic, some more than once.

Krag-Jorgensen

The Krag-Jorgensen rifle served with the US Army as well as in its native Norway. Its integral magazine could be loaded more quickly than most others, and a partially emptied magazine could be easily 'topped off' with additional rounds.

SPECIFICATIONS	
Country of Origin:	Norway
Date:	1886
Calibre:	7.62mm (.3in)
Operation:	Bolt action
Weight:	3.375kg (7.4lb)
Overall Length:	986mm (38.8in)
Barrel Length:	520mm (20.5in)
Muzzle Velocity:	580m/sec (1900ft/sec)
Feed/Magazine:	5-round magazine
Range:	500m (1640ft)

Ross

Although it performed well on the range, the Canadian Ross rifle suffered from serious defects. It was prone to jamming, both due to mechanical problems and to a general susceptibility to dirt.

SPECIFICATIONS	
Country of Origin:	Canada
Date:	1903
Calibre:	7.7mm (.303in)
Operation:	Bolt action
Weight:	4.48kg (9.875lb)
Overall Length:	1285mm (50.6in)
Barrel Length:	765mm (30.1in)
Muzzle Velocity:	792m/sec (2600ft/sec)
Feed/Magazine:	5-round magazine
Range:	500m (1640ft)

TIMELINE

1886

1903

Pattern 1914 Enfield Rifle (P14)

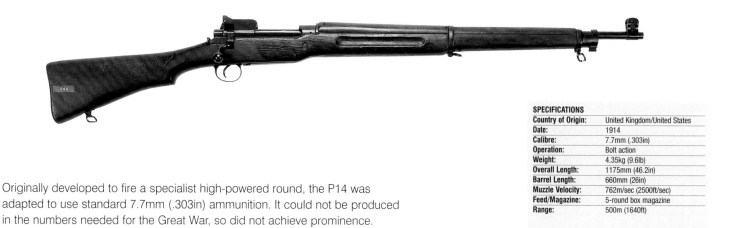

Originally developed to fire a specialist high-powered round, the P14 was adapted to use standard 7.7mm (.303in) ammunition. It could not be produced in the numbers needed for the Great War, so did not achieve prominence.

SPECIFICATIONS	
Country of Origin:	United Kingdom/United States
Date:	1914
Calibre:	7.7mm (.303in)
Operation:	Bolt action
Weight:	4.35kg (9.6lb)
Overall Length:	1175mm (46.2in)
Barrel Length:	660mm (26in)
Muzzle Velocity:	762m/sec (2500ft/sec)
Feed/Magazine:	5-round box magazine
Range:	500m (1640ft)

Mousqueton Berthier Mle 1892/M16

One of the most successful and long-lived variants of the Berthier system was the short carbine version of the five-shot Mle 1916 Berthier, designated 'Mousqueton Berthier Mle 1892/M16'. This carbine proved popular with mounted cavalry and reconnaissance troops.

SPECIFICATIONS	
Country of Origin:	France
Date:	1916
Calibre:	8mm (.314in)
Operation:	Bolt action
Weight:	3.1kg (6.8lb)
Overall Length:	945mm (37.2in)
Barrel Length:	453mm (17.8in)
Muzzle Velocity:	640m/sec (3000ft/sec)
Feed/Magazine:	5-round charger loaded magazine
Range:	500m (1640ft)

M1917 Enfield Rifle

Developed from the advanced but ill-fated P14, the M1917 was adapted to fire US 7.62 x 63mm (.30-06) ammunition and put into mass production. Over two million were made, with many later going to British Home Guard units.

SPECIFICATIONS	
Country of Origin:	United Kingdom/United States
Date:	1917
Calibre:	7.62mm (.3in)
Operation:	Bolt action
Weight:	4.17kg (9.2lb)
Overall Length:	1175mm (46.25in)
Barrel Length:	660mm (26in)
Muzzle Velocity:	823m/sec (2700ft/sec)
Feed/Magazine:	6-round magazine, 5-round-clip-fed reloading
Range:	500m (1640ft)

The Lee-Enfield

The Lee-Enfield rifle was the standard British infantry weapon of the Great War. Several variants existed, resulting from incremental development over many years. The definitive Short Magazine Lee-Enfield was a world-beating weapon that remained in service for many decades.

Magazine Lee-Enfield (MLE)

Developed from the Lee-Metford rifle, the Magazine Lee-Enfield (MLE) was introduced in 1895, with a shortened carbine variant arriving the following year. The weapon's name was derived from the Enfield factory where it was made, and the designer, James Paris Lee.

SPECIFICATIONS	
Country of Origin:	United Kingdom
Date:	1895
Calibre:	7.7mm (.303in)
Operation:	Bolt action
Weight:	4.17kg (9.2lb)
Overall Length:	1257mm (49.5in)
Barrel Length:	540mm (22in)
Muzzle Velocity:	751m/sec (2465ft/sec)
Feed/Magazine:	10-round box, loaded with 5-round charger clips
Range:	500m (1640ft)

Short Magazine Lee-Enfield (SMLE) Mk I

The word 'Short' in the weapon's name referred to its length, not that of the magazine it used. The SMLE was somewhere between a standard battle rifle and a carbine in length, making it easy to handle.

SPECIFICATIONS	
Country of Origin:	United Kingdom
Date:	1904
Calibre:	7.7mm (.303in)
Operation:	Bolt action
Weight:	4.14kg (9.125lb)
Overall Length:	1129mm (44.4in)
Barrel Length:	640mm (25.2in)
Muzzle Velocity:	751m/sec (2465ft/sec)
Feed/Magazine:	10-round box, loaded with 5-round charger clips
Range:	500m (1640ft)

TIMELINE

1895   1904   1906

Short Magazine Lee-Enfield (SMLE) Mk II

The Mk II SMLE entered service in 1906. Rather than a new model as such, it was a conversion of older 'long' Lee-Enfields into what was effectively a Mk I configuration.

SPECIFICATIONS	
Country of Origin:	United Kingdom
Date:	1906
Calibre:	7.7mm (.303in)
Operation:	Bolt action
Weight:	4.14kg (9.125lb)
Overall Length:	1129mm (44.4in)
Barrel Length:	640mm (25.2in)
Muzzle Velocity:	751m/sec (2465ft/sec)
Feed/Magazine:	10-round box, loaded with 5-round charger clips
Range:	500m (1640ft)

Short Magazine Lee-Enfield (SMLE) Mk III

The definitive SMLE appeared in 1907, with slight modifications including the ability to fire higher-velocity ammunition. A wartime expedient version, designated Mk III*, went into production in 1915. This version was later redesignated Rifle No 1 Mk III*.

SPECIFICATIONS	
Country of Origin:	United Kingdom
Date:	1907
Calibre:	7.7mm (.303in)
Operation:	Bolt action
Weight:	3.93kg (8.625lb)
Overall Length:	1133mm (44.6in)
Barrel Length:	640mm (25.2in)
Muzzle Velocity:	634m/sec (2080ft/sec)
Feed/Magazine:	10-round box, loaded with 5-round charger clips
Range:	500m (1640ft)

Short Magazine Lee-Enfield (SMLE) Mk III with grenade launcher

The Mk III SMLE could be converted into a grenade launcher. As grenade launcher rifles were prone to bursting, the body and upper barrel were wrapped in brass wire and soldered together. The grenade is a No 5 Mk I 1916.

SPECIFICATIONS*	
Country of Origin:	United Kingdom
Date:	1916
Calibre:	7.7mm (.303in)
Operation:	Bolt action
Weight:	3.93kg (8.625lb)
Overall Length:	1133mm (44.6in)
Barrel Length:	640mm (25.2in)
Muzzle Velocity:	634m/sec (2080ft/sec)
Feed/Magazine:	N/A
Range (Grenade):	100m (328ft)
(*Of rifle without grenade)	

1907

1916

Military Bolt-Action Rifles

Just as breech loaders drove their predecessors from the battlefield, nations facing the new generation of bolt-action infantry rifles needed to obtain comparable weapons or risk utter defeat. The bolt-action rifle represented a huge leap forward in infantry firepower.

Mosin-Nagant Rifle

The Mosin-Nagant rifle combined elements of designs by Sergei Mosin and the Nagant brothers to create a weapon that was virtually indestructible despite its complexity. A series of developed versions armed the Russian military for decades.

SPECIFICATIONS	
Country of Origin:	Russia
Date:	1891
Calibre:	7.62mm (.3in)
Operation:	Bolt action
Weight:	4.37kg (9.625lb)
Overall Length:	1305mm (51.4in)
Barrel Length:	802mm (31.6in)
Muzzle Velocity:	810m/sec (2657ft/sec)
Feed/Magazine:	5-round box magazine
Range:	500m (1640ft), 750m (2460ft) + with optics

Fucile Modello 91 (Mannlicher-Carcano)

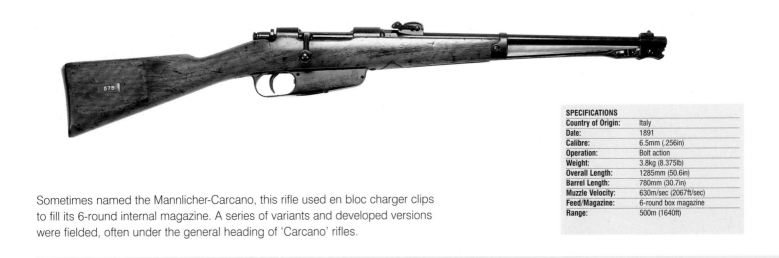

Sometimes named the Mannlicher-Carcano, this rifle used en bloc charger clips to fill its 6-round internal magazine. A series of variants and developed versions were fielded, often under the general heading of 'Carcano' rifles.

SPECIFICATIONS	
Country of Origin:	Italy
Date:	1891
Calibre:	6.5mm (.256in)
Operation:	Bolt action
Weight:	3.8kg (8.375lb)
Overall Length:	1285mm (50.6in)
Barrel Length:	780mm (30.7in)
Muzzle Velocity:	630m/sec (2067ft/sec)
Feed/Magazine:	6-round box magazine
Range:	500m (1640ft)

TIMELINE

1891

Arisaka Type 30

The first of the Arisaka family of rifles, the Type 30 used a weak 6.5 x 50mm (.256 x 1.97in) round. A shorter carbine variant was issued to cavalry, but both versions proved unsatisfactory and the search for a replacement was soon underway.

SPECIFICATIONS	
Country of Origin:	Japan
Date:	1897
Calibre:	6.5mm (.256in)
Operation:	Bolt action
Weight:	3.95kg (8.7lb)
Overall Length:	1280mm (50.7in)
Barrel Length:	800mm (31.5in)
Muzzle Velocity:	765m/sec (2509ft/sec)
Feed/Magazine:	5-round internal magazine
Range:	500m (1640ft)

Springfield Model 1903

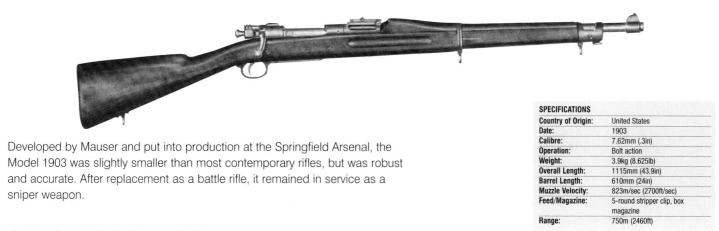

Developed by Mauser and put into production at the Springfield Arsenal, the Model 1903 was slightly smaller than most contemporary rifles, but was robust and accurate. After replacement as a battle rifle, it remained in service as a sniper weapon.

SPECIFICATIONS	
Country of Origin:	United States
Date:	1903
Calibre:	7.62mm (.3in)
Operation:	Bolt action
Weight:	3.9kg (8.625lb)
Overall Length:	1115mm (43.9in)
Barrel Length:	610mm (24in)
Muzzle Velocity:	823m/sec (2700ft/sec)
Feed/Magazine:	5-round stripper clip, box magazine
Range:	750m (2460ft)

Arisaka 38th Year Rifle

Developed from the Type 30 rifle, the Type 38 (or 38th Year Rifle) also used the low-powered 6.5mm (.256in) cartridge. It was effective out to about 400m (1312ft) and served through both world wars.

SPECIFICATIONS	
Country of Origin:	Japan
Date:	1905
Calibre:	6.5mm (.256in)
Operation:	Bolt action
Weight:	4.2kg (9.25lb)
Overall Length:	1275mm (50.2in)
Barrel Length:	797.5mm (31.4in)
Muzzle Velocity:	731m/sec (2400ft/sec)
Feed/Magazine:	5-round box magazine
Range:	500m (1640ft)

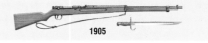

Bolt-Action Rifles: Springfield Model 1903

A bolt-action rifle, like any firearm, has to perform three main tasks. It must transfer ammunition from wherever it is stored to the firing chamber, fire it in a manner that ensures both a reasonable degree of accuracy and also the safety of the user, and then get rid of the expended cartridge so that the next one can be loaded.

The key to all these actions is the bolt, which is manually operated by the user. Pulling the bolt to the rear opens the breech and operates the ejector mechanism, flipping the cartridge (whether expended or not) out of the weapon. Pushing it forward again allows the next round to be pushed into the chamber by the magazine spring.

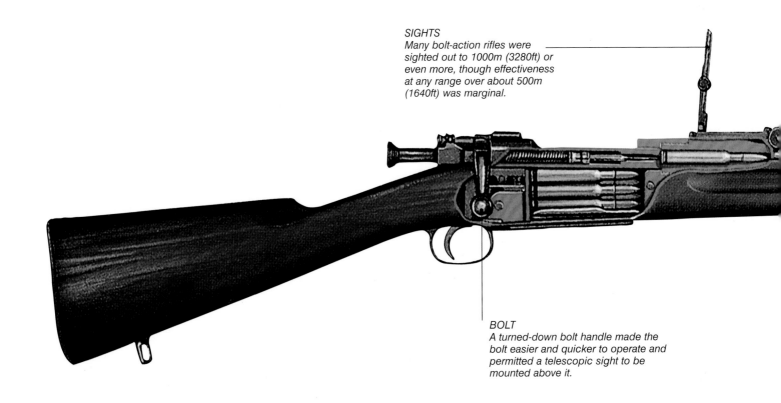

SIGHTS
Many bolt-action rifles were sighted out to 1000m (3280ft) or even more, though effectiveness at any range over about 500m (1640ft) was marginal.

BOLT
A turned-down bolt handle made the bolt easier and quicker to operate and permitted a telescopic sight to be mounted above it.

SPECIFICATIONS	
Country of Origin:	United States
Date:	1903
Calibre:	7.62mm (.3in)
Operation:	Bolt action
Weight:	3.9kg (8.625lb)
Overall Length:	1115mm (43.9in)
Barrel Length:	610mm (24in)
Muzzle Velocity:	823m/sec (2700ft/sec)
Feed/Magazine:	5-round stripper clip, box magazine
Range:	750m (2460ft)

Fully closing the bolt seals the firing chamber and ensures that no gases escape to injure the user when the weapon is fired. A positive lock on the bolt is critical to safety; a potentially lethal malfunction can occur if a weak or overstressed bolt is thrown back into the user's face by gas pressure in the chamber.

CHAMBER
Once chambered, the round is securely locked in. This prevents gas escape that would reduce muzzle velocity and perhaps injure the weapon's user.

FORESIGHT
Most bolt-action infantry rifles had a simple post front sight, but in the mid-twentieth century a hooded sight became popular.

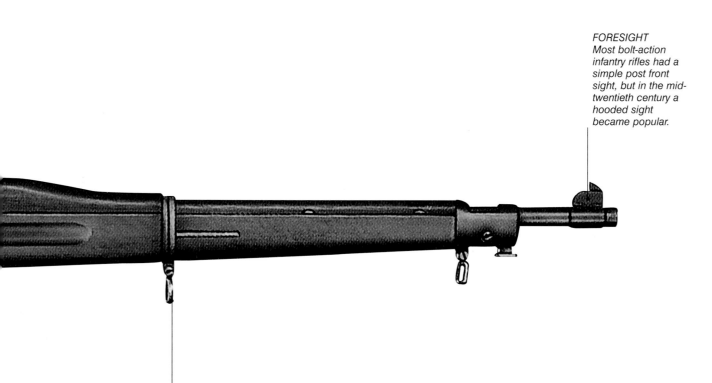

FURNITURE
Good quality furniture was important to accuracy; a warped wooden forearm would pull the barrel out of alignment.

A good rifle chambers and ejects rounds smoothly, and provides a solid seal on the chamber when firing, all without requiring undue effort on the part of the user. It is not possible to shoot accurately and quickly while fighting with a weapon's bolt; a clean and crisp action is the heart of an effective rifle.

M1918 Browning Automatic Rifle (BAR)

One problem facing the armies of the Great War was how to provide automatic fire support for advancing troops. The medium machine guns of the day were too bulky to carry forward over no-man's-land, and without them the ability of advancing troops to repel a counterattack was limited.

The answer was to provide a lighter automatic support weapon which did not need a heavy tripod and water-cooling apparatus, and which could carry its ammunition in a convenient magazine or drum.

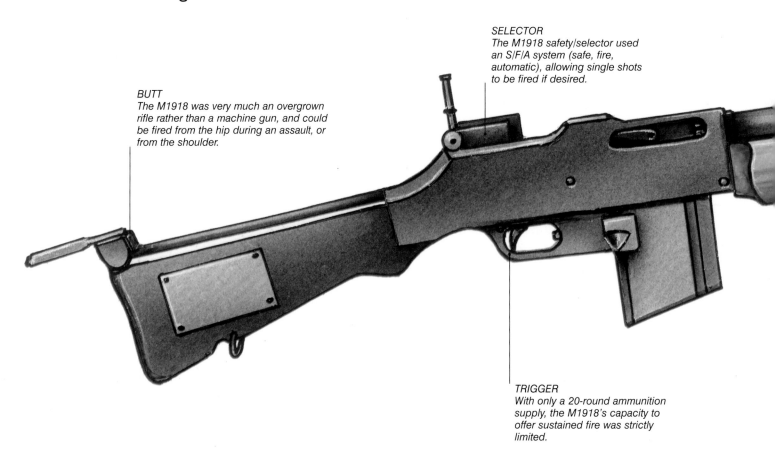

SELECTOR
The M1918 safety/selector used an S/F/A system (safe, fire, automatic), allowing single shots to be fired if desired.

BUTT
The M1918 was very much an overgrown rifle rather than a machine gun, and could be fired from the hip during an assault, or from the shoulder.

TRIGGER
With only a 20-round ammunition supply, the M1918's capacity to offer sustained fire was strictly limited.

SPECIFICATIONS	
Country of Origin:	United States
Date:	1917
Calibre:	7.62mm (.3in)
Operation:	Gas-operated
Weight:	7.26kg (16lb)
Overall Length:	1194mm (47in)
Barrel Length:	610mm (24in)
Muzzle Velocity:	853m/sec (2800ft/sec)
Feed/Magazine:	20-round straight box
Range:	1000–1500m (3280–4921ft)

Of the various attempts to provide a light automatic support weapon, the Browning Automatic Rifle was one of the most effective. It was not a true machine gun; for one thing it did not have a quick-change barrel to prevent overheating under sustained fire, and its ammunition capacity was limited. However, the BAR enabled an infantry squad to lay down automatic fire to suppress an enemy position or repel a counterattack, without impeding mobility.

It has been suggested that the BAR was an early assault rifle, but this is not really true. It was chambered for full-power 'battle rifle' ammunition and certainly was not a short, lightweight assault weapon. What it definitely was, was a highly effective squad-level automatic weapon. This was something the infantry needed in 1918 and still need today.

GAS PISTON
The M1918 was operated by gas drawn from the barrel, driving a long piston to cycle the weapon. It fired from an open bolt.

OTHER MODELS
Fabrique Nationale bought the rights to produce the Browning Automatic Rifle in 1920, and produced a range of variants to various specifications.

Light Machine Guns

Medium machine guns were excellent for defence but lacked mobility. In an effort to provide automatic fire support for an advance, lighter machine guns were developed by the combatant nations.

Lewis Gun Mk 1

The innovative Lewis Gun was gas operated, using the expanding propellant gases from one round to work the action and to draw air into the jacket to cool the weapon. It could use 97- and 47-round ammunition drums.

SPECIFICATIONS	
Country of Origin:	United States
Date:	1914
Calibre:	7.7mm (.303in)
Operation:	Gas-operated, air-cooled
Weight:	11.8kg (26lb)
Overall Length:	965mm (38in)
Barrel Length:	665mm (26.25in)
Muzzle Velocity:	600m/sec (1970ft/sec)
Feed/Magazine:	Magazine-fed
Cyclic Rate:	550rpm
Range:	1000m (3280ft) +

Bergmann MG15

The Bergmann MG15 was the world's first light machine gun to use a disintegrating-link belt of ammunition. A 100-round belt could be loaded into a drum for mobile fire support.

SPECIFICATIONS	
Country of Origin:	Germany
Date:	1915
Calibre:	7.9mm (.307in) Mauser
Operation:	Recoil, air-cooled
Weight:	12.9kg (28.5lb)
Overall Length:	1120mm (44in)
Barrel Length:	725mm (28.5in)
Muzzle Velocity:	890m/sec (2925ft/sec)
Feed/Magazine:	Belt-fed (belt contained in drum)
Cyclic Rate:	500rpm
Range:	2000m (6560ft) +

TIMELINE

 1914

 1915

Fusil Mitrailleur M'15 (Chauchat)

The Chauchat light machine gun was used in vast numbers by the French and US armies. The US variant, chambered for 7.62 x 63mm (.30-06) ammunition, proved highly unreliable; the 8mm (.314in) French version was somewhat better.

SPECIFICATIONS	
Country of Origin:	France
Date:	1915
Calibre:	8mm (.314in) Lebel
Operation:	Recoil, air-cooled
Weight:	9kg (20lb)
Overall Length:	1145mm (45in)
Barrel Length:	470mm (18.5in)
Muzzle Velocity:	700m/sec (2300ft/sec)
Feed/Magazine:	Magazine-fed
Cyclic Rate:	250rpm
Range:	1000m (3280ft)

Villar-Perosa M1915

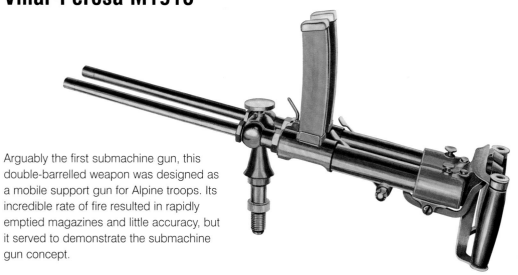

Arguably the first submachine gun, this double-barrelled weapon was designed as a mobile support gun for Alpine troops. Its incredible rate of fire resulted in rapidly emptied magazines and little accuracy, but it served to demonstrate the submachine gun concept.

SPECIFICATIONS	
Country of Origin:	Italy
Date:	1915
Calibre:	9mm (.35in)
Operation:	Blowback
Weight:	6.5kg (14.33lb)
Overall Length:	558.8mm (21in)
Barrel Length:	320mm (12.6in)
Muzzle Velocity:	320m/sec (1050ft/sec)
Feed/Magazine:	Box magazine
Cyclic Rate:	350rpm
Range:	2000m (6560ft) +

Villar-Perosa OVP M1918

Essentially half a Villar-Perosa M1915 with a rifle-style shoulder stock, the OVP was capable of single shots or automatic fire and represented a significant step towards a workable submachine gun design.

SPECIFICATIONS	
Country of Origin:	Italy
Date:	1915
Calibre:	9mm (0.35in)
Operation:	Blowback
Weight:	3.62kg (8lb)
Overall Length:	901.69mm (35.5in)
Barrel Length:	Not known
Muzzle Velocity:	301.82m/sec (990ft/sec)
Feed/Magazine:	25-round detachable box magazine
Range:	70m (230ft)

1915

Bergmann MP18

The world's first blowback-operated submachine gun, the MP18 was developed by Hugo Schmeisser in 1916. It saw action in 1918, in a trench-clearing role, but was too late to influence the course of the war. Although MP18 production ended in the 1920s, its design formed the basis of most submachine guns manufactured between 1920 and 1960.

BUTT
If the buttstock of a loaded gun was given a hard knock while the bolt was fully forward, the gun could accidentally fire because of the bolt overcoming the action spring resistance and moving far enough backwards to pick up a round and fire.

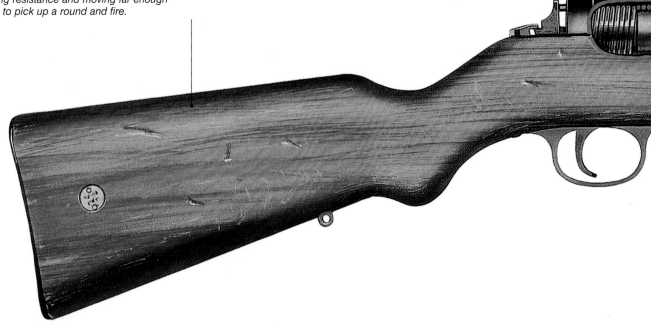

SPECIFICATIONS	
Country of Origin:	Germany
Date:	1918
Calibre:	9mm (.35in) Parabellum
Operation:	Blowback
Weight:	4.2kg (9.25lb)
Overall Length:	815mm (32in)
Barrel Length:	195mm (7.75in)
Muzzle Velocity:	395m/sec (1300ft/sec)
Feed/Magazine:	32-round detachable drum magazine
Range:	70m (230ft)

Full-scale production of the MP18 did not begin until early 1918. Though technically not the world's first submachine gun, being beaten by the Italian Villar-Perosa M1915 of 1915, in modern usage of the term the MP18 is considered the world's first submachine gun, since the Villar-Perosa had been designed to be used as a light machine gun on aircraft before it was adapted to infantry use.

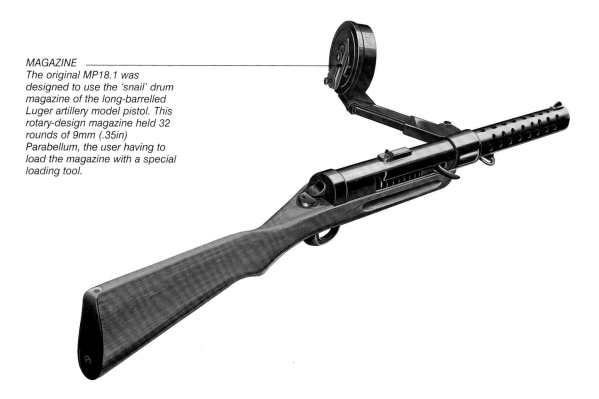

MAGAZINE
The original MP18.1 was designed to use the 'snail' drum magazine of the long-barrelled Luger artillery model pistol. This rotary-design magazine held 32 rounds of 9mm (.35in) Parabellum, the user having to load the magazine with a special loading tool.

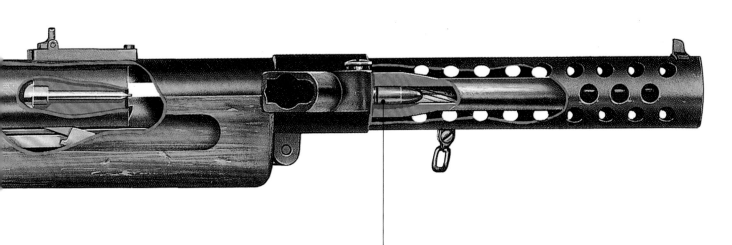

OPERATION
Blowback operation uses the rearward motion of the cartridge case to work the weapon's action. Gas pressure from firing pushes the case backwards, with the inertia of the bolt giving the projectile time to leave the barrel of the weapon.

Medium Machine Guns

Most automatic weapons of the Great War period fall into the category of medium machine guns. Firing rifle-calibre ammunition at rifle distances, they nevertheless were more like artillery weapons in terms of mobility and crew requirements.

Maxim Maschinengewehr '08

The Maxim '08 was one of the two most prevalent automatic support weapons of the war. A water-cooled weapon using a short-recoil system, it was extremely heavy and hard to move, being mounted on a metal sledge.

SPECIFICATIONS	
Country of Origin:	Germany
Date:	1908
Calibre:	7.92mm (.312in) Mauser
Operation:	Short recoil, water-cooled
Weight:	26.44kg (58.25lb)
Overall Length:	1175mm (46.25in)
Barrel Length:	719mm (28.33in)
Muzzle Velocity:	829m/sec (2925ft/sec)
Feed/Magazine:	Belt-fed (250-round fabric belt)
Cyclic Rate:	300–450rpm
Range:	1500m (4921ft)

Maxim Maschinengewehr '08/15 (bipod version)

Various efforts were made to make the Maxim '08 more mobile, doing away with the heavy sledge mount in favour of a tripod or a bipod. It was still necessary to carry water for the cooling system however.

SPECIFICATIONS	
Country of Origin:	Germany
Date:	1908
Calibre:	7.92mm (.312in) Mauser
Operation:	Short recoil
Weight:	18kg (39.75lb)
Overall Length:	1398mm (55in)
Barrel Length:	719mm (28.33in)
Muzzle Velocity:	900m/sec (2953ft/sec)
Feed/Magazine:	50-, 100- or 250-round fabric belt
Cyclic Rate:	450rpm
Range:	1500m (4921ft)

TIMELINE   1908   1913

Perino M1913

The Italian Perino machine gun used a mix of recoil and gas operation and had a clever cooling system. The original 1900 version was excessively heavy, but this was corrected with the M1913.

SPECIFICATIONS	
Country of Origin:	Italy
Date:	1913
Calibre:	6.5mm (.256in) M95
Operation:	Combined recoil/gas-operated, water-/air-cooled
Weight:	13.65kg (30lb)
Overall Length:	1180mm (46.5in)
Barrel Length:	655mm (25.75in)
Muzzle Velocity:	640m/sec (210ft/sec)
Feed/Magazine:	Strip-fed
Cyclic Rate:	500rpm
Range:	1500m (4921ft)

Fiat-Revelli Modello 14

The Modello 14 was unpleasant to fire and highly prone to stoppages from a variety of causes; not least its tendency to split cartridge cases in the chamber. Its feed system used 10 10-round clips set in a revolving drum.

SPECIFICATIONS	
Country of Origin:	Italy
Date:	1914
Calibre:	6.5mm (.256in) M95
Operation:	Delayed blowback, water-cooled
Weight:	17kg (37.75lb)
Overall Length:	1180mm (46.5in)
Barrel Length:	655mm (25.75in)
Muzzle Velocity:	640m/sec (210ft/sec)
Feed/Magazine:	Magazine-fed
Cyclic Rate:	400rpm
Range:	1500m (4921ft)

Hotchkiss Mle 1914

SPECIFICATIONS	
Country of Origin:	France
Date:	1914
Calibre:	8mm (.314in)
Operation:	Gas-operated, air-cooled
Weight:	23.6kg (52lb)
Overall Length:	1270mm (50in)
Barrel Length:	775mm (30.5in)
Muzzle Velocity:	725m/sec (2380ft/sec)
Feed/Magazine:	Strip-fed
Cyclic Rate:	600rpm
Range:	2000m (6560ft)

The Mle 1914 improved upon previous Hotchkiss gas-operated designs by enabling the user to link three-round ammunition strips into a 249-round belt. It was reliable but still too heavy for its intended use as a mobile infantry weapon.

Water-Cooled Machine Guns

Most early machine guns were water-cooled, using a jacket around the barrel to draw off heat. Maintaining an adequate supply of water was every bit as important to sustained fire as providing sufficient ammunition.

Schwarzlose M07/12

The choice of delayed-blowback operation necessitated that the Schwarzlose had a short barrel, which in turn limited effective range to about 1000m (3280ft). The M07/12 was the most popular of four variants.

SPECIFICATIONS	
Country of Origin:	Austria-Hungary
Date:	1907
Calibre:	8mm (.314in)
Operation:	Blowback, water-cooled
Weight:	20kg (44lb)
Overall Length:	1070mm (42in)
Barrel Length:	525mm (20.75in)
Muzzle Velocity:	618m/sec (2030ft/sec)
Feed/Magazine:	Belt-fed
Cyclic Rate:	425rpm
Range:	1000m (3280ft) +

Skoda M1909

A delayed-blowback weapon which was originally limited to a very slow 250rpm, the M1909 was gradually improved but never really overcame the basic inefficiency of its design. Skoda ceased manufacturing machine guns in 1913.

SPECIFICATIONS	
Country of Origin:	Austria-Hungary
Date:	1909
Calibre:	8mm (.314in)
Operation:	Delayed blowback, water-cooled
Weight:	44kg (20lb)
Overall Length:	1070mm (42in)
Barrel Length:	525mm (20.75in)
Muzzle Velocity:	618m/sec (2030ft/sec)
Feed/Magazine:	Belt-fed
Cyclic Rate:	425rpm
Range:	1000m (3280ft)

TIMELINE

1907

1909

Pulemet Maksima Obrazets 1910

A licensed copy of the Maxim Gun, the M1910 differed mainly in its mounting. Rather than a tripod, it was fixed to a two-wheeled carriage which brought the weapon's overall weight to over 70kg (154lb).

SPECIFICATIONS	
Country of Origin:	Russia
Date:	1910
Calibre:	7.62mm (.3in)
Operation:	Recoil, water-cooled
Weight:	23.8kg (52.47lb)
Overall Length:	1107mm (43.6in)
Barrel Length:	720mm (28.35in)
Muzzle Velocity:	863m/sec (2831ft/sec)
Feed/Magazine:	Belt-fed
Cyclic Rate:	520–600rpm
Range:	Not known

Browning M1917

A bulky weapon firing at 450rpm, the M1917 was capable of sustained fire from a fixed position and was thus eminently suitable for defensive operations or mounting aboard an aircraft or vehicle.

SPECIFICATIONS	
Country of Origin:	United States
Date:	1917
Calibre:	7.62mm (.3in)
Operation:	Recoil, water-cooled
Weight:	15kg (32.75lb)
Overall Length:	980mm (38.5in)
Barrel Length:	610mm (24in)
Muzzle Velocity:	850m/sec (2800ft/sec)
Feed/Magazine:	Belt-fed
Cyclic Rate:	450rpm
Range:	2000m (6560ft) +

Browning M1917A1

Country of Origin:	United States
Date:	1918
Calibre:	7.62mm (.3in)
Operation:	Recoil, water-cooled
Weight:	15kg (32.75lb)
Overall Length:	980mm (38.5in)
Barrel Length:	610mm (24in)
Muzzle Velocity:	850m/sec (2800ft/sec)
Feed/Magazine:	Belt-fed
Cyclic Rate:	600rpm
Range:	2000m (6560ft) +

The M1917 arrived at the front in the last few weeks of the war, and saw fairly limited action. After the war it was developed further and served as the M1917A1 until the 1960s.

1910

1917

1918

Vickers Mk I

Hiram Maxim's company, formed to produce his machine gun, merged with Vickers and Nordenfeldt in 1896. An improved version of the Maxim Gun was marketed by this firm, becoming known as the Vickers Machine Gun. It was originally designated as a heavy machine gun, though the advent of larger-calibre weapons caused a redesignation to medium.

The Vickers was also used to arm many aircraft of the Great War. It was replaced in this role between the wars but was still in service with ground units, despite experiments intended to find a replacement, at the outbreak of World War II. Again, it gave good service in all theatres of war.

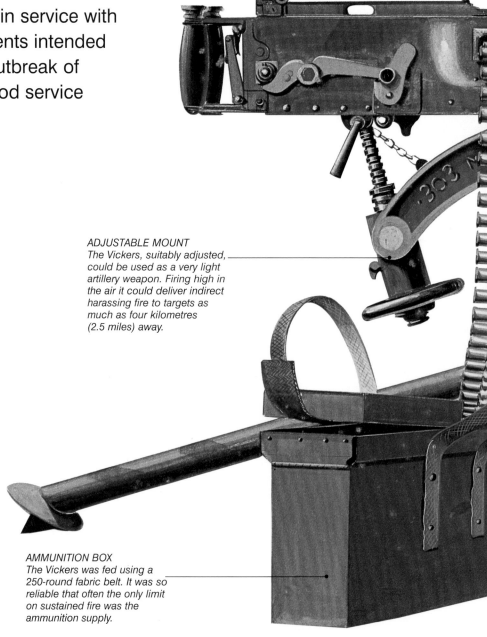

ADJUSTABLE MOUNT
The Vickers, suitably adjusted, could be used as a very light artillery weapon. Firing high in the air it could deliver indirect harassing fire to targets as much as four kilometres (2.5 miles) away.

The water-cooled Vickers Machine Gun proved to be supremely reliable, even in the trench conditions of the Great War. It was used in a variety of roles including infantry support and anti-aircraft defence, and for a time was deployed with specialist units of the British Machine Gun Corps.

AMMUNITION BOX
The Vickers was fed using a 250-round fabric belt. It was so reliable that often the only limit on sustained fire was the ammunition supply.

SPECIFICATIONS	
Country of Origin:	United Kingdom
Date:	1912
Calibre:	7.7mm (.303in)
Operation:	Recoil, water-cooled
Weight:	18kg (40lb)
Overall Length:	1155mm (40.5in)
Barrel Length:	725mm (28.5in)
Muzzle Velocity:	600m/sec (1970ft/sec)
Feed/Magazine:	Belt-fed
Cyclic Rate:	600rpm
Range:	2000m (6560ft) + ; later 3000m (9842ft)

MUZZLE
A muzzle booster ensured that the Vickers produced enough recoil force to cycle its action.

WATER JACKET
The barrel was cooled by a water-filled jacket surrounding it. The water began to boil after about 750 rounds of fire at a high rate.

WATER CAN
Some cooling water could be recycled by using a condenser hose into a can. Maintaining a suitable water supply was always something of a problem.

TRIPOD
The Vickers was heavy and required an equally bulky tripod or similar mount. This limited its mobility during an advance or retreat.

Specialist and Experimental Machine Guns

Within a few years of its invention, the machine gun had matured into a highly effective weapon system and was beginning to find new roles to fill. Experimentation produced a considerable range of variations on the automatic support weapon theme.

Taisho 3

The Taisho 3 machine gun was largely copied from the Hotchkiss Mle 1900, which had impressed the Japanese authorities in the Russo-Japanese War. The weapon's tripod design was innovative, allowing the weapon to be moved intact by its crew.

SPECIFICATIONS	
Country of Origin:	Japan
Date:	1914
Calibre:	6.5mm (.256in) Arisaka
Operation:	Gas-operated, air-cooled
Weight:	28kg (62lb)
Overall Length:	1155mm (45in)
Barrel Length:	750mm (29.5in)
Muzzle Velocity:	760m/sec (2500ft/sec)
Feed/Magazine:	Strip-fed
Cyclic Rate:	400rpm
Range:	1500m (4921ft)

Parabellum-Maschinengewehr Modell 14

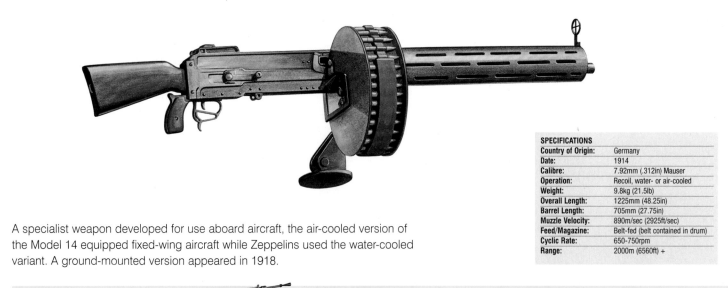

A specialist weapon developed for use aboard aircraft, the air-cooled version of the Model 14 equipped fixed-wing aircraft while Zeppelins used the water-cooled variant. A ground-mounted version appeared in 1918.

SPECIFICATIONS	
Country of Origin:	Germany
Date:	1914
Calibre:	7.92mm (.312in) Mauser
Operation:	Recoil, water- or air-cooled
Weight:	9.8kg (21.5lb)
Overall Length:	1225mm (48.25in)
Barrel Length:	705mm (27.75in)
Muzzle Velocity:	890m/sec (2925ft/sec)
Feed/Magazine:	Belt-fed (belt contained in drum)
Cyclic Rate:	650-750rpm
Range:	2000m (6560ft) +

TIMELINE

1914

Vickers Class C (Aircraft Mounting)

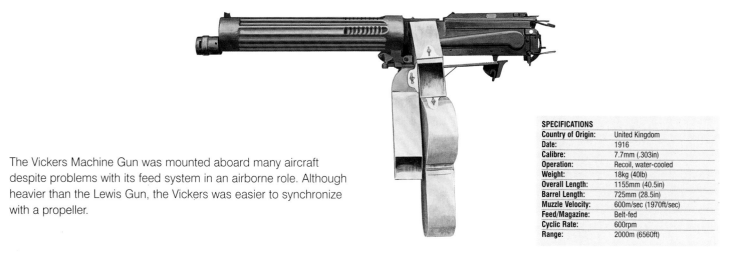

The Vickers Machine Gun was mounted aboard many aircraft despite problems with its feed system in an airborne role. Although heavier than the Lewis Gun, the Vickers was easier to synchronize with a propeller.

SPECIFICATIONS	
Country of Origin:	United Kingdom
Date:	1916
Calibre:	7.7mm (.303in)
Operation:	Recoil, water-cooled
Weight:	18kg (40lb)
Overall Length:	1155mm (40.5in)
Barrel Length:	725mm (28.5in)
Muzzle Velocity:	600m/sec (1970ft/sec)
Feed/Magazine:	Belt-fed
Cyclic Rate:	600rpm
Range:	2000m (6560ft)

Twin Lewis

The air-cooled Lewis Gun was a natural choice for aircraft armament. It was the first machine gun to be fired from an aircraft and became a standard armament, often in twin mounts to increase fire volume.

SPECIFICATIONS	
Country of Origin:	United States
Date:	1916
Calibre:	7.7mm (.303in)
Operation:	Gas-operated, air-cooled
Weight:	11.8kg (26lb)
Overall Length:	965mm (38in)
Barrel Length:	665mm (26.25in)
Muzzle Velocity:	600m/sec (1970ft/sec)
Feed/Magazine:	Magazine-fed
Cyclic Rate:	550rpm
Range:	1000m (3280ft) +

SEMAG 20mm

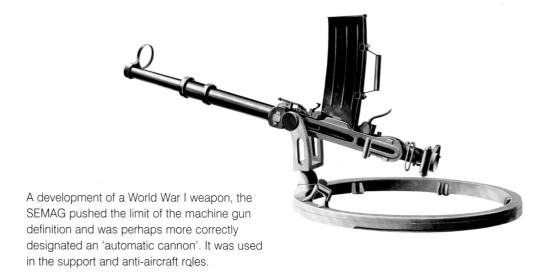

A development of a World War I weapon, the SEMAG pushed the limit of the machine gun definition and was perhaps more correctly designated an 'automatic cannon'. It was used in the support and anti-aircraft roles.

SPECIFICATIONS	
Country of Origin:	Switzerland
Date:	1923
Calibre:	20mm (.78in)
Operation:	Advanced Primer Ignition (API) blowback
Weight:	43kg (94.8lb)
Overall Length:	Variable
Barrel Length:	1400mm (55in)
Muzzle Velocity:	820m/sec (2700ft/sec)
Feed/Magazine:	Belt-fed
Cycle Rate:	450rpm
Range:	2000m (6560ft)

1916

1923

INTERWAR YEARS

World War I put immense numbers of weapons to the test, and prompted rapid development of weapons technology. It also caused a revolution in military thinking, demonstrating the need for infantry weapons other than infantry rifles.

Handguns, shotguns and sub-machine guns proved their worth in bitter trench-clearing actions, and developments in these fields fed back into the civilian and law enforcement markets. This occurred at a time of great economic and social upheaval, and these weapons found their way onto the streets in the hands of gangsters, government agents and revolutionaries.

Left: French colonial troops search buildings somewhere in Algeria. They are armed with Lebel Berthier 1915 bolt-action rifles.

Guns for Self-Defence

Although by no means military battlefield weapons, handguns are effective in close-range combat. In a civilian environment, a small and concealable handgun may be the only weapon available when combat begins.

Smith & Wesson .44 Triple Lock

This weapon was more correctly designated as a .44 Special version of the S&W Hand Ejector. The 'triple lock' was a third locking lug on the cylinder crane, to enable the gun to handle its powerful cartridge. This feature was later dropped.

SPECIFICATIONS	
Country of Origin:	United States
Date:	1908
Calibre:	11.2mm (.44in)
Operation:	Double-action revolver
Weight:	1.08kg (2.4lb)
Overall Length:	298mm (11.75in)
Barrel Length:	185mm (7.3in)
Muzzle Velocity:	198m/sec (650ft/sec)
Feed/Magazine:	6-round cylinder
Range:	30m (98ft)

Unceta Victoria

The Victoria was the first in a long line of handguns produced by a manufacturer better known by its later title: Astra. The Victoria was heavily influenced by Browning designs and was adopted by the French Army.

SPECIFICATIONS	
Country of Origin:	Spain
Date:	1911
Calibre:	7.65mm (.301in)
Operation:	Blowback
Weight:	.57kg (1.25lb)
Overall Length:	146mm (5.75in)
Barrel Length:	81mm (3.2in)
Muzzle Velocity:	229m/sec (750ft/sec)
Feed/Magazine:	7-round detachable box magazine
Range:	30m (98ft)

TIMELINE

 1908
 1911
 1918

Remington 51

A very small 'pocket' semi-automatic pistol, the Remington 51 was introduced in a tough marketplace. It never achieved the large-scale popularity it perhaps deserved, largely due to the Great Depression.

SPECIFICATIONS	
Country of Origin:	United States
Date:	1918
Calibre:	8.1mm (.32in) ACP
Operation:	Hesitation-locked
Weight:	.6kg (1.3lb)
Overall Length:	168mm (6.6in)
Barrel Length:	83mm (3.25in)
Muzzle Velocity:	Not known
Feed/Magazine:	Detachable single-stack box magazine
Range:	30m (98ft)

Colt Detective Special

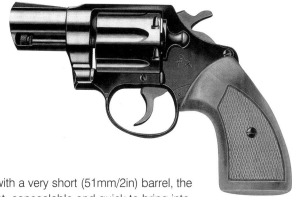

Effectively a Colt Police Positive revolver with a very short (51mm/2in) barrel, the Detective Special was designed to be light, concealable and quick to bring into action thanks to its minimal length.

SPECIFICATIONS	
Country of Origin:	UNITED STATES
Date:	1927
Calibre:	9.6mm (.38in) Special
Operation:	Revolver
Weight:	.6kg (1.3lb)
Overall Length:	171mm (6.7in)
Barrel Length:	54mm (2.13in)
Muzzle Velocity:	213m/sec (700ft/sec)
Feed/Magazine:	6-round cylinder
Range:	30m (98ft)

Smith & Wesson .357 M27

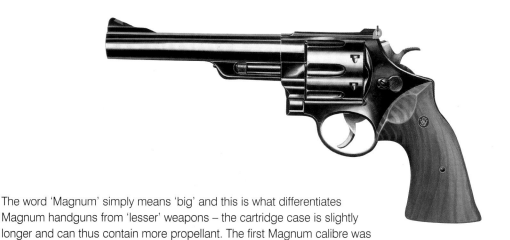

The word 'Magnum' simply means 'big' and this is what differentiates Magnum handguns from 'lesser' weapons – the cartridge case is slightly longer and can thus contain more propellant. The first Magnum calibre was .357, which was essentially a lengthened .38 Special round. Both 9.6mm (.38in) and 9.1mm (.357in) weapons use a 9.1mm (.357in) diameter bullet.

SPECIFICATIONS	
Country of Origin:	United States
Date:	1935
Calibre:	9.1mm (.357in) Magnum
Operation:	Double action revolver
Weight:	1.45kg (3.19lb)
Overall Length:	Not known
Barrel Length:	102mm (4in)/153mm (6in)
Muzzle Velocity:	198m/sec (650ft/sec)
Feed/Magazine:	6-round cylinder
Range:	30m (98ft)

1927

1935

Browning HP-35

At the time of his death, John Moses Browning was working on what would become one of the most successful handguns of all time. When it was finished, the new weapon went on sale as the Browning High Power. It has also been known as the HP-35 and GP-35 (for *Grande Puissance*, French for 'High Power').

The 'High Power' designation refers to the weapon's huge (for the time) magazine capacity of 13 rounds rather than ascribing any special capabilities to its 9mm (.35in) ammunition. This was achieved by using a slightly wider magazine than the usual single-stack layout, allowing rounds to be staggered. This made the HP-35 slightly wider than many contemporary handguns, but not unduly so.

The HP-35 achieved massive sales and influenced a whole generation of single-action semi-automatic pistols. Such weapons can be carried with a round in the chamber and the hammer either cocked (Condition One) or uncocked (Condition Two). In the latter case, the hammer has to be manually cocked before firing.

If the Browning HP-35 is carried Condition Three (no round chambered, hammer uncocked) then the act of working the slide to chamber the first round also cocks the hammer and readies the weapon. In all cases the safety catch should be on until the user is ready to fire.

SPECIFICATIONS	
Country of Origin:	Belgium/United States
Date:	1935
Calibre:	9mm (.35in) Parabellum
Operation:	Short recoil
Weight:	.99kg (2.19lb)
Overall Length:	197mm (7.75in)
Barrel Length:	118mm (4.65in)
Muzzle Velocity:	335m/sec (1100ft/sec)
Feed/Magazine:	13-round detachable box
Range:	30m (98ft)

Sometimes minimally trained users are taught to carry the
Browning HP-35 Condition Three and never touch the safety. This
can raise after-action safety issues but it is a useful technique for
occasions where semi-automatic handguns are to be used but
there is no time for training.

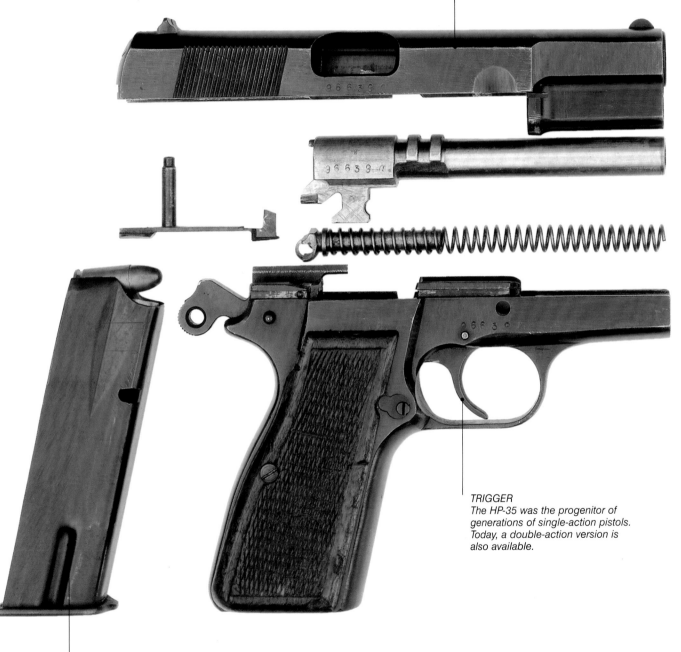

SLIDE
*The HP-35 operates on a short-
recoil system, where barrel
and slide recoil together briefly.
The slide is then unlocked from
the barrel and continues
rearwards to eject the spent
round and chamber the next.*

TRIGGER
*The HP-35 was the progenitor of
generations of single-action pistols.
Today, a double-action version is
also available.*

MAGAZINE
*A 13-round magazine represented a
huge capacity in 1935 and is still
very respectable today.*

Interwar Semi-Automatics

By the end of the Great War, the semi-automatic pistol was a proven weapon system, offering significant advantages over the revolver in many circumstances. Development continued through the 1920s and 1930s, producing a new generation of weapons.

Nambu 14th Year (Type 14 Nambu/Taisho 14)

An updated version of the rather poor Type 4 Nambu, the Type 14 added a safety catch and an enlarged trigger guard to allow it to be used wearing gloves. It remained an unreliable weapon firing an underpowered round, however.

SPECIFICATIONS	
Country of Origin:	Japan
Date:	1906
Calibre:	8mm (.314in) Nambu
Operation:	Short recoil
Weight:	.9kg (1.98lb)
Overall Length:	227mm (8.93in)
Barrel Length:	121mm (4.76in)
Muzzle Velocity:	335m/sec (1100ft/sec)
Feed/Magazine:	8-round detachable box magazine
Range:	30m (98ft)

Star Model B

The Star Models A and B were essentially copies of the Colt M1911. The Model B was chambered for 9mm (.35) Parabellum, and was developed through a series of models. Some were taken into German service in World War II.

SPECIFICATIONS	
Country of Origin:	Spain
Date:	1924
Calibre:	9mm (.35in)
Operation:	Short recoil
Weight:	1.1kg (2.4lb)
Overall Length:	215mm (8.46in)
Barrel Length:	122mm (4.8in)
Muzzle Velocity:	Not known
Feed/Magazine:	Not known
Range:	Not known

TIMELINE

 1906

 1924

 1929

Walther PPK

The PPK was a version of the PP intended for use by plainclothes police. Its small size made it ideal as a concealable weapon, and being a double-action pistol it could be drawn and fired immediately.

SPECIFICATIONS	
Country of Origin:	Germany
Date:	1929
Calibre:	5.6mm (.22in) LR, 6.35mm (.25in) or 7.65mm (.301in) Browning, 9mm (.35in) Short
Operation:	Blowback
Weight:	.59kg (1.3lb)
Overall Length:	148mm (5.8in)
Barrel Length:	80mm (3.15in)
Muzzle Velocity:	290m/sec (950ft/sec)
Feed/Magazine:	7-round detachable box magazine
Range:	30m (98ft)

Beretta Modello 1934

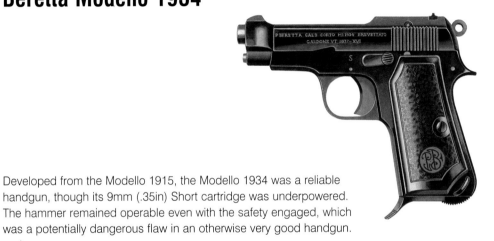

Developed from the Modello 1915, the Modello 1934 was a reliable handgun, though its 9mm (.35in) Short cartridge was underpowered. The hammer remained operable even with the safety engaged, which was a potentially dangerous flaw in an otherwise very good handgun.

SPECIFICATIONS	
Country of Origin:	Italy
Date:	1934
Calibre:	9mm (.35in) Short
Operation:	Blowback
Weight:	.65kg (1.4lb)
Overall Length:	152mm (6in)
Barrel Length:	95mm (3.7in)
Muzzle Velocity:	229m/sec (750ft/sec)
Feed/Magazine:	9-round magazine
Range:	30m (98ft)

94 Shiki Kenju (Type 94)

Designed for cheap mass-production, the Type 94 became more expensive as modifications were added. It was issued to aircrew and vehicle crews and was more robust than the Type 14, but suffered from using the same weak round.

SPECIFICATIONS	
Country of Origin:	Japan
Date:	1934
Calibre:	8mm (.314in)
Operation:	Not known
Weight:	.688kg (1.52lb)
Overall Length:	183mm (7.2in)
Barrel Length:	96mm (3.78in)
Muzzle Velocity:	305m/sec (1000ft/sec)
Feed/Magazine:	6-round box
Range:	Not known

1934

Walther P38

The Walther PP family, and especially the P38, are widely regarded as some of the best handguns of the twentieth century. Built around the 9mm (.35in) Parabellum cartridge which had become the standard military sidearm ammunition in Germany, the P38 was much simpler to produce and maintain than the Parabellum '08 it was intended to replace, but could match its performance.

A modified version of the earlier Walther PP chambered for 9mm (.35in) Parabellum ammunition, the double-action P38 was intended to replace all other pistols in German army service but had not done so by the outbreak of war.

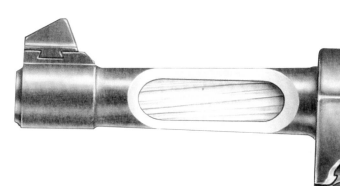

SPECIFICATIONS	
Country of Origin:	Germany
Date:	1938
Calibre:	9mm (.35in) Parabellum
Operation:	Short recoil
Weight:	.96kg (2.11lb)
Overall Length:	213mm (8.38in)
Barrel Length:	127mm (5in)
Muzzle Velocity:	350m/sec (1150ft/sec)
Feed/Magazine:	8-round detachable box magazine
Range:	30m (98ft)

The original P38 had a fully concealed hammer, but in accordance with the wishes of the German Army, a version with a portion of the hammer exposed (to allow manual cocking) was introduced. Designated Model HP (Heerpistole), this became the official German Army sidearm, though other weapons remained in service as too few P38s were available.

Production of the P38 ceased at the end of the war, but was resumed in 1957. At this time the P38 was re-instated as the German Army's service pistol, now under the designation Pistole 1. It remained in service almost to the end of the century.

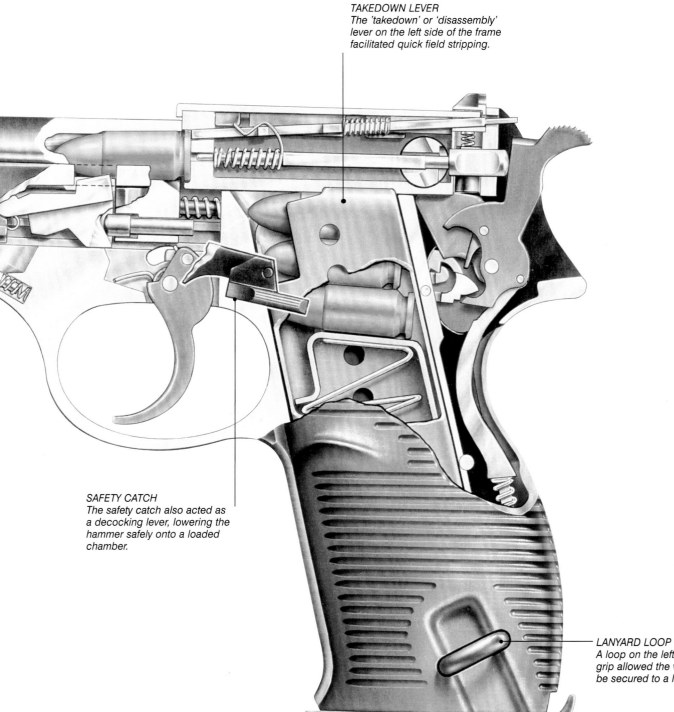

TAKEDOWN LEVER
The 'takedown' or 'disassembly' lever on the left side of the frame facilitated quick field stripping.

SAFETY CATCH
The safety catch also acted as a decocking lever, lowering the hammer safely onto a loaded chamber.

LANYARD LOOP
A loop on the left side of the grip allowed the weapon to be secured to a lanyard.

Japanese Infantry Weapons

Japan followed a rather different path to most Western nations in terms of weapon development. One reason was the (on average) lighter body frame of the Japanese infantryman, who could thus not shoot accurately with a high-recoil weapon.

Type 89 Grenade Launcher

A lightweight, small-calibre mortar or grenade discharger, the Type 89 was capable of being operated by a single crewman, and was deployed in large numbers. Despite its short range it was an effective light support weapon

SPECIFICATIONS	
Country of Origin:	Japan
Date:	1929
Calibre:	50mm (1.97in)
Operation:	Spring, manual
Weight:	4.7kg (10.3lb)
Overall Length:	610mm (24in)
Barrel Length:	254mm (10in)
Muzzle Velocity:	N/A
Feed/Magazine:	N/A
Range:	120m (394ft)

Type 97 Sniper Rifle

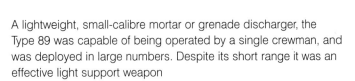

The Type 97 sniper rifle was an adaptation of the Type 38 rifle, firing a relatively weak 6.5 x 50mm (.256 x 1.97in) cartridge. It did have the advantage of very little muzzle flash, making it hard to locate a sniper's position.

SPECIFICATIONS	
Country of Origin:	Japan
Date:	1937
Calibre:	6.5mm (.256in) Arisaka
Operation:	Bolt action
Weight:	3.95kg (8.7lb)
Overall Length:	1280mm (50.4in)
Barrel Length:	797mm (31.4in)
Muzzle Velocity:	762.1m/sec (2500ft/sec)
Feed/Magazine:	5-round internal magazine, stripper-clip-loaded
Range:	800m (2620ft)

TIMELINE

1929

1937

Type 99 rifle

The Type 99 rifle was developed from the Type 38, but used a more potent 7.7 x 58mm (.303 x 2.28in) cartridge. The previous 6.5mm (.256in) round was discovered to be underpowered when facing troops armed with Western weapons.

SPECIFICATIONS	
Country of Origin:	Japan
Date:	1939
Calibre:	7.7mm (.303in) Arisaka
Operation:	Bolt action
Weight:	3.7kg (8.16lb)
Overall Length:	1120mm (44.1in)
BarrelLength:	657mm (25.87in)
Muzzle Velocity:	730m/sec (2394ft/sec)
Feed/Magazine:	5-round internal box magazine, stripper-clip-loaded
Range:	500m (1640ft)

Type 99 Sniper Rifle

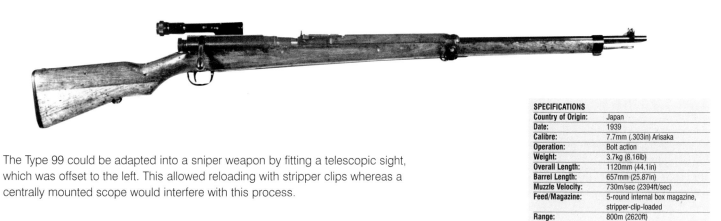

The Type 99 could be adapted into a sniper weapon by fitting a telescopic sight, which was offset to the left. This allowed reloading with stripper clips whereas a centrally mounted scope would interfere with this process.

SPECIFICATIONS	
Country of Origin:	Japan
Date:	1939
Calibre:	7.7mm (.303in) Arisaka
Operation:	Bolt action
Weight:	3.7kg (8.16lb)
Overall Length:	1120mm (44.1in)
Barrel Length:	657mm (25.87in)
Muzzle Velocity:	730m/sec (2394ft/sec)
Feed/Magazine:	5-round internal box magazine, stripper-clip-loaded
Range:	800m (2620ft)

Type 99 with Type 2 Grenade Launcher

The Type 99 rifle was a robust weapon, though late-war examples were hurriedly thrown together and were sometimes poor. A grenade-launching adaptor was available for the Type 99, which would also fit the Type 38 rifle.

SPECIFICATIONS*	
Country of Origin:	Japan
Date:	1939
Calibre:	7.7mm (.303in) Arisaka
Operation:	Bolt action
Weight:	3.7kg (8.16lb)
Overall Length:	1120mm (44.1in)
Barrel Length:	657mm (25.87in)
Muzzle Velocity:	730m/sec (2394ft/sec)
Feed/Magazine:	N/A
Range (Grenade):	100m (360ft)
* Of rifle without grenade	

Interwar Light Machine Guns

The light machine gun (LMG) was introduced in World War I, and like any experimental weapon system, suffered from a number of teething troubles. Development continued after the war, with the LMG emerging as an efficient weapon system.

Hotchkiss M1922/26

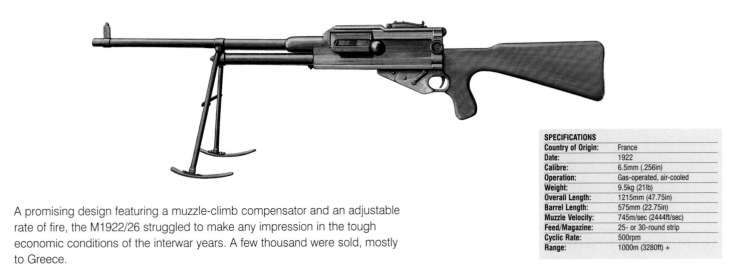

A promising design featuring a muzzle-climb compensator and an adjustable rate of fire, the M1922/26 struggled to make any impression in the tough economic conditions of the interwar years. A few thousand were sold, mostly to Greece.

SPECIFICATIONS	
Country of Origin:	France
Date:	1922
Calibre:	6.5mm (.256in)
Operation:	Gas-operated, air-cooled
Weight:	9.5kg (21lb)
Overall Length:	1215mm (47.75in)
Barrel Length:	575mm (22.75in)
Muzzle Velocity:	745m/sec (2444ft/sec)
Feed/Magazine:	25- or 30-round strip
Cyclic Rate:	500rpm
Range:	1000m (3280ft) +

Fusil Mitrailleur Mle 24/29

The Mle 24 did away with the 8mm (.314in) Lebel cartridge in favour of a rimless 7.5mm (.295in) round that caused fewer stoppages, and was then developed into the Mle 1924/29 Châtellerault, which became the standard French LMG.

SPECIFICATIONS	
Country of Origin:	France
Date:	1924
Calibre:	7.5mm (.295in) M29
Operation:	Gas-operated, air-cooled
Weight:	9.25kg (20.25lb)
Overall Length:	1080mm (42.5in)
Barrel Length:	500mm (19.75in)
Muzzle Velocity:	825m/sec (2707ft/sec)
Cyclic Rate:	500rpm
Feed/Magazine:	25-round box magazine
Range:	1000m (3280ft) +

TIMELINE 1922 1924 1930

Lehky Kulomet ZB vz30

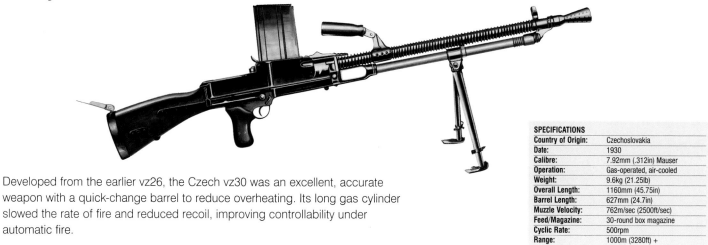

Developed from the earlier vz26, the Czech vz30 was an excellent, accurate weapon with a quick-change barrel to reduce overheating. Its long gas cylinder slowed the rate of fire and reduced recoil, improving controllability under automatic fire.

SPECIFICATIONS	
Country of Origin:	Czechoslovakia
Date:	1930
Calibre:	7.92mm (.312in) Mauser
Operation:	Gas-operated, air-cooled
Weight:	9.6kg (21.25lb)
Overall Length:	1160mm (45.75in)
Barrel Length:	627mm (24.7in)
Muzzle Velocity:	762m/sec (2500ft/sec)
Feed/Magazine:	30-round box magazine
Cyclic Rate:	500rpm
Range:	1000m (3280ft) +

Lehky Kulomet ZGB vz33

Coming from a long line of excellent Czech light machine guns, the vz33 was the immediate predecessor of the Bren Gun, which gained its name from the vz33's origins at Brno in Czechoslovakia and Enfield in Britain where the Bren was developed.

SPECIFICATIONS	
Country of Origin:	Czechoslovakia
Date:	1933
Calibre:	7.92mm (.312in) Mauser
Operation:	Gas-operated, air-cooled
Weight:	10.25kg (22.5lb)
Overall Length:	1150mm (45.25in)
Barrel Length:	635mm (25in)
Muzzle Velocity:	730m/sec (2400ft/sec)
Feed/Magazine:	30-round box magazine
Cyclic Rate:	500rpm
Range:	1000m (3280ft)

Mark 1 Bren

With its relatively light weight and impressive accuracy, the Bren was an excellent squad-level support weapon that was developed through five main variants before becoming the L4, chambered for 7.62mm (.3in) NATO ammunition. L4 Brens saw action as late as the Falklands War in 1982.

SPECIFICATIONS	
Country of Origin:	United Kingdom
Date:	1937
Calibre:	7.7mm (.303in)
Operation:	Gas-operated, air-cooled
Weight:	10.25kg (22.5lb)
Overall Length:	1150mm (45.25in)
Barrel Length:	635mm (25in)
Muzzle Velocity:	730m/sec (2400ft/sec)
Feed/Magazine:	30-round box magazine
Cyclic Rate:	500rpm
Range:	1000m (3280ft)

1933

1937

Bren Gun (Mark 2)

The Bren Gun was a huge success in its role as a squad-level support weapon. It was much lighter than a belt-fed machine gun and could be used in the manner of a rifle. Indeed, it was accurate enough for sharpshooting. The Mk 1 version had a pistol-style foregrip for 'assault' firing but this was deleted on later models.

SPECIFICATIONS	
Country of Origin:	United Kingdom
Date:	1941
Calibre:	7.7mm (.303in) British
Operation:	Gas-operated, air-cooled
Weight:	10.25kg (22.5lb)
Overall Length:	1150mm (45.25in)
Barrel Length:	625mm (25in)
Muzzle Velocity:	730m/sec (2400ft/sec)
Feed/Magazine:	30-round box magazine
Cyclic Rate:	500rpm
Range:	1000m (3280ft)

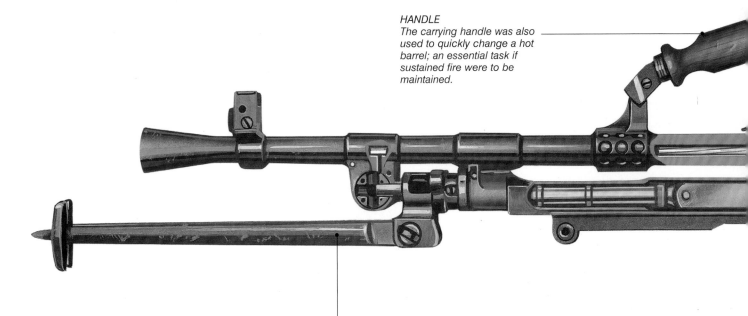

HANDLE
The carrying handle was also used to quickly change a hot barrel; an essential task if sustained fire were to be maintained.

BIPOD
Although the Bren could be deployed on a tripod, it was best suited to a mobile role, resting its bipod on whatever cover or support presented itself.

The Bren's ammunition supply was very limited, making sustained firing problematical, and its impressive accuracy could be a problem when laying down suppressive fire. A weapon that distributed large amounts of ammunition over an area was perhaps more desirable for harassing or suppressing enemy troops. Despite these drawbacks, the Bren was popular and effective. Such was its importance that British doctrine in World War II was for every infantryman to know how to use the section's Bren.

Brens were also used to arm vehicles and as anti-aircraft weapons. A large-capacity magazine was available for this role. The Universal Carrier, an infantry-carrying tracked vehicle developed by the British Army, was also known as the Bren Carrier, because it could be mounted with a Bren Gun both at the front and on a central mounting. This model (see right) has a centrally mounted Bren Gun and was used in the Western Desert by the British Eighth Army in 1942.

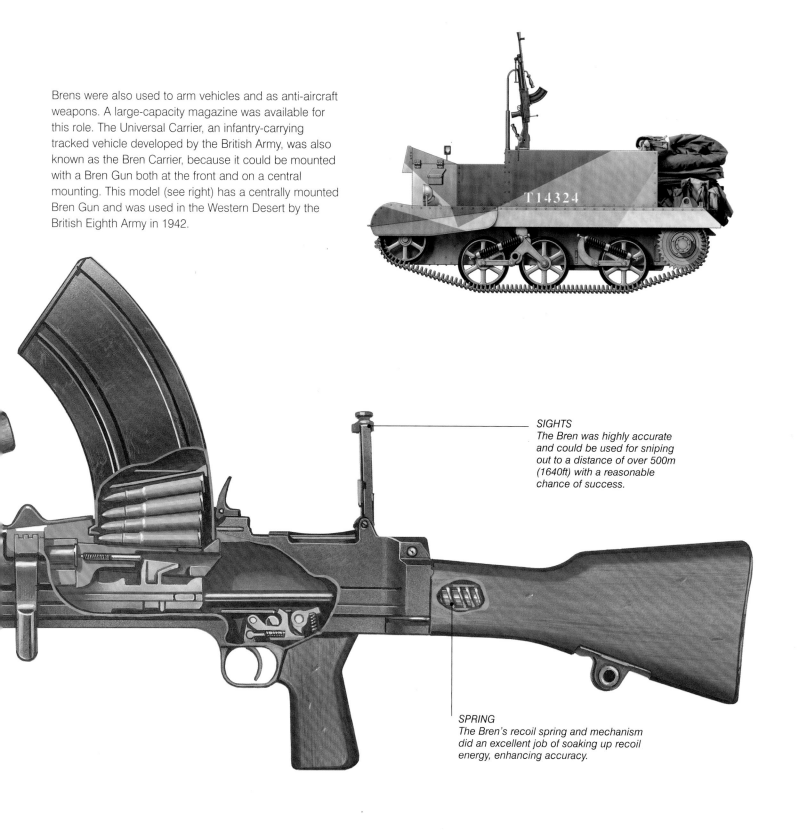

SIGHTS
The Bren was highly accurate and could be used for sniping out to a distance of over 500m (1640ft) with a reasonable chance of success.

SPRING
The Bren's recoil spring and mechanism did an excellent job of soaking up recoil energy, enhancing accuracy.

Japanese Machine Guns

Japanese plans to provide the army with up-to-date support weapons were interrupted by the outbreak of war. Although new weapons did enter service, as a rule they served alongside rather than replaced their predecessors.

Type 11/Taisho 11

The Type 11 was Japan's first true light machine gun. It used a 30-round hopper feed system, loaded using six stripper clips of the sort used by the 6.5mm (.256in) Arisaka 38 rifle. The feed system was not always very reliable.

SPECIFICATIONS	
Country of Origin:	Japan
Date:	1922
Calibre:	6.5mm (.256in) Arisaka
Operation:	Gas-operated, air-cooled
Weight:	10.2kg (22.5lb)
Overall Length:	1155mm (45in)
Barrel Length:	749mm (29.5in)
Muzzle Velocity:	731m/sec (2400ft/sec)
Feed/Magazine:	30-round hopper feed
Cyclic Rate:	400rpm
Range:	1500m (4921ft)

Type 89

One of the better Japanese automatic weapons of the war, the Type 89 was an aircraft weapon with a heavy barrel to dissipate heat. It was mounted aboard a range of fighter aircraft.

SPECIFICATIONS	
Country of Origin:	Japan
Date:	1929
Calibre:	7.7mm (.303in)
Operation:	Recoil
Weight:	16.78kg (37lb)
Overall Length:	1051mm (41.4in)
Barrel Length:	685mm (27in)
Muzzle Velocity:	Not known
Feed/Magazine:	69-round drum magazine
Cyclic Rate:	600rpm +
Range:	2000m (6560ft) +

TIMELINE			
	 1922	 1929	 1932

Type 92

The Japanese Type 92 was little different from the preceding Taisho 3 model. It fired the heavier 7.7mm (.303in) round and was often nicknamed the 'Woodpecker' by Australian troops, for its stuttering sound.

SPECIFICATIONS	
Country of Origin:	Japan
Date:	1932
Calibre:	7.7mm (.303in)
Operation:	Gas-operated, air-cooled
Weight:	55kg (122lb)
Overall Length:	1160mm (45in)
Barrel Length:	700mm (27.5in)
Muzzle Velocity:	715m/sec (2350ft/sec)
Feed/Magazine:	30-round box magazine
Cyclic Rate:	450rpm
Range:	2000m (6560ft)

Type 96

Intended to replace the Taisho 11, the Type 96 had an improved feed system that used a box magazine rather than the problematical hopper. Despite the inaccuracy of the weapon, a telescopic sight was developed for it.

SPECIFICATIONS	
Country of Origin:	Japan
Date:	1936
Calibre:	6.5mm (.256in) Arisaka
Operation:	Gas-operated, air-cooled
Weight:	9kg (20lb)
Overall Length:	1055mm (41.5in)
Barrel Length:	555mm (21.75in)
Muzzle Velocity:	730m/sec (2300ft/sec)
Feed/Magazine:	30-round box magazine
Cyclic Rate:	550rpm
Range:	1000m (3280ft)

Type 1 Heavy Machine Gun

The Type 1 Heavy Machine Gun was the standard heavy machine gun in the Imperial Japanese Army during World War II from 1941. It is essentially a smaller, lighter version of the Type 92.

SPECIFICATIONS	
Country of Origin:	Japan
Date:	1941
Calibre:	7.7mm (.303in) Arisaka
Operation:	Gas-operated
Weight:	31.8kg (70.1lb)
Overall Length:	1077mm (42.4in)
Barrel Length:	589mm (23.2in)
Muzzle Velocity:	770m/sec (2500ft/sec)
Feed/Magazine:	30-round metallic feed trays
Cyclic Rate:	450rpm
Range:	1400m (4593ft)

1936

1941

Browning M2HB

The water-cooled Browning M1917 heavy machinegun saw action in World War I and proved successful. Browning's guns were developed over subsequent years into a family of weapons that is still in use today, though some versions were more successful than others. In order to provide the US military with a machine gun effective against vehicles and aircraft, Browning developed the water-cooled M1921 from the M1917. By the 1930s this had developed into the air-cooled M2 heavy machine gun. One of the mst enduring heavy machineguns of all time, this weapon is still in service today with both US and other armed forces around the world. More than 3 million have bene used by the world's armies.

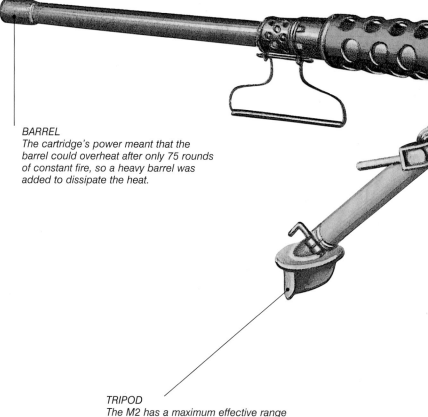

BARREL
The cartridge's power meant that the barrel could overheat after only 75 rounds of constant fire, so a heavy barrel was added to dissipate the heat.

TRIPOD
The M2 has a maximum effective range of 1.8 kilometers (1.2 miles) when fired from the M3 tripod.

SPECIFICATIONS	
Country of Origin:	United States
Date:	1921
Calibre:	12.7mm (.5in)
Operation:	Short recoil, air-cooled
Weight:	38.5kg (84lb)
Overall Length:	1655mm (65in)
Barrel Length:	1143mm (45in)
Muzzle Velocity:	898m/sec (2950ft/sec)
Feed/Magazine:	110-round belt
Cyclic Rate:	450–550rpm
Range:	1800m (5905ft) effective

Overheating was a problem with the early M2 models, so a new 'heavy barrel' version designated M2HB was developed. This weapon has been produced in the millions and remains in service today as a ground-based and vehicle weapon.

AMMUNITION
There are several types of ammunition used in the M2HB. From World War II through to the Vietnam War, standard ball, armour-piercing (AP), armour-piercing incendiary (API) and armour-piercing incendiary tracer (APIT) rounds were used.

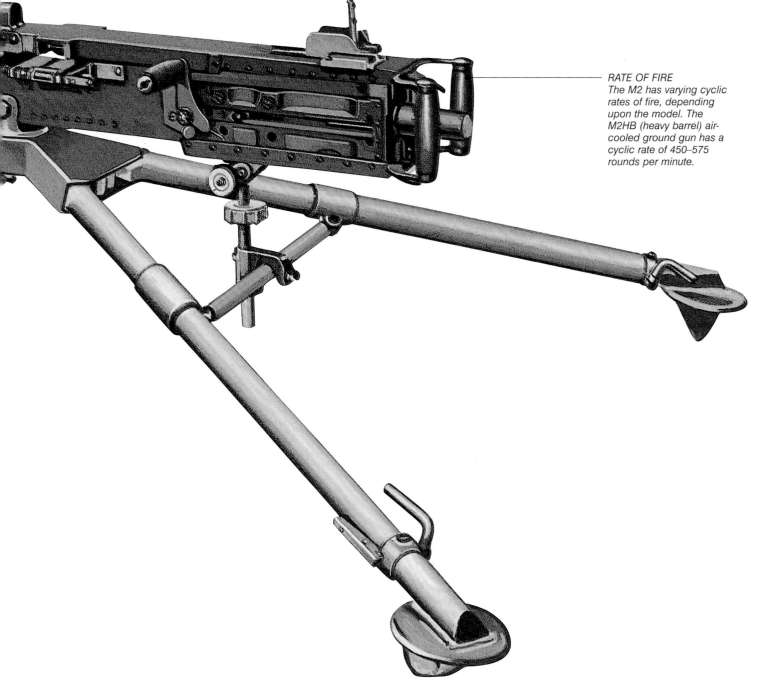

RATE OF FIRE
The M2 has varying cyclic rates of fire, depending upon the model. The M2HB (heavy barrel) air-cooled ground gun has a cyclic rate of 450–575 rounds per minute.

Browning M1919A4

The main drawback with the Browning M1917 was its requirement for a water jacket to cool the barrel. Water was heavy to carry on the move and was not always easy to obtain even in fixed positions. The M1919 solved this problem by using an air-cooled barrel which was much lighter. In fact, it was initially too light. Early models of the M1919 tended to overheat under sustained fire, so a heavier barrel was substituted on the A2 and later variants.

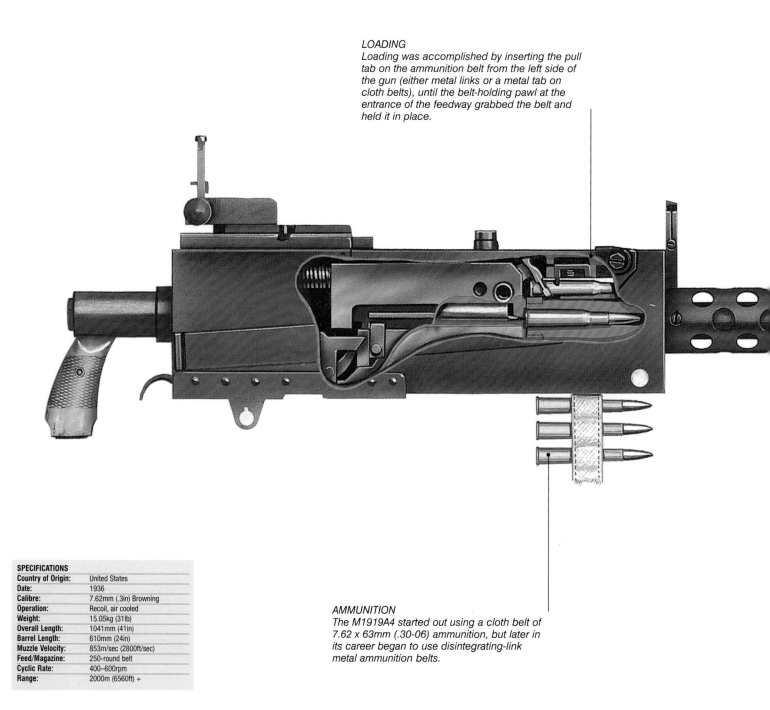

LOADING
Loading was accomplished by inserting the pull tab on the ammunition belt from the left side of the gun (either metal links or a metal tab on cloth belts), until the belt-holding pawl at the entrance of the feedway grabbed the belt and held it in place.

SPECIFICATIONS	
Country of Origin:	United States
Date:	1936
Calibre:	7.62mm (.3in) Browning
Operation:	Recoil, air cooled
Weight:	15.05kg (31lb)
Overall Length:	1041mm (41in)
Barrel Length:	610mm (24in)
Muzzle Velocity:	853m/sec (2800ft/sec)
Feed/Magazine:	250-round belt
Cyclic Rate:	400–600rpm
Range:	2000m (6560ft) +

AMMUNITION
The M1919A4 started out using a cloth belt of 7.62 x 63mm (.30-06) ammunition, but later in its career began to use disintegrating-link metal ammunition belts.

The definitive M1919 was the A4 version, which was mounted on a variety of vehicles as well as on a tripod for infantry support. The A5 version was almost identical, but was designed to be internally mounted as a co-axial or turret weapon in a tank or armoured car.

BARREL
The M1919 survived the changeover to 7.62 x 51mm (.3 x 1in) NATO standard ammunition almost unchanged, and many examples remained in US service until the 1990s. Some armed forces elsewhere in the world still use this weapon.

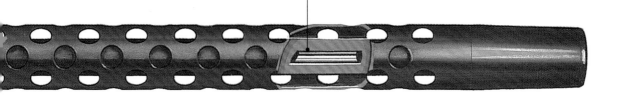

As a company or battalion support weapon, the M1919 required at least a two-man team. In practice, four men were normally involved: the gunner (who fired the gun and when advancing carried the tripod and box of ammo), the assistant gunner (who helped feed the gun and carried the gun plus a box of spare parts and tools), and two ammunition carriers.

WORLD WAR II

World War II was the first 'modern' conflict. Armoured vehicles and air power had matured from their experimental origins in the previous war into potent and far-reaching weapons systems, enabling rapid offensives to cover great distances.

At the same time, average combat ranges continued to drop as close-quarters urban combat became ever more prevalent. This was the domain of the sub-machine gun, the flamethrower and, later in the war, the assault rifle. Assault rifles did not become common before the war ended, but infantry firepower took another leap forward as the semi-automatic rifle became commonplace. Often firing the same round as its bolt-action predecessor, the semi-automatic rifle enabled the individual soldier to reload quicker and shoot faster; usually with no less accuracy.

Left: US Marines pose for a photo in the jungle of Bougainville, Solomon Islands, 1943. Most are armed with M1 Garand rifles, although a few are carrying the 1903 Springfield and M1 Carbine, both popular with troops involved in jungle warfare.

Russian and East European Semi-Automatics

Handguns never received much priority in Russia as they were never seen as serious combat weapons, and some rather mediocre designs resulted. Other nations in Eastern Europe produced some very good handguns, however.

Tokarev TT30

The TT30 was developed as a replacement for the Nagant revolvers then in Soviet service. It was chambered for the 7.62 x 25mm (.3 x .98in) Tokarev round and proved robust, but required further development before it was adopted.

SPECIFICATIONS	
Country of Origin:	USSR
Date:	1930
Calibre:	7.62mm (.3in)
Operation:	Short recoil
Weight:	.83kg (1.83lb)
Overall Length:	194mm (7.6in)
Barrel Length:	116mm (4.57in)
Muzzle Velocity:	420m/sec (1380ft/sec)
Feed/Magazine:	8-round detachable box magazine
Range:	50m (164ft)

Tula-Tokarev TT33

Alterations to the trigger, frame and barrel of the TT30 resulted in the TT33, of which over two million were made. Although hampered by a weak cartridge and lacking a safety catch, it was a reliable and robust weapon.

SPECIFICATIONS	
Country of Origin:	USSR
Date:	1933
Calibre:	7.62mm (.3in) Soviet
Operation:	Short recoil
Weight:	.83kg (1.83lb)
Overall Length:	194mm (7.6in)
Barrel Length:	116mm (4.57in)
Muzzle Velocity:	415m/sec (1362ft/sec)
Feed/Magazine:	8-round detachable box magazine
Range:	30m (98ft)

TIMELINE

1930

1933

Lahti L-35

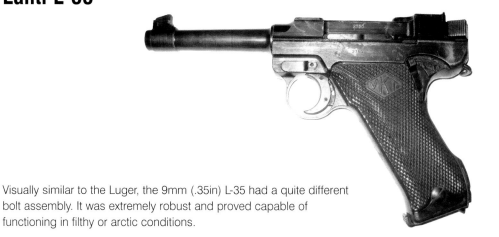

Visually similar to the Luger, the 9mm (.35in) L-35 had a quite different bolt assembly. It was extremely robust and proved capable of functioning in filthy or arctic conditions.

SPECIFICATIONS	
Country of Origin:	Finland
Date:	1935
Calibre:	9mm (0.35in)
Operation:	Toggle-locked, short recoil
Weight:	1.2 kg (2.6lb)
Overall Length:	245mm (9.65in)
Barrel Length:	107mm (4.21in)
Muzzle Velocity:	335.3m/sec (1100ft/sec)
Feed/Magazine:	8-round detachable box magazine
Range:	50m (164ft)

Radom wz35

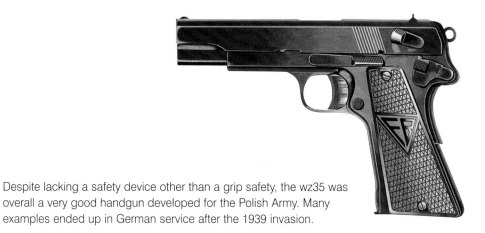

Despite lacking a safety device other than a grip safety, the wz35 was overall a very good handgun developed for the Polish Army. Many examples ended up in German service after the 1939 invasion.

SPECIFICATIONS	
Country of Origin:	Poland
Date:	1935
Calibre:	9mm (.35in) Parabellum
Operation:	Short recoil
Weight:	1.022kg (2.25lb)
Overall Length:	197mm (7.76in)
Barrel Length:	115mm (4.53in)
Muzzle Velocity:	350m/sec (1150ft/sec)
Feed/Magazine:	8-round detachable box magazine
Range:	30m (98ft)

CZ Model 38

Chambered for a weak 9mm (.35in) Short cartridge and suffering from a very heavy trigger pull, the Model 38 was not a success. The invading Germany Army, short of pistols, took most of the production run into service anyway.

SPECIFICATIONS	
Country of Origin:	Czechoslovakia
Date:	1938
Calibre:	9mm (0.35in) Short
Operation:	Short recoil
Weight:	.909kg (2lb)
Overall Length:	198mm (7.8in)
Barrel Length:	119mm (4.69in)
Muzzle Velocity:	296m/sec (970ft/sec)
Feed/Magazine:	8-round box magazine
Range:	30m (98ft)

1935

1938

Welrod Silent Pistol

A number of innovative weapons were developed during World War II, for use by covert operatives and resistance fighters. The elimination of a single political figure or key military officer could cause very significant disruption to the enemy in a region. However, unless the operative was willing to undertake a suicide mission, the assassination had to be covert.

In order to give the assassin a chance to complete the mission and escape, a silent firearm was desirable. A gun provided a range of options not available with a knife or other hand weapon; the target could be shot through a window or other opening without the assassin having to come into physical contact.

REAR OF RECEIVER
Although it had an eight-round magazine, the Welrod was intended for single precise shots. Chambering a new round was a relatively slow process.

HANDGRIP
The Welrod's magazine was integral to its handgrip; the whole grip was removed for reloading.

SPECIFICATIONS	
Country of Origin:	United Kingdom
Date:	1940
Calibre:	7.65mm (.301in) (.32 ACP)
Operation:	Rotary bolt
Weight:	1.090kg (2.4lb)
Overall Length:	310mm (12in)
Barrel Length:	95mm (less silencer)
Muzzle Velocity:	Not known
Feed/Magazine:	8-round magazine
Range:	20m (65ft)

The Welrod assassination pistol was developed for the British Special Operations Executive and had an integral silencer. The only safety device was a grip safety, and reloading was manual rather than semi-automatic. To chamber the next round, the cap at the rear of the weapon was twisted and pulled back, then pushed home again.

BARREL
The Welrod pistol's silencer was integral to its design and could not be removed.

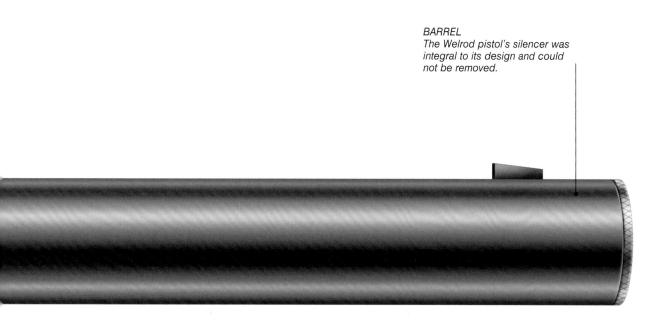

Stopping power was less important to an assassin than to a combat soldier; a target that did not die immediately but succumbed to blood loss was just as dead as one who dropped instantly, so small-calibre weapons were not a major drawback. Indeed, some assassinations have been carried out by 'zippering' the target with a series of small-calibre shots close together. This makes stopping the bleeding far more difficult than with a single, larger wound.

Liberator M1942

A number of weapons were developed to be used by resistance fighters, including simple multi-shot shotguns and similarly basic weapons. The idea was that these weapons could be airdropped into occupied countries where potential resistance forces would find them and thus gain the means to fight back against the invader.

Many of these weapons were very crude and cheaply made, which meant that they were only of value to desperate resistance fighters – a well-equipped military force would get no value out of these weapons even if the shipment was captured. Of them all, one of the crudest was the Liberator pistol.

SPECIFICATIONS

Country of Origin:	United States
Date:	1942
Calibre:	11.4mm (.45in)
Operation:	Manual
Weight:	.454kg (1lb)
Overall Length:	141mm (5.55in)
Barrel Length:	102mm (4in)
Muzzle Velocity:	250m/sec (820ft/sec)
Feed/Magazine:	Single shot
Range:	8m (26.2ft)

REAR OF BARREL
Ejecting a spent round from the Liberator required pushing a suitable implement down the barrel and prodding the cartridge case out of the rear of the weapon.

BARREL
As a smoothbore weapon, the Liberator had an extremely short effective range.

A single-shot smoothbore handgun firing an 11.4mm/ .45in (.45 ACP) round, the Liberator was intended for close-range assassination rather than combat, allowing a resistance fighter to eliminate an enemy sentry or perhaps a higher-value target. Rather optimistically, each weapon was provided with 10 rounds of ammunition. Reloading was less than rapid, as the spent cartridge was ejected by poking it out of the mechanism with a stick.

In theory a user might be able to 'trade up' his Liberator for the weapon of his victim and thus increase his firepower, but it is not known how many Liberator pistols were ever used, nor how successful these attempts were.

REAR BLOCK
The cocking piece was manually pulled to the rear and turned aside for loading and ejection.

FRAME
The Liberator was intended to be made as cheaply as possible. It showed.

HANDGRIP
Five additional rounds were carried in the handgrip, but these had to be removed and manually loaded into the weapon.

Bolt-Action Rifles

At the outbreak of the war, the standard infantry arm was still the bolt-action rifle. Although somewhat lighter and shorter than those of previous generations, the bolt-action rifles used by early World War II troops were functionally identical.

Mauser Kar 98 Kurz K

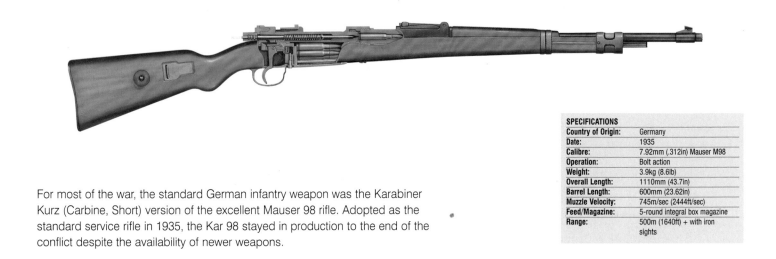

For most of the war, the standard German infantry weapon was the Karabiner Kurz (Carbine, Short) version of the excellent Mauser 98 rifle. Adopted as the standard service rifle in 1935, the Kar 98 stayed in production to the end of the conflict despite the availability of newer weapons.

SPECIFICATIONS	
Country of Origin:	Germany
Date:	1935
Calibre:	7.92mm (.312in) Mauser M98
Operation:	Bolt action
Weight:	3.9kg (8.6lb)
Overall Length:	1110mm (43.7in)
Barrel Length:	600mm (23.62in)
Muzzle Velocity:	745m/sec (2444ft/sec)
Feed/Magazine:	5-round integral box magazine
Range:	500m (1640ft) + with iron sights

Fusil MAS36

Chambered for the new 7.5 x 54mm (.295 x 2.1in) round, the MAS36 was one of the last bolt-action service rifles to be adopted. It remained in production for nearly two decades, with several variants made.

SPECIFICATIONS	
Country of Origin:	France
Date:	1936
Calibre:	7.5mm (.295in)
Operation:	Bolt action
Weight:	3.7kg (4.1lb)
Overall Length:	1020mm (40in)
Barrel Length:	575mm (22.6in)
Muzzle Velocity:	853.6m/sec (2800ft/sec)
Feed/Magazine:	5-round internal box magazine, clip-fed
Range:	320–365m (1050–1198ft)

TIMELINE   1935   1936

Mosin-Nagant M1938 Carbine

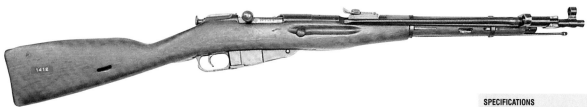

A shortened ('carbine') version of the venerable Mosin-Nagant rifle, the M1938 was sufficiently accurate to be used as a sniping weapon. It retained the same 5-round internal magazine as the original rifle.

SPECIFICATIONS	
Country of Origin:	USSR
Date:	1938
Calibre:	7.62mm (.3in)
Operation:	Bolt action
Weight:	3.45kg (7.62lb)
Overall Length:	1020mm (40in)
Barrel Length:	510mm (20in)
Muzzle Velocity:	800m/sec (2625ft/sec)
Feed/Magazine:	5-round non-detachable magazine
Range:	500m (1640ft)

Lee-Enfield Rifle No 4 Mk 1

The British Army started the war with the SMLE Mk III as its standard weapon, but it soon became apparent that a version more amenable to wartime mass production was needed. About four million of the resulting weapon were made.

SPECIFICATIONS	
Country of Origin:	United Kingdom
Date:	1939
Calibre:	7.7mm (.303in) British Service
Operation:	Bolt action
Weight:	4.11kg (9.06lb)
Overall Length:	1128mm (44.43in)
Barrel Length:	640mm (25.2in)
Muzzle Velocity:	751m/sec (2464ft/sec)
Feed/Magazine:	10-round detachable box magazine
Range:	1000m (3280ft) +

Lee-Enfield Rifle No 5/Jungle Carbine

Despite a rubber shoulder protector and a flash hider, the shortened 'Jungle Carbine' suffered from excessive recoil and muzzle blast. Also hampered by sights that routinely drifted out of alignment, the Rifle No 5 was abandoned in 1947.

SPECIFICATIONS	
Country of Origin:	United Kingdom
Date:	1944
Calibre:	7.7mm (.303in) British Service
Operation:	Bolt action
Weight:	3.24kg (7.14lb)
Overall Length:	1000mm (39.37in)
Barrel Length:	478mm (18.7in)
Muzzle Velocity:	610m/sec (2000ft/sec)
Feed/Magazine:	10-round detachable box magazine
Range:	1000m (3280ft)

1938

1939

1944

Sniper Rifles

Few sniper weapons of the WWII period were custom designed. Most were simply bolt-action service rifles selected from among the thousands manufactured and fitted with a suitable scope. In the right hands, these weapons proved deadly indeed.

Mauser Kar 98K Sniper Version

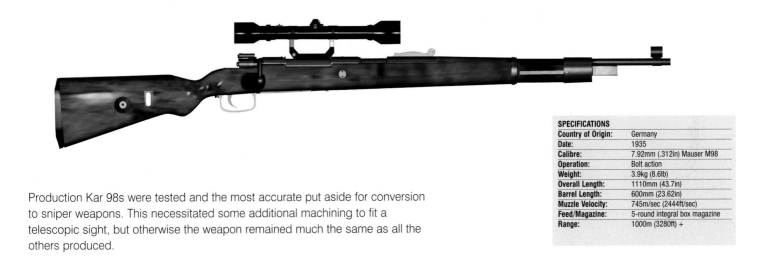

Production Kar 98s were tested and the most accurate put aside for conversion to sniper weapons. This necessitated some additional machining to fit a telescopic sight, but otherwise the weapon remained much the same as all the others produced.

SPECIFICATIONS	
Country of Origin:	Germany
Date:	1935
Calibre:	7.92mm (.312in) Mauser M98
Operation:	Bolt action
Weight:	3.9kg (8.6lb)
Overall Length:	1110mm (43.7in)
Barrel Length:	600mm (23.62in)
Muzzle Velocity:	745m/sec (2444ft/sec)
Feed/Magazine:	5-round integral box magazine
Range:	1000m (3280ft) +

Springfield Model 1903/A3

The M1903A4 was a moderately successful conversion of the obsolescent bolt-action service rifle. Its main drawback was that the scope prevented the use of a charger to rapidly load the magazine.

SPECIFICATIONS	
Country of Origin:	United States
Date:	1942
Calibre:	7.62mm (.3in) M1906
Operation:	Bolt action
Weight:	3.94kg (8.68lb)
Overall Length:	1097mm (43.19in)
Barrel Length:	610mm (24in)
Muzzle Velocity:	853m/sec (2800ft/sec)
Feed/Magazine:	5-round internal box magazine
Range:	1000m (3280ft) +

TIMELINE

1935

1942

Lee-Enfield Rifle No. 4 Mk. 1(T) Sniper Rifle

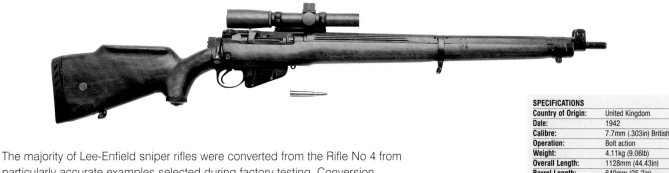

The majority of Lee-Enfield sniper rifles were converted from the Rifle No 4 from particularly accurate examples selected during factory testing. Conversion required little more than the addition of a cheek-piece and a telescopic sight.

SPECIFICATIONS	
Country of Origin:	United Kingdom
Date:	1942
Calibre:	7.7mm (.303in) British Service
Operation:	Bolt action
Weight:	4.11kg (9.06lb)
Overall Length:	1128mm (44.43in)
Barrel Length:	640mm (25.2in)
Muzzle Velocity:	751m/sec (2464ft/sec)
Feed/Magazine:	10-round detachable box magazine
Range:	1000m (3280ft) +

De Lisle Carbine

A silenced short-range sniping weapon created by mating the Lee-Enfield action to a Thompson sub-machine gun barrel, the de Lisle carbine was almost completely silent. Its 11.4mm/.45in (.45 ACP) round was accurate out to about 250m (820ft).

SPECIFICATIONS	
Country of Origin:	United Kingdom
Date:	1943
Calibre:	11.4mm (.45in) .45 ACP
Operation:	Bolt action
Weight:	3.7kg (8.15lb)
Overall Length:	960mm (37.79in)
Barrel Length:	210mm (8.26in)
Muzzle Velocity:	260m/sec (853ft/sec)
Feed/Magazine:	7-round detachable box magazine
Range:	400m (1312ft)

Garand M1C

Late in the war, a sniper version of the semi-automatic Garand M1 became available. Examples saw action, but the Garand did not supplant the M1903 sniper variant until the Korean War.

SPECIFICATIONS	
Country of Origin:	United States
Date:	1944
Calibre:	7.62mm (.3in) US .30-06
Operation:	Gas-operated
Weight:	4.37kg (9.5lb)
Overall Length:	1103mm (43.5in)
Barrel Length:	610mm (24in)
Muzzle Velocity:	853m/sec (2800ft/sec)
Feed/Magazine:	8-round internal box magazine
Range:	1000m (3280ft) +

1942

1943

1944

M1 Garand

By modern standards, the M1 Garand is somewhat archaic, but for the time it was a huge leap forward in infantry firepower. Its powerful 7.62mm/.3in .30-06 round could be delivered accurately and rapidly from an eight-round internal magazine, and this could be quickly replenished.

The first M1 model was prone to jamming due to the way that gas was tapped to work the action, but from 1939 onwards an alternative system, taking gas from a port under the muzzle, was used which greatly improved reliability.

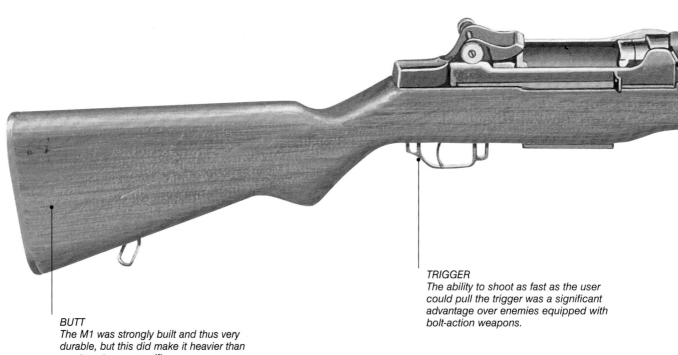

TRIGGER
The ability to shoot as fast as the user could pull the trigger was a significant advantage over enemies equipped with bolt-action weapons.

BUTT
The M1 was strongly built and thus very durable, but this did make it heavier than most contemporary rifles.

SPECIFICATIONS	
Country of Origin:	United States
Date:	1936
Calibre:	7.62mm (.3in) US .30-06
Operation:	Gas-operated
Weight:	4.37kg (9.5lb)
Overall Length:	1103mm (43.5in)
Barrel Length:	610mm (24in)
Muzzle Velocity:	853m/sec (2800ft/sec)
Feed/Magazine:	8-round internal box magazine
Range:	500m (1640ft) +

One drawback in the M1 that was never remedied was the loading system. The eight-round en bloc ammunition clips used by the Garand meant that the magazine could not be 'topped off', and the loud 'ping' as an expended clip was ejected could alert enemy troops to a user's vulnerability.

Despite the loading system issue, the M1 Garand was an excellent combat rifle whose firepower greatly enhanced the capability of the troops that used it. The Garand was named by General Eisenhower as one of the five inventions that won World War II; it is the only personal weapon on the list.

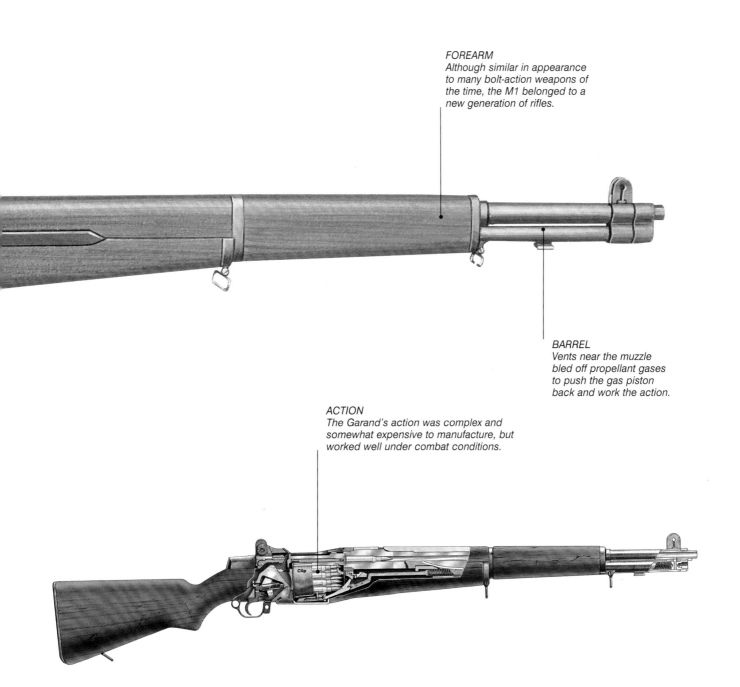

FOREARM
Although similar in appearance to many bolt-action weapons of the time, the M1 belonged to a new generation of rifles.

BARREL
Vents near the muzzle bled off propellant gases to push the gas piston back and work the action.

ACTION
The Garand's action was complex and somewhat expensive to manufacture, but worked well under combat conditions.

Clip

Semi-Automatic Rifles

Although most armies started the war largely armed with bolt-action rifles, semi-automatic weapons had been available for several years and were gradually being adopted. It took time for these more effective weapons to become available in sufficient numbers.

Fusil Automatique Modèle 1917

Developed from the M1886 Lebel rifle, the M1917 used the same ammunition and many of its components. Its internal magazine was loaded with 5-round clips. It saw action in World War I and remained in service into the 1940s.

SPECIFICATIONS	
Country of Origin:	France
Date:	1917
Calibre:	8mm (.314in) Lebel
Operation:	Gas, rotating bolt
Weight:	5.25kg (116lb)
Overall Length:	1331mm (52.4in)
Barrel Length:	798mm (31.4in)
Muzzle Velocity:	853m/sec (2800ft/sec)
Feed/Magazine:	5-round box magazine
Range:	300m (984ft)

M1 Garand with M11 A2 rifle grenade

A number of variants on the Garand were fielded, but other than the sniper version most did not see action. An exception was the grenade-launching variant, but older M1903s were generally preferred for this role.

SPECIFICATIONS*	
Country of Origin:	United States
Date:	1936
Calibre:	7.62mm (.3in) US .30-06
Operation:	Gas-operated
Weight:	4.37kg (9.5lb)
Overall Length:	1103mm (43.5in)
Barrel Length:	610mm (24in)
Muzzle Velocity:	853m/sec (2800ft/sec)
Feed/Magazine:	N/A
Range (Grenade):	100m (328ft)
* Of rifle without grenade	

TIMELINE

1917   1936   1940

Tokarev SVT-40

Developed from the earlier SVT-38, the SVT-40 became available to re-equip some Soviet infantry units just in time for the German invasion. The increased firepower of these formations came as an unpleasant surprise for the invaders.

SPECIFICATIONS	
Country of Origin:	USSR
Date:	1940
Calibre:	7.62mm (.3in)
Operation:	Gas-operated
Weight:	3.90kg (8.6lb)
Overall Length:	1226mm (48.27in)
Barrel Length:	610mm (25in)
Muzzle Velocity:	840m/sec (2755ft/sec)
Feed/Magazine:	10-round detachable box magazine
Range:	500m (1640ft) +

Carbine, Caliber .30, M1

Conceived as a lightweight weapon for support troops, the M1 carbine fired a pistol cartridge which limited its range and stopping power. It was nevertheless a popular and effective weapon, of which six million or more were made.

SPECIFICATIONS	
Country of Origin:	United States
Date:	1942
Calibre:	7.62mm (.3in) Carbine
Operation:	Gas-operated
Weight:	2.5kg (5.47lb)
Overall Length:	905mm (35.7in)
Barrel Length:	457mm (18in)
Muzzle Velocity:	595m/sec (1950ft/sec)
Feed/Magazine:	15- or 30-round detachable box magazine
Range:	c.300m (984ft)

Gewehr 43

Designed by Walther, the Gewehr 43 was accurate and effective but complex and thus slow to produce. It was issued in small numbers; semi-automatic weapons never became as prevalent in the German Army as in some other nations' forces.

SPECIFICATIONS	
Country of Origin:	Germany
Date:	1943
Calibre:	8mm (.314in) IS
Operation:	Gas-operated
Weight:	4.1kg (9.7lb)
Overall Length:	1130mm (44.49in)
Muzzle Velocity:	853.6m/sec (2800ft/sec)
Feed/Magazine:	10-round detachable box magazine
Range:	500m (1640ft); 800m (2620ft) with scope

1942

1943

Early Assault Rifles

The term *Sturmgewehr* (Storm Rifle) is attributed to Adolf Hitler, describing the fully automatic weapon that became designated StG44. Assault rifles are optimized for close combat, often in urban terrain, rather than long-range marksmanship in the open.

Tokarev AVT-40

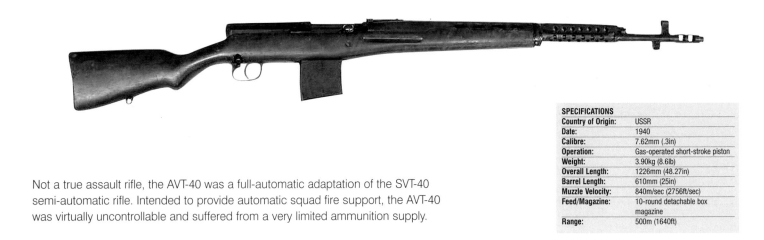

Not a true assault rifle, the AVT-40 was a full-automatic adaptation of the SVT-40 semi-automatic rifle. Intended to provide automatic squad fire support, the AVT-40 was virtually uncontrollable and suffered from a very limited ammunition supply.

SPECIFICATIONS	
Country of Origin:	USSR
Date:	1940
Calibre:	7.62mm (.3in)
Operation:	Gas-operated short-stroke piston
Weight:	3.90kg (8.6lb)
Overall Length:	1226mm (48.27in)
Barrel Length:	610mm (25in)
Muzzle Velocity:	840m/sec (2756ft/sec)
Feed/Magazine:	10-round detachable box magazine
Range:	500m (1640ft)

Charlton Automatic Rifle

Shortage of automatic support weapons prompted the conversion of Lee-Enfield and Lee-Metford rifles to full-automatic capability. The Charlton Automatic Rifle was capable of using a Bren magazine or its own 10-round magazine.

SPECIFICATIONS	
Country of Origin:	New Zealand
Date:	1941
Calibre:	7.7mm (.303in)
Operation:	Gas-operated semi-automatic
Weight:	7.3kg (16lb)
Overall Length:	1150mm (44.5in)
Barrel Length:	Not known
Muzzle Velocity:	744m/sec (2440ft/sec)
Feed/Magazine:	10-round magazine
Range:	910m (2985ft)

TIMELINE   1940   1941   1942

Fallschirmjägergewehr 42 (FG42)

Developed for paratroops (Fallschirmjäger), the FG42 fell somewhere between a light machine gun and an assault rifle. It fired a full-power rifle cartridge from a 20-round magazine which, at 750rpm, tended to be emptied rather quickly.

SPECIFICATIONS	
Country of Origin:	Germany
Date:	1942
Calibre:	7.92mm (.312in) Mauser
Operation:	Gas-operated
Weight:	4.53kg (9.99lb)
Overall Length:	940mm (37in)
Barrel Length:	502mm (19.76in)
Muzzle Velocity:	761m/sec (2500ft/sec)
Feed/Magazine:	20-round detachable box magazine
Range:	400m (1312ft) +

Maschinenkarabiner 42 (H) / Machinenpistole 43

The large numbers of sub-machine guns used by Soviet troops in urban combat gave them an advantage that the German Army needed to counter. However, Hitler originally blocked the Maschinenkarabiner 42 project, so it was quietly continued under the MP43 designation.

SPECIFICATIONS	
Country of Origin:	Germany
Date:	1943
Calibre:	7.92mm (.312in) Kurz
Operation:	Gas-operated
Weight:	5.1kg (11.24lb)
Overall Length:	940mm (37in)
Barrel Length:	418mm (16.5in)
Muzzle Velocity:	700m/sec (2300ft/sec)
Feed/Magazine:	30-round detachable box magazine
Range:	c.300m (984ft)

Sturmgewehr 44

Finally approved by Hitler, the MP43 project went into service as the StG44. Firing a short 7.92mm (.312in) cartridge, it offered controllable automatic fire and was accurate out to 400m (1312ft). The 'Storm Rifle' inspired a whole generation of assault rifles.

SPECIFICATIONS	
Country of Origin:	Germany
Date:	1944
Calibre:	7.92mm (.312in) Kurz
Operation:	Gas-operated
Weight:	5.1kg (11.24lb)
Overall Length:	940mm (37in)
Barrel Length:	418mm (16.5in)
Muzzle Velocity:	700m/sec (2300ft/sec)
Feed/Magazine:	30-round detachable box magazine
Range:	c.400m (1312ft)

1943 1944

Gas-Operated vs Manual

Both gas-operated and bolt-action weapons use the same basic system. A bolt moves back and forth to eject the spent case, to allow the magazine spring to push a new round into the chamber, and then to close and seal the chamber ready for firing.

The only real difference is how the bolt is operated. A bolt-action weapon needs a protrusion for the user to grasp, which in turn requires that a hand be taken off the weapon. A gas-operated weapon can in theory have a wholly internal action, though in practice there is usually a manual cocking handle which by definition must be external.

FALLSCHIRMJÄGERGEWEHR 42
The FG 42 was a selective fire battle rifle produced in Germany from 1942. The weapon was developed specifically for the use with airborne troops and was deployed in very limited numbers until the end of the war. It combined the characteristics and firepower of a light machine gun in a lightweight form no larger than the standard-issue Kar 98k rifle. Considered one of the most advanced weapon designs of its time, the FG 42 helped to shape the modern assault rifle concept.

SPECIFICATIONS	
Country of Origin:	Germany
Date:	1942
Calibre:	7.92mm (.312in) Mauser
Operation:	Gas-operated
Weight:	4.53kg (9.99lb)
Overall Length:	940mm (37in)
Barrel Length:	502mm (19.76in)
Muzzle Velocity:	761m/sec (2500ft/sec)
Feed/Magazine:	20-round detachable box magazine
Range:	400m (1312ft) +

GAS OPERATION
The FG 42 had a gas-operated turning bolt action geared to a spiral recoil spring. This system used pressurized exhaust gases from the bore and channeled them through a port drilled in the barrel into a gas cylinder located under the barrel.

GAS-OPERATION

Hot gases formed by the detonation of propellant in the firing chamber push the round down the barrel until it passes the vent. This gives the gases an additional route for expansion. The gas piston, which is connected to the bolt, is rapidly pushed backwards. This opens the ejection port and ejects the spent cartridge before rearward movement is arrested by a spring.

The bolt is then pushed forward again, picking up a new round and chambering it before closing and sealing the chamber. Exactly at what point the weapon is recocked depends upon the design of the weapon. The gas piston and recoil spring help absorb some of the weapon's recoil, a factor which can aid accuracy during rapid fire.

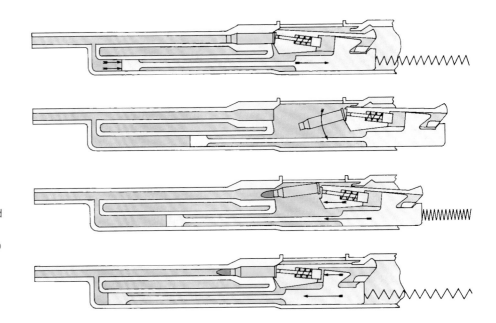

PISTON
The rapid build-up of propellant gases imparted rearward pressure on a long-stroke piston, driving it backwards.

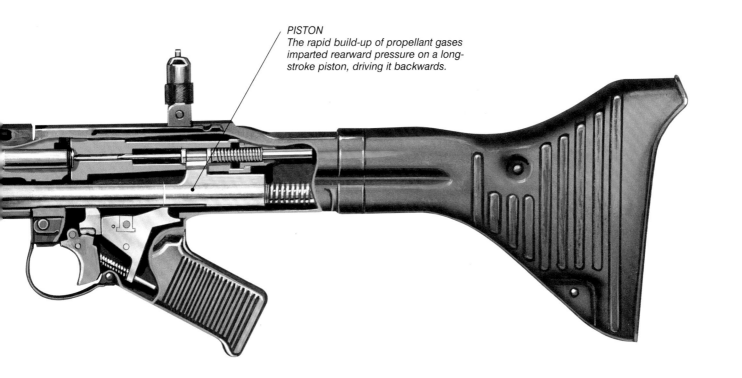

SKS Carbine

World War II was largely characterized by short-range firefights in urban terrain, jungles, and in close terrain such as the Normandy Bocage. Increased use of motorized transport also created a need for a shorter infantry weapon that could be easily manoeuvred into and out of vehicles.

The end result of this trend was the assault rifle, a lightweight carbine-like rifle firing a lighter cartridge than a typical 'battle' rifle, and optimized for combat at 200–400m (656–1312ft) rather than accurate fire at 800m (2620ft) or beyond. However, there were a number of steps along the way.

ACTION/MAGAZINE
The use of stripper clips to reload internal-magazine weapons is the likely origin of the misnomer 'clip' often applied to a detachable magazine.

SPECIFICATIONS	
Country of Origin:	USSR
Date:	1945
Calibre:	7.62mm (.3in)
Operation:	Gas-operated short-stroke piston
Weight:	3.85kg (8.49lb)
Overall Length:	1021mm (40.2in)
Barrel Length:	521mm (20.5in)
Muzzle Velocity:	735m/sec (2411ft/sec)
Feed/Magazine:	10-round integral box magazine
Range:	400m (1312ft)

The SKS carbine appeared in 1945. It is not a true assault rifle, but it illustrates the direction in which weapon design was going. Firing a short 7.62 x 39mm (.3 x 1.54in) round (which would be used in the AK47 two years later), the SKS was short and handy. However, it was a semi-automatic weapon and was limited by its ammunition capacity.

BAYONET
The SKS was equipped with a permanently attached folding bayonet. Such devices were uncommon compared with the more usual detachable knife/bayonet.

FOREARM
The SKS was one of the last conventional-layout rifles used by the Soviet Army. Within a few years the radically different AK47 would enter service.

The SKS was fed from a 10-round internal magazine which was loaded manually or with a stripper clip. It thus had some of the characteristics of an assault rifle – light cartridge, short length and reduced weight – but lacked the capacity for automatic fire and, more importantly perhaps, fast reloading that a true assault rifle required.

The Sten Family

At the outbreak of World War II, Britain needed a simple light automatic weapon that could be thrown together quickly and cheaply. The Sten was crude, but could be built in the huge numbers required.

Sten Mk I

The original Sten gun had wooden furniture and a flash hider and a foregrip which folded up to make the weapon easier to carry. The magazine was copied from the German MP40 and was equally prone to stoppages.

SPECIFICATIONS	
Country of Origin:	United Kingdom
Date:	1940
Calibre:	9mm (.35in) Parabellum
Operation:	Blowback
Weight:	3.1kg (7lb)
Overall Length:	760mm (29.9in)
Barrel Length:	196mm (7.7in)
Muzzle Velocity:	365m/sec (1198ft/sec)
Feed/Magazine:	32-round detachable box magazine
Range:	60m (196ft)

Sten Mk II

The definitive Sten gun was of (extremely crude) all-metal construction. Its 47 parts were mainly of stamped metal; only the bolt and barrel were machined. The Mk II Sten was supplied to resistance fighters as well as thousands of Allied troops.

SPECIFICATIONS	
Country of Origin:	United Kingdom
Date:	1942
Calibre:	9mm (.35in) Parabellum
Operation:	Blowback
Weight:	2.95kg (6.5lb)
Overall Length:	762mm (30in)
Barrel Length:	196mm (7.7in)
Muzzle Velocity:	380m/sec (1247ft/sec)
Feed/Magazine:	32-round detachable box magazine
Range:	70m (230ft)

TIMELINE 1940 1942 1943

Sten Mk II 'Silent Sten'

A suppressed version of the Sten Mk II was developed for use by Special Operations Executive (SOE) operatives. It saw action in Europe and Southeast Asia, and was used later by Australian special forces in Vietnam.

SPECIFICATIONS	
Country of Origin:	United Kingdom
Date:	1943
Calibre:	9mm (.35in) Parabellum
Operation:	Blowback
Weight:	2.95kg (6.5lb)
Overall Length:	762mm (30in)
Barrel Length:	196mm (7.7in)
Muzzle Velocity:	380m/sec (1247ft/sec)
Feed/Magazine:	32-round detachable box magazine
Range:	70m (230ft)

Sten Mk IV (Prototype)

A miniaturized Sten that never developed past the prototype stage, the Mk IV was characterized by a pistol grip and a very short barrel with a flash hider.

SPECIFICATIONS	
Country of Origin:	United Kingdom
Date:	1944
Calibre:	9mm (.35in) Parabellum
Operation:	Blowback
Weight:	Not known
Overall Length:	Not known
Barrel Length:	Not known
Muzzle Velocity:	380m/sec (1247ft/sec)
Feed/Magazine:	32-round detachable box magazine
Range:	N/A

Sten Mk V

Intended for airborne troops, the Sten Mk V gained a fixed wooden stock and foregrip. It could be fitted with a bayonet, though this was of very limited use.

SPECIFICATIONS	
Country of Origin:	United Kingdom
Date:	1944
Calibre:	9mm (.35in) Parabellum
Operation:	Blowback
Weight:	3.86kg (8.5lb)
Overall Length:	762mm (30in)
Barrel Length:	196mm (7.7in)
Muzzle Velocity:	380m/sec (1247ft/sec)
Feed/Magazine:	32-round detachable box magazine
Range:	70m (230ft)

1944

Sten Gun

The Sten gun was named for the initials of its creators (Shepherd and Turpin), plus the Enfield factory where it was developed. The designers' main aim was to create an expedient weapon that could be rushed into mass production. They succeeded, but the Sten's cheapness came at a price.

The Sten was simply and crudely built, and could be assembled in any workshop – indeed there are tales of Stens built by schoolboys. It was extremely cheap, did not use up resources needed for other weapons, and could use captured German 9mm (.35in) ammunition if need be.

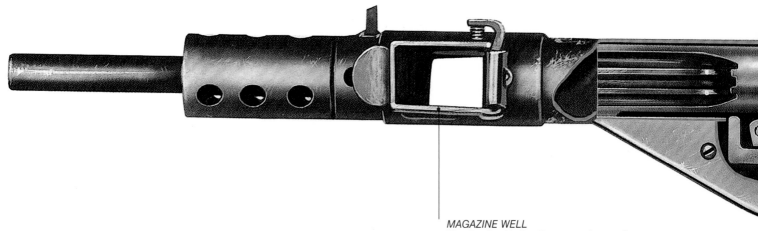

MAGAZINE WELL
The Sten's side-loading magazine made a handy foregrip, but this could move it out of alignment and cause a jam.

SPECIFICATIONS	
Country of Origin:	United Kingdom
Date:	1942
Calibre:	9mm (.35in) Parabellum
Operation:	Blowback
Weight:	2.95kg (6.5lb)
Overall Length:	762mm (30in)
Barrel Length:	196mm (7.7in)
Muzzle Velocity:	380m/sec (1247ft/sec)
Feed/Magazine:	32-round detachable box magazine
Range:	70m (230ft)

One snag with the Sten was a proneness to jamming. It shared this defect with the MP40, from which its magazine was copied. It also had a lamentable habit of discharging if knocked, and on top of that it could be difficult to maintain due to its many ragged and sharp edges.

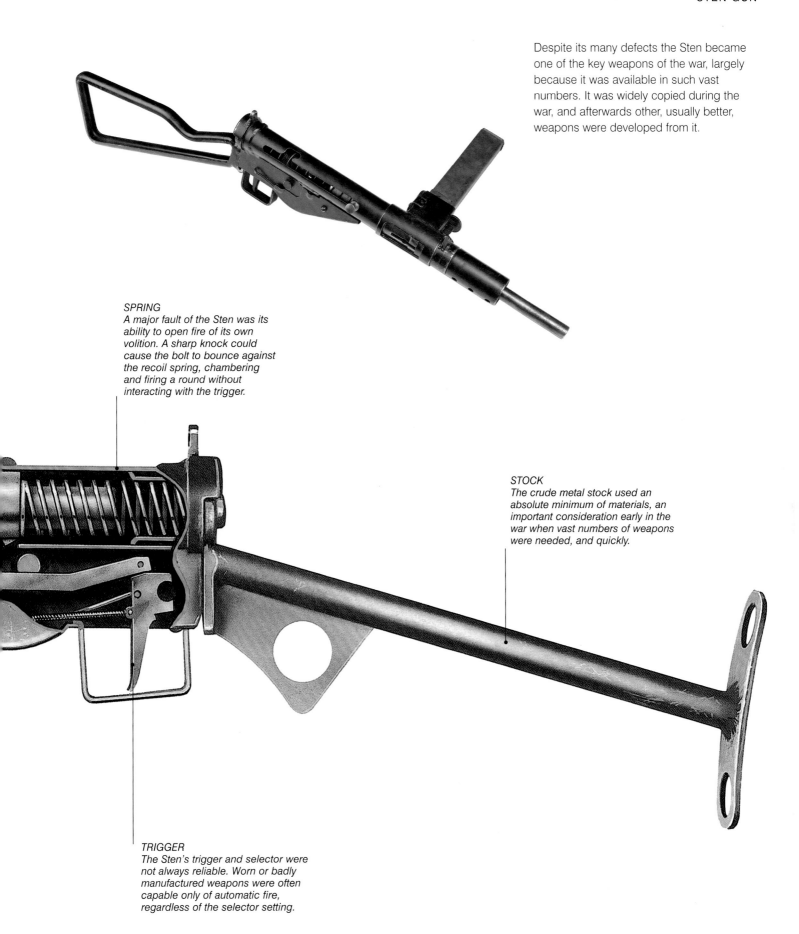

Despite its many defects the Sten became one of the key weapons of the war, largely because it was available in such vast numbers. It was widely copied during the war, and afterwards other, usually better, weapons were developed from it.

SPRING
A major fault of the Sten was its ability to open fire of its own volition. A sharp knock could cause the bolt to bounce against the recoil spring, chambering and firing a round without interacting with the trigger.

STOCK
The crude metal stock used an absolute minimum of materials, an important consideration early in the war when vast numbers of weapons were needed, and quickly.

TRIGGER
The Sten's trigger and selector were not always reliable. Worn or badly manufactured weapons were often capable only of automatic fire, regardless of the selector setting.

German Submachine Guns

Having successfully experimented with submachine guns (SMGs) in the last months of World War I, the German Army was prohibited from owning them by the Treaty of Versailles. As the terms of the treaty were gradually discarded, SMGs re-entered German service. German submachine guns were usually designated with the abbreviation 'MP' for *Maschinenpistole*.

MP28

Developed for law enforcement use (which was allowed under the Treaty of Versailles), the MP28 was essentially a slightly modified MP18, quantities of which had been retained despite the treaty's prohibition.

SPECIFICATIONS	
Country of Origin:	Germany
Date:	1928
Calibre:	9mm (.35in) Parabellum
Operation:	Open bolt blowback
Weight:	4.18kg (9.2lb)
Overall Length:	832mm (32.8in)
Barrel Length:	200mm (7.9in)
Muzzle Velocity:	380m/sec (1247ft/sec)
Feed/Magazine:	32-round detachable drum magazine
Range:	70m (230ft)

Erma MPE

The MPE entered production in 1930 and achieved considerable export success, notably in Central and South America. It was extensively used in the Spanish Civil War.

SPECIFICATIONS	
Country of Origin:	Germany
Date:	1930
Calibre:	9mm (.35in) Parabellum
Operation:	Blowback
Weight:	4.15kg (9.13lb)
Overall Length:	902mm (35.5in)
Barrel Length:	254mm (10in)
Muzzle Velocity:	395m/sec (1300ft/sec)
Feed/Magazine:	20- or 32-round box magazine
Cyclic Rate:	500rpm
Range:	70m (230ft)

TIMELINE

1928

1930

1938

MP38

Cheaply manufactured from metal stampings, the MP38 was generally reliable but prone to jamming if the user pulled back on the magazine when using it as a foregrip. It was also susceptible to accidental discharges if knocked.

SPECIFICATIONS	
Country of Origin:	Germany
Date:	1938
Calibre:	9mm (.35in) Parabellum
Operation:	Blowback
Weight:	4.1kg (9.1lb)
Overall Length:	832mm (32.75in) stock extended; 630mm (24.75in) stock folded
Barrel Length:	248mm (9.75in)
Muzzle Velocity:	395m/sec (1300ft/sec)
Feed/Magazine:	32-round box magazine
Cyclic Rate:	500rpm
Range:	70m (230ft)

MP40

The MP40 used simplified production methods to ensure that large numbers could be quickly built. It is often wrongly called a 'Schmeisser', but in fact Hugo Schmeisser was not involved in its design.

SPECIFICATIONS	
Country of Origin:	Germany
Date:	1940
Calibre:	9mm (.35in) Parabellum
Operation:	Blowback
Weight:	3.97kg (8.75lb)
Overall Length:	832mm (32.75in) stock extended; 630mm (24.75in) stock folded
Barrel Length:	248mm (9.75in)
Muzzle Velocity:	395m/sec (1300ft/sec)
Feed/Magazine:	32-round box magazine
Cyclic Rate:	500rpm
Range:	70m (230ft)

MP41

The MP41 was designed by Hugo Schmeisser. It essentially mated the MP40 receiver to the stock and selector of an MP28. Most of the weapons made were privately purchased by SS troops.

SPECIFICATIONS	
Country of Origin:	Germany
Date:	1941
Calibre:	9mm (.35in) Parabellum
Operation:	Blowback
Weight:	3.87kg (8.5lb)
Overall Length:	860mm (33.8in)
Barrel Length:	250mm (9.8mm)
Muzzle Velocity:	381m/sec (1250ft/sec)
Feed/Magazine:	32-round box magazine
Cyclic Rate:	500rpm
Range:	150-200m (492-656ft)

1940   1941

MP40

Prior to the development of the MP38 and the MP40 that was developed from it, weapons tended to be carefully machined and provided with high-quality fittings. The MP38 changed all that, and the MP40 took the trend still further.

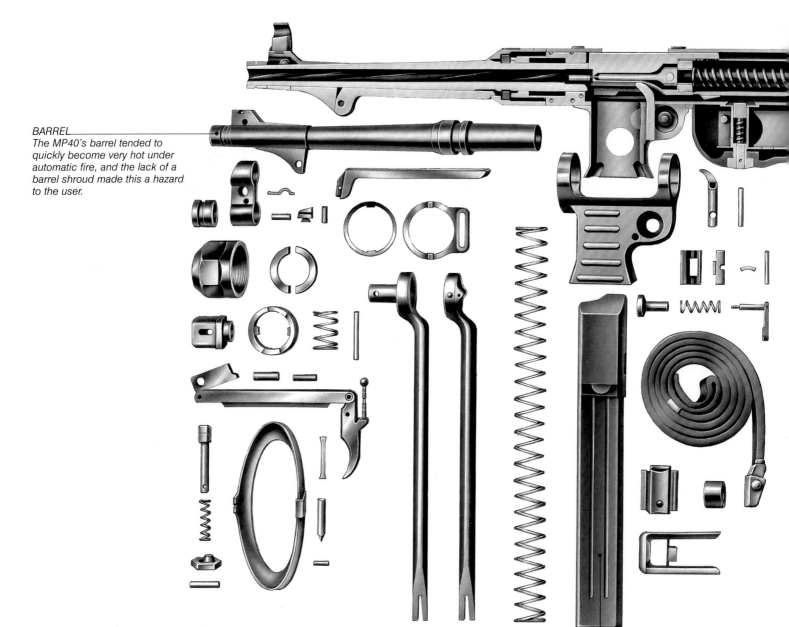

BARREL
The MP40's barrel tended to quickly become very hot under automatic fire, and the lack of a barrel shroud made this a hazard to the user.

Rather than high-quality machining, the MP40 used cheap metal stampings, a wire stock and plastic parts rather than elegant wooden ones. It looked, and indeed was, a little crude, but it fulfilled the basic function it was designed for – it delivered automatic fire when it was called upon to do so.

MAGAZINE
The long single-stacked magazine made a handy foregrip, but this practice was discouraged in training as it could cause stoppages.

The main difference between the MP38 and MP40, apart from simplified production, was the machining of a slot over the 'home' position of the breech block, allowing a pin to be inserted to prevent the weapon from firing. Prior to this, a cocked MP38 could (and sometimes did) initiate automatic fire all by itself if dropped. The Sten gun, another cheap submachine gun, suffered from a similar habit of trying to murder its users.

SPECIFICATIONS	
Country of Origin:	Germany
Date:	1940
Calibre:	9mm (.35in) Parabellum
Operation:	Blowback
Weight:	3.97kg (8.75lb)
Overall Length:	832mm (32.75in) stock extended; 630mm (24.75in) stock folded
Barrel Length:	248mm (9.75in)
Muzzle Velocity:	395m/sec (1300ft/sec)
Feed/Magazine:	32-round box magazine
Cyclic Rate:	500rpm
Range:	70m (230ft)

SPRING
The MP40 used blowback operation, firing from an open bolt like most submachine guns.

STOCK
The folding metal stock was an innovation, and influenced a great many other designs long after the MP40 was retired.

HANDGUARD
The handguard, running from the trigger guard to the magazine well, could be used to support the weapon with the left hand. An alternative position was to grip the magazine-well.

Side-Loading Submachine Guns

The side-loading submachine gun is no longer common, but during the World War II period there were several such examples. Most owed their design to the influential MP18, the first combat-proven SMG.

Steyr-Solothurn S1-100

In order to get around the Treaty of Versailles, Germany contracted out some of its arms development to other European countries. The S1-100 was one result. It was adopted by Austria and achieved considerable overseas sales.

SPECIFICATIONS	
Country of Origin:	Austria
Date:	1930
Calibre:	9mm (.35in)
Operation:	Blowback
Weight:	4.48kg (9.88lb)
Overall Length:	850mm (33.46in)
Barrel Length:	200mm (7.87in)
Muzzle Velocity:	418m/sec (1370ft/sec)
Feed/Magazine:	32-round box magazine
Cyclic Rate:	500rpm
Range:	100m (328ft)

ZK 383

Despite being chambered for a 9mm (.35in) pistol round, the Czech ZK 383 was intended as a squad support weapon. It achieved some export success before the war; most wartime-made weapons went to the Waffen-SS.

SPECIFICATIONS	
Country of Origin:	Czechoslovakia
Date:	1938
Calibre:	9mm (.35in)
Operation:	Blowback
Weight:	4.83kg (10.65lb)
Overall Length:	875mm (34.45in)
Barrel Length:	325mm (12.8in)
Muzzle Velocity:	365m/sec (1200ft/sec)
Feed/Magazine:	30-round box magazine
Range:	100m (328ft)

TIMELINE

1930

1938

1941

Lanchester

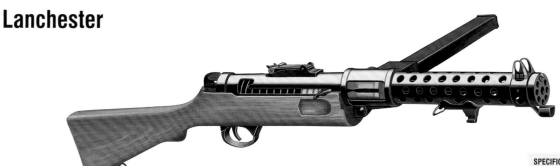

The very well put-together Lanchester was essentially a copy of the Bergmann MP28. It used the furniture of a Lee-Enfield rifle and was made from high-quality materials. However, this made it expensive and slow to produce.

SPECIFICATIONS	
Country of Origin:	United Kingdom
Date:	1941
Calibre:	9mm (.35in) Parabellum
Operation:	Blowback
Weight:	4.34kg (9.56lb)
Overall Length:	850mm (33.5in)
Barrel Length:	203mm (8in)
Muzzle Velocity:	380m/sec (1247ft/sec)
Feed/Magazine:	50-round box magazine
Cyclic Rate:	600rpm
Range:	70m (230ft)

Type 100

The Type 100 was the only Japanese SMG of the war. Firing the weak 8mm (.314in) Nambu pistol round, it initially had low rate of fire of 400rpm. Even the upgraded 1944 version was outgunned by Western weapons.

SPECIFICATIONS	
Country of Origin:	Japan
Date:	1942
Calibre:	8mm (.314in) Nambu
Operation:	Blowback
Weight:	3.83kg (8.44lb)
Overall Length:	890mm (35in)
Barrel Length:	228mm (9in)
Muzzle Velocity:	335m/sec (1100ft/sec)
Feed/Magazine:	30-round box magazine
Cyclic Rate:	450rpm (1940); 800rpm (1944)
Range:	70m (230ft)

Patchett Mk 1

The Patchett was developed as an improved replacement for the Sten gun. It proved its worth in action at Arnhem in 1944, and was eventually developed through a Mk 2 model into the Sterling SMG.

SPECIFICATIONS	
Country of Origin:	United Kingdom
Date:	1944
Calibre:	9mm (.35in) Parabellum
Operation:	Blowback
Weight:	2.7kg (6lb)
Overall Length:	685mm (27in)
Barrel Length:	195mm (7.75in)
Muzzle Velocity:	395m/sec (1295ft/sec)
Feed/Magazine:	32-round detachable box magazine
Cyclic Rate:	550rpm
Range:	70m (230ft)

1942

1944

US Submachine Guns

The term 'submachine gun' was coined to describe the Thompson M1921. Thus, although it was not the first weapon of its type, the Thompson submachine gun deserves recognition as the first weapon to be labelled as such.

Thompson Model 1921

With its high firepower and the excellent stopping power of its 11.4mm/.45in .45 ACP round, the M1921 was an immediate commercial success. It was favoured by both criminals and law enforcement agencies, causing some militaries to view its 'gangster' image with suspicion.

SPECIFICATIONS	
Country of Origin:	United States
Date:	1921
Calibre:	11.4mm (.45in) M1911
Operation:	Delayed blowback
Weight:	4.88kg (10.75lb)
Overall Length:	857mm (33.75in)
Barrel Length:	266mm (10.5in)
Muzzle Velocity:	280m/sec (920ft/sec)
Feed/Magazine:	18-, 20-, 30-round detachable box magazine; 50- or 100-round drum magazine
Cyclic Rate:	800rpm
Range:	120m (394ft)

Thompson Model 1928

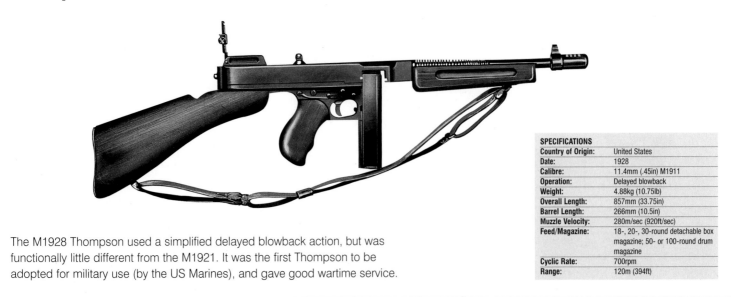

The M1928 Thompson used a simplified delayed blowback action, but was functionally little different from the M1921. It was the first Thompson to be adopted for military use (by the US Marines), and gave good wartime service.

SPECIFICATIONS	
Country of Origin:	United States
Date:	1928
Calibre:	11.4mm (.45in) M1911
Operation:	Delayed blowback
Weight:	4.88kg (10.75lb)
Overall Length:	857mm (33.75in)
Barrel Length:	266mm (10.5in)
Muzzle Velocity:	280m/sec (920ft/sec)
Feed/Magazine:	18-, 20-, 30-round detachable box magazine; 50- or 100-round drum magazine
Cyclic Rate:	700rpm
Range:	120m (394ft)

TIMELINE   1921   1928

Reising Model 55

A complex weapon firing from a closed bolt rather than the more usual open-bolt blowback action, the Reising Model 55 was intended for use by airborne troops but was too susceptible to dirt for military use.

SPECIFICATIONS	
Country of Origin:	United States
Date:	1941
Calibre:	11.4mm (.45in) M1911
Operation:	Delayed blowback
Weight:	2.89kg (6.37lb)
Overall Length:	787mm (31in)
Barrel Length:	266mm (10.5in)
Muzzle Velocity:	280m/sec (920ft/sec)
Feed/Magazine:	12- or 25-round box magazine
Cyclic Rate:	500rpm
Range:	120m (394ft)

Thompson M1

The M1 was a simplified Thompson which was much cheaper to produce for military use. It could not use the high-capacity drum magazine of previous versions, but a 30-round box magazine was introduced to partially compensate.

SPECIFICATIONS	
Country of Origin:	United States
Date:	1942
Calibre:	11.4mm (.45in) M1911
Operation:	Delayed blowback
Weight:	4.74kg (10.45lb) loaded
Overall Length:	813mm (32in)
Barrel Length:	267mm (10.5in)
Muzzle Velocity:	280m/sec (920ft/sec)
Feed/Magazine:	20- or 30-round box magazine
Cyclic Rate:	700rpm
Range:	120m (394ft)

United Defense M42

Designed as a commercial product, the M42 was apparently taken into US service to supply covert units and resistance organizations. Although of high quality it never made much impression in the mainstream marketplace.

SPECIFICATIONS	
Country of Origin:	United States
Date:	1942
Calibre:	11.4mm (.45in) M1911
Operation:	Delayed blowback
Weight:	4.1kg (10lb)
Overall Length:	820mm (32.3in)
Barrel Length:	279mm (11in)
Muzzle Velocity:	335.3m/sec (1100ft/sec)
Feed/Magazine:	25-round box magazine
Cyclic Rate:	900rpm
Range:	120m (394ft)

Thompson Submachine Gun M1928

The Thompson submachine gun was a fearsomely powerful weapon, delivering an 11.4mm (.45in) round at 700–800rpm. It was never especially accurate as a result of its heavy recoil, rate of fire and firing from an open bolt. The latter means that the bolt began the firing cycle to the rear and ran forward to chamber and then fire a round.

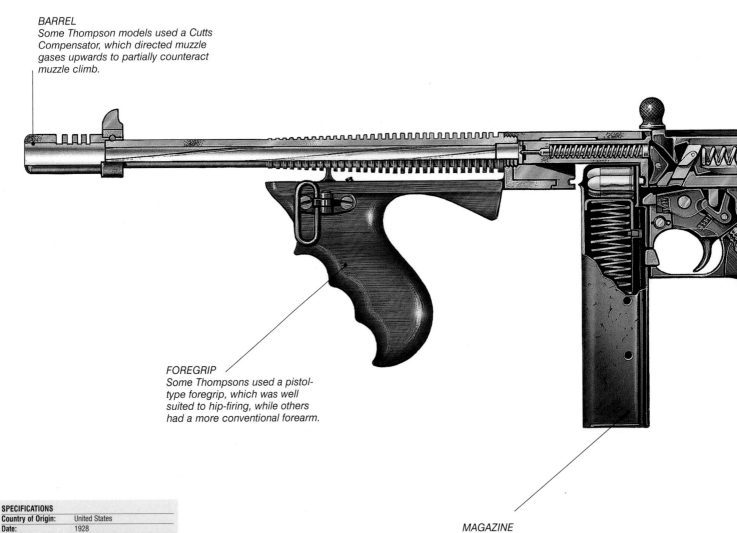

BARREL
Some Thompson models used a Cutts Compensator, which directed muzzle gases upwards to partially counteract muzzle climb.

FOREGRIP
Some Thompsons used a pistol-type foregrip, which was well suited to hip-firing, while others had a more conventional forearm.

MAGAZINE
Although the drum magazine was made famous by Hollywood, most Thompsons used a smaller box-type magazine.

SPECIFICATIONS	
Country of Origin:	United States
Date:	1928
Calibre:	11.4mm (.45in) M1911
Operation:	Delayed blowback
Weight:	4.88kg (10.75lb)
Overall Length:	857mm (33.75in)
Barrel Length:	266mm (10.5in)
Muzzle Velocity:	280m/sec (920ft/sec)
Feed/Magazine:	18-, 20-, 30-round detachable box magazine; 50- or 100-round drum magazine
Cyclic Rate:	700rpm
Range:	120m (394ft)

Various attempts to improve controllability included the Cutts Compensator (which was intended to reduce muzzle climb) and a pistol-style foregrip. However, submachine guns are intended for firepower rather than precision, and in this area the Thompson excelled.

Although the weapon was heavy, had a short range and did not penetrate cover well, it was well liked by the troops that used it, not least for its reliability. The 50-round drum magazine proved to be too bulky and noisy for military use, as well as prone to jamming. The alternative, a 20-round box magazine, was supplemented with a 30-round 'stick' which proved highly effective.

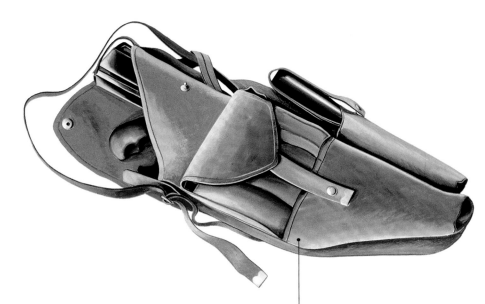

CARRYING POUCH
The carrying pouch was first developed for the M1917 submachine gun, with separate pockets for the various parts of the weapon.

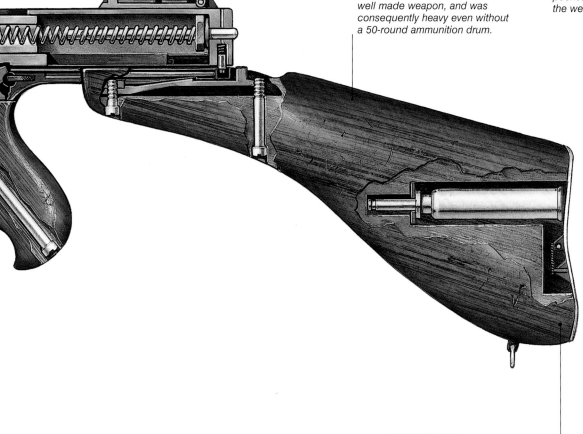

STOCK
The Thompson was a sturdy and well made weapon, and was consequently heavy even without a 50-round ammunition drum.

INSIDE STOCK
A hollow compartment in the stock contained an oiling bottle. On some models the stock could be quickly detached by removing two screws.

Experimental and Variant Submachine Guns

Of the submachine guns developed during the World War II period, some were successful, some innovative, and some both. There were, however, a few blind alleys to explore along the way.

Star SI35

SPECIFICATIONS	
Country of Origin:	Spain
Date:	1935
Calibre:	9mm (.35in) Largo
Operation:	Delayed blowback
Weight:	3.74kg (8.25lb)
Overall Length:	900mm (35.45in)
Barrel Length:	269mm (10.6in)
Muzzle Velocity:	410m/sec (1345ft/sec)
Feed/Magazine:	10-, 30-, 40-round detachable box magazine
Cyclic Rate:	300 or 700rpm
Range:	50m (164ft)

The Star SI35 had a number of interesting features, such as a selectable rate of fire and a mechanism to hold the bolt open once the magazine was empty. However, it was passed over in favour of simpler weapons.

Moschetto Auto Beretta (MAB) 38

SPECIFICATIONS	
Country of Origin:	Italy
Date:	1938
Calibre:	9mm (.35in) Parabellum
Operation:	Blowback
Weight:	2.72kg (6lb)
Overall Length:	798mm (31.4in)
Barrel Length:	198mm (7.79in)
Muzzle Velocity:	395m/sec (1295ft/sec)
Feed/Magazine:	34-round detachable box magazine
Range:	70m (230ft)

The Beretta 1938A was a fine weapon, but like many designs it was not suitable for wartime mass production. A simplified version designated Model 1938/42 was implemented, making extensive use of cheap sheet steel.

TIMELINE   1935   1938

MAS 38

Despite its slightly odd outlines, the MAS 38 was a well-designed weapon, though limited by its weak 7.65mm (.301in) Longue cartridge. On the plus side, it had little recoil and thus did not suffer much from muzzle climb.

SPECIFICATIONS	
Country of Origin:	France
Date:	1938
Calibre:	7.65mm (.301in) Longue
Operation:	Blowback
Weight:	4.1kg (9.1lb)
Overall Length:	832mm (32.75in)
Barrel Length:	247mm (9.75in)
Muzzle Velocity:	395m/sec (1300ft/sec)
Feed/Magazine:	32-round box magazine
Cyclic Rate:	500rpm
Range:	70m (230ft)

Furrer MP41/44

An attempt to build a submachine gun around the Maxim toggle-lock, which was not really suitable for a small automatic weapon, resulted in this vastly overcomplex and unreliable weapon. It was rightly rejected for service with the Swiss Army.

SPECIFICATIONS	
Country of Origin:	Switzerland
Date:	1941
Calibre:	9mm (.35in) Parabellum
Operation:	Recoil, toggle-locked
Weight:	5.2kg (11.5lb)
Overall Length:	775mm (30.5in)
Barrel Length:	247mm (9.72in)
Muzzle Velocity:	395m/sec (1295ft/sec)
Feed/Magazine:	40-round detachable box magazine
Cyclic Rate:	800rpm
Range:	70m (230ft)

MP3008

Facing invasion by the Allies, Germany sought a cheap, mass-produced submachine gun to arm its Volkssturm militia. The result was the MP3008, a Sten copy with the magazine feeding from underneath instead of the side.

SPECIFICATIONS	
Country of Origin:	Germany
Date:	1945
Calibre:	9mm (.35in) Parabellum
Operation:	Blowback
Weight:	3.2kg (7.05lb)
Overall Length:	760mm (29.9in)
Barrel Length:	196mm (7.7in)
Muzzle Velocity:	365m/sec (1198ft/sec)
Feed/Magazine:	32-round detachable box magazine
Range:	70m (230ft)

1941

1945

Finnish and Soviet Submachine Guns

A number of distinctive submachine guns were produced in Finland and Soviet Russia during the war period. Although most commonly associated with drum feed, these weapons also used a stick magazine which was far less cumbersome to carry.

Suomi KP/-31

The Suomi Model 31 was extremely influential as it proved the viability of a large (71-round) drum magazine. It was extremely well machined, and thus was accurate out to about 300m (984ft) – much further than most submachine guns.

SPECIFICATIONS	
Country of Origin:	Finland
Date:	1931
Calibre:	9mm (.35in) Parabellum
Operation:	Blowback
Weight:	4.87kg (10.74lb)
Overall Length:	870mm (34.25in)
Barrel Length:	319mm (12.52in)
Muzzle Velocity:	400m/sec (1310ft/sec)
Feed/Magazine:	30- or 50-round detachable box magazine or 71-round drum magazine
Cyclic Rate:	900rpm
Range:	100m (328ft) +

PPD-1934/38

Derived from the Suomi as well as the German MP18 and MP28, the PPD was a high-quality weapon with a chromium-lined barrel to reduce wear. It was expensive to produce, however.

SPECIFICATIONS	
Country of Origin:	USSR
Date:	1934
Calibre:	7.62mm (.3in) Soviet
Operation:	Blowback
Weight:	5.69kg (12.54lb) loaded
Overall Length:	780mm (30.71in)
Barrel Length:	269mm (10.60in)
Muzzle Velocity:	488m/sec (1600ft/sec)
Feed/Magazine:	25-round box magazine or 71-round drum magazine
Cyclic Rate:	800rpm
Range:	100m (328ft) +

TIMELINE

1931   1934

PPS-42

Needing vast numbers of cheap submachine guns to resist the German invasion, the Soviet Union turned to a weapon made of cheap stamped metal. The PPS-42 proved incredibly reliable and robust, so much so that both sides prized it highly.

SPECIFICATIONS	
Country of Origin:	USSR
Date:	1942
Calibre:	7.62mm (.3in) Soviet
Operation:	Blowback
Weight:	2.95kg (6.5lb)
Overall Length:	907mm (35.7in)
Barrel Length:	273mm (10.7in)
Muzzle Velocity:	500m/sec (1640ft/sec)
Feed/Magazine:	35-round detachable box magazine
Cyclic Rate:	650rpm
Range:	100m (328ft) +

PPS-43

The PPS-43, a slightly modified PPS-42, was designed and produced in the besieged city of Leningrad. Despite its crude construction, this weapon became popular with vehicle crews and enjoyed a long service career.

SPECIFICATIONS	
Country of Origin:	USSR
Date:	1943
Calibre:	7.62mm (.3in) Soviet
Operation:	Blowback
Weight:	3.36kg (7.4lb)
Overall Length:	820mm (32.3in)
Barrel Length:	254mm (10in)
Muzzle Velocity:	500m/sec (1640ft/sec)
Feed/Magazine:	35-round detachable box magazine
Cyclic Rate:	650rpm
Range:	100m (328ft) plus

Konepistooli M44

Essentially a copy of the Soviet PPS-43, the M44 was a simple and effective weapon that could use a 50-round box magazine or the Suomi 71-round drum. It was later adapted to take the 36-round Carl Gustav magazine.

SPECIFICATIONS	
Country of Origin:	Finland
Date:	1944
Calibre:	9mm (.35in) Parabellum
Operation:	Blowback
Weight:	2.8kg (6.17lb)
Overall Length:	825mm (32.48in)
Barrel Length:	247mm (9.72in)
Muzzle Velocity:	395m/sec (1300ft/sec)
Feed/Magazine:	50-round box magazine or 71-round drum magazine
Cyclic Rate:	650rpm
Range:	70m (230ft)

1942   1943   1944

PPSh-41

Designed from the outset to be cheap and quick to produce in huge numbers, the PPSh-41 was nevertheless one of the finest weapons of World War II. Durable and reliable, its chrome-lined barrel was resistant to wear even under the harsh combat conditions encountered in Russia.

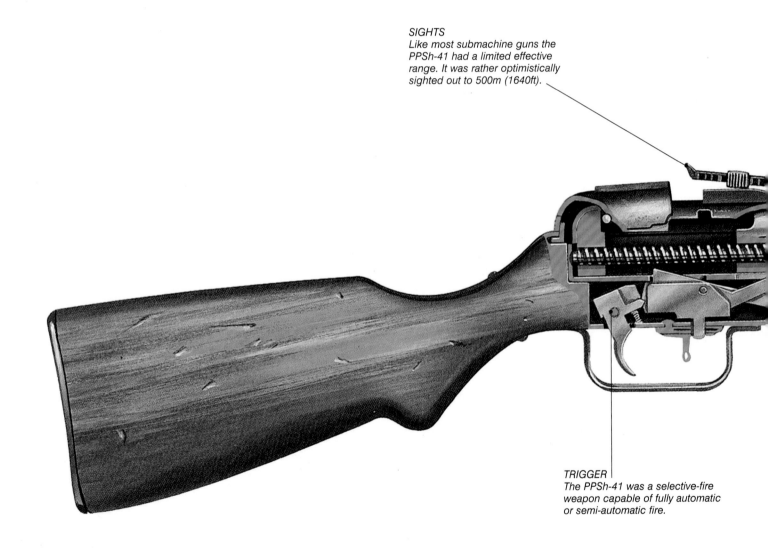

SIGHTS
Like most submachine guns the PPSh-41 had a limited effective range. It was rather optimistically sighted out to 500m (1640ft).

TRIGGER
The PPSh-41 was a selective-fire weapon capable of fully automatic or semi-automatic fire.

SPECIFICATIONS	
Country of Origin:	USSR
Date:	1941
Calibre:	7.62mm (.3in) Soviet
Operation:	Blowback
Weight:	3.64kg (8lb)
Overall Length:	838mm (33in)
Barrel Length:	266mm (10.5in)
Muzzle Velocity:	490m/sec (1600ft/sec)
Feed/Magazine:	35-round box magazine or 71-round drum magazine
Cyclic Rate:	900rpm
Range:	120m (394ft)

The PPSh-41 could use a bulky 71-round drum or a more convenient 35-round curved magazine. It fired a 7.62 x 25mm (.3 x .98in) pistol round which produced little felt recoil. With the weapon's high cyclic rate this enabled a user to put a lot of rounds into a target and made the PPSh-41 extremely deadly in close-quarters combat.

CHAMBER
Although it was quickly and simply made, the PPSh-41 had a chrome-lined barrel and chamber to resist corrosion.

BARREL
The barrel shroud protected the user from coming into contact with an extremely hot barrel.

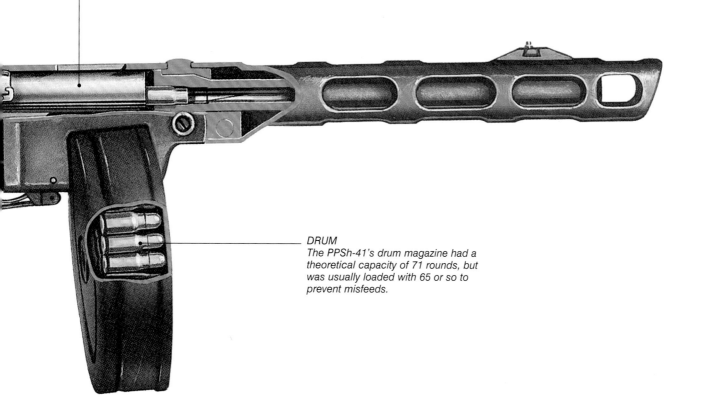

DRUM
The PPSh-41's drum magazine had a theoretical capacity of 71 rounds, but was usually loaded with 65 or so to prevent misfeeds.

The PPSh-41 was well respected by both sides in World War II, with German troops obtaining them whenever they could. Some were adapted to use German ammunition as many soldiers relied on captured or scavenged stocks.

9mm vs .45 calibre Submachine Guns

The two main calibres used for submachine guns in World War II were 9mm (.35in) and 11.4mm/.45in (.45 ACP). Each had its own advantages and drawbacks, and some designers created weapons that could be chambered for either.

Owen

The 9mm (.35in) Owen SMG was remarkable mainly for its top-mounted magazine and quick-release barrel. It was extremely reliable and was preferred by its Australian users to the Austen.

SPECIFICATIONS	
Country of Origin:	Australia
Date:	1941
Calibre:	9mm (.35in) Parabellum
Operation:	Blowback
Weight:	4.21kg (9.28lb)
Overall Length:	813mm (32in)
Barrel Length:	247mm (9.75in)
Muzzle Velocity:	380m/sec (1247ft/sec)
Feed/Magazine:	33-round detachable box magazine
Cyclic Rate:	700rpm
Range:	70m (230ft)

Austen

The Austen was derived from the Sten, but was fitted with a foregrip. Considerable use of die-casting was made in its manufacture. A suppressed variant and an improved Mk 2 were fielded later in the war.

SPECIFICATIONS	
Country of Origin:	Australia
Date:	1942
Calibre:	9mm (.35in) Parabellum
Operation:	Blowback
Weight:	3.98kg (8.75lb)
Overall Length:	845mm (33.25in)
Barrel Length:	196mm (7.75in)
Muzzle Velocity:	380m/sec (1246ft/sec)
Feed/Magazine:	28-round detachable box magazine
Cyclic Rate:	500rpm
Range:	50m (164ft)

TIMELINE
1941
1942

M2 (Hyde-Inland M2)

The M2, chambered for 11.4mm/.45in (.45 ACP), was intended as a possible replacement for the M1 (Thompson), and could use its magazines. However, it took too long to manufacture and was not adopted.

SPECIFICATIONS	
Country of Origin:	United States
Date:	1942
Calibre:	11.4mm (.45in) .45 ACP
Operation:	Blowback
Weight:	4.19kg (9.24lb)
Overall Length:	813mm (32in)
Barrel Length:	305mm (12in)
Muzzle Velocity:	292m/sec (960ft/sec)
Feed/Magazine:	Detachable box magazine (Thompson)
Cyclic Rate:	500rpm
Range:	50m (164ft)

M3 'Grease Gun'

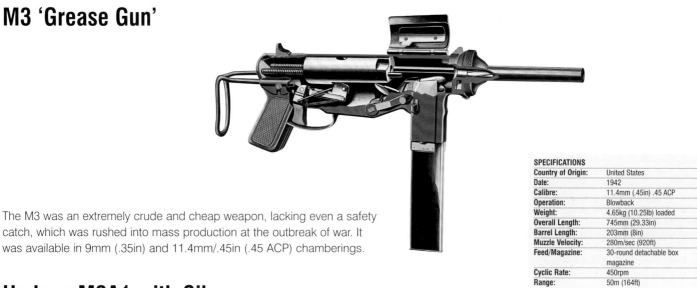

The M3 was an extremely crude and cheap weapon, lacking even a safety catch, which was rushed into mass production at the outbreak of war. It was available in 9mm (.35in) and 11.4mm/.45in (.45 ACP) chamberings.

SPECIFICATIONS	
Country of Origin:	United States
Date:	1942
Calibre:	11.4mm (.45in) .45 ACP
Operation:	Blowback
Weight:	4.65kg (10.25lb) loaded
Overall Length:	745mm (29.33in)
Barrel Length:	203mm (8in)
Muzzle Velocity:	280m/sec (920ft)
Feed/Magazine:	30-round detachable box magazine
Cyclic Rate:	450rpm
Range:	50m (164ft)

Hudson M3A1 with Silencer

A variant of the M3 'Grease Gun' was manufactured for the Office of Strategic Services. Chambered for the relatively low velocity 11.4mm/.45in (.45 ACP) round, it had an integral silencer.

SPECIFICATIONS	
Country of Origin:	United States
Date:	1944
Calibre:	9mm (.35in) or 11.4mm (.45in) .45 ACP
Operation:	Blowback
Weight:	3.7kg (8.15lb)
Overall Length:	762mm (30in)
Barrel Length:	203mm (8in)
Muzzle Velocity:	275m/sec (900ft/sec)
Feed/Magazine:	30-round detachable box magazine
Cyclic Rate:	450rpm
Range:	50m (164ft)

1944

M3A1 'Grease Gun'

The M3A1 was designed to be mass-produced cheaply, and as such it was a no-frills weapon which made up for its mediocre performance by simply being present in huge numbers. In this regard, it was exactly what the US needed early in World War II. It was designed to be converted from 9mm (.35in) to 11.4mm/.45in (.45 ACP) – the two standard submachine gun calibres available at that time – with minimal effort.

SIGHTS
The fixed sights consisted of a rear aperture sight pre-set for firing at 90m (295ft) and a front blade foresight.

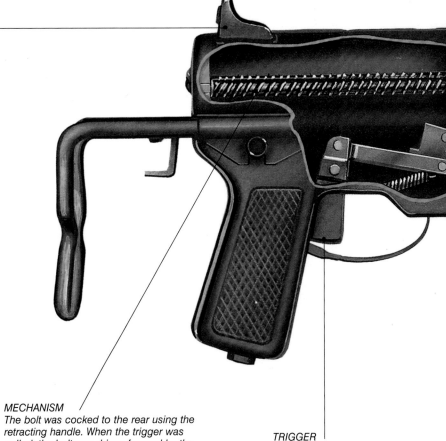

MECHANISM
The bolt was cocked to the rear using the retracting handle. When the trigger was pulled, the bolt was driven forward by the recoil springs, stripping a round from the feed lips of the magazine and guiding the round into the chamber.

TRIGGER
This submachine gun had no mechanical means of disabling the trigger; the insertion of a loaded magazine would load the gun.

SPECIFICATIONS	
Country of Origin:	United States
Date:	1944
Calibre:	9mm (.35in) Parabellum or 11.4mm (.45in) .45 ACP
Operation:	Blowback
Weight:	3.7kg (8.15lb)
Overall Length:	762mm (30in)
Barrel Length:	203mm (8in)
Muzzle Velocity:	275m/sec (900ft/sec)
Feed/Magazine:	30-round detachable box magazine
Cyclic Rate:	450rpm
Range:	50m (164ft)

Although intended to be a short-term expedient weapon, the M3A1 showed remarkable longevity; its final service with the US military was in the 1990s as a weapon for vehicle crews.

Despite being a distinctly basic weapon, the M3A1 was cleverly designed. Its stock could be removed to fulfil several functions: one of the arms could be used to clean the barrel, and both together were used to remove it. The stock also had a built-in magazine loading tool which was little more than an 'L' shaped section of metal but greatly reduced fatigue when loading ammunition into the 30-round magazines.

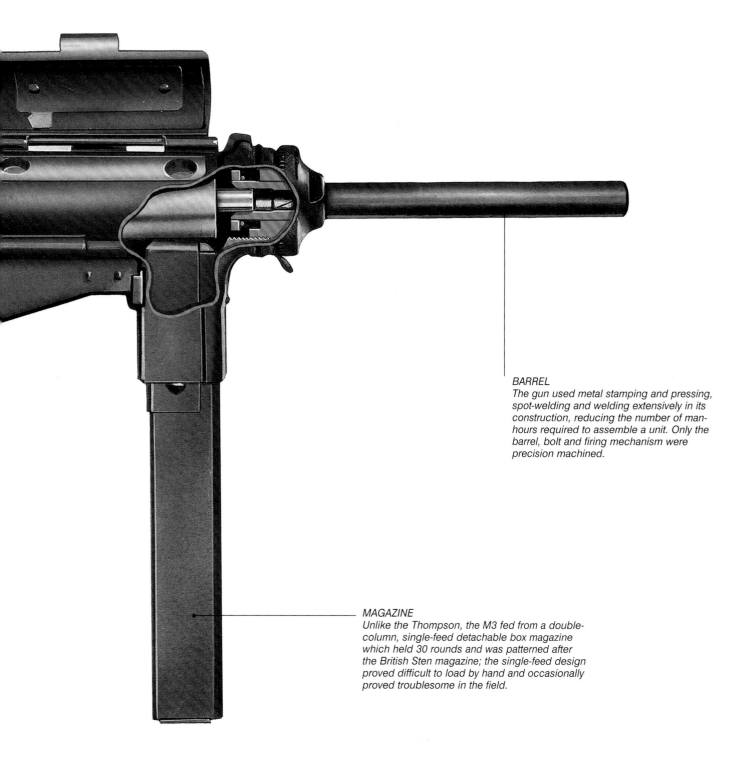

BARREL
The gun used metal stamping and pressing, spot-welding and welding extensively in its construction, reducing the number of man-hours required to assemble a unit. Only the barrel, bolt and firing mechanism were precision machined.

MAGAZINE
Unlike the Thompson, the M3 fed from a double-column, single-feed detachable box magazine which held 30 rounds and was patterned after the British Sten magazine; the single-feed design proved difficult to load by hand and occasionally proved troublesome in the field.

General-Purpose Machine Guns

Interwar German designers got around the prohibition on developing medium or heavy machine guns by coming up with a lighter weapon that could fulfil many roles, creating a class of weapon that came to dominate the light support niche.

Degtyarev DP

The DP was a very robust weapon whose main defect was its awkward drum feed system, which was prone to damage. Despite this, the DP gave good service during the war and remained in production into the 1950s.

SPECIFICATIONS	
Country of Origin:	USSR/Russia
Date:	1928
Calibre:	7.62mm (.3in) Soviet
Operation:	Gas-operated, air-cooled
Weight:	9.12kg (20.1lb)
Overall Length:	1290mm (50.8in)
Barrel Length:	605mm (23.8in)
Muzzle Velocity:	840m/sec (2756ft/sec)
Feed/Magazine:	47-round drum magazine
Cyclic Rate:	475rpm
Range:	2000m (6560ft)

Fucile Mitragliatore Breda Modello 30

The Modello 30 had some clever features, including a hinged magazine which was opened and filled with rifle chargers to reload the weapon. However, it was prone to damage which rendered the weapon useless.

SPECIFICATIONS	
Country of Origin:	Italy
Date:	1930
Calibre:	6.5mm (.256in) M95 and others
Operation:	Blowback, air-cooled
Weight:	10.2kg (22.5lb)
Overall Length:	1230mm (48.5in)
Barrel Length:	520mm (20.5in)
Muzzle Velocity:	610m/sec (2000ft/sec)
Feed/Magazine:	20-round integral box magazine
Cyclic Rate:	475rpm
Range:	1000m (3280ft)

TIMELINE

1928

Solothurn MG30

The MG30 was never built in large numbers, but it was the forefather of the excellent MG34. Its trigger system, which allowed single shots or full-automatic fire to be selected by trigger use, was retained on the MG34.

SPECIFICATIONS	
Country of Origin:	Germany
Date:	1930
Calibre:	7.5mm (.295in) Schmidt-Rubin
Operation:	Recoil, air-cooled
Weight:	7.7kg (17lb)
Overall Length:	1175mm (46.25in)
Barrel Length:	595mm (23.42in)
Muzzle Velocity:	800m/sec (2650ft/sec)
Feed/Magazine:	25-round detachable box magazine
Cyclic Rate:	500rpm
Range:	2000m (6560ft) +

Maschinengewehr MG13

The MG13 was a conversion of a World War I water-cooled weapon to air-cooled operation. It was adopted for service in 1930 but was not a great success. It was retired in favour of the altogether better MG34.

SPECIFICATIONS	
Country of Origin:	Germany
Date:	1930
Calibre:	7.92mm (.312in) Mauser
Operation:	Short recoil
Weight:	13.3kg (29.32lb)
Overall Length:	1443mm (56.8in)
Barrel Length:	Not known
Muzzle Velocity:	890m/sec (2919.2ft/sec)
Feed/Magazine:	25-round box magazine or 75-round saddle drum magazine
Cyclic Rate:	600rpm
Range:	2000m (6560ft)

Breda Model 30

SPECIFICATIONS	
Country of Origin:	Italy
Date:	1930
Calibre:	6.5mm (0.255in)
Operation:	Blowback
Weight:	10.2kg (22.5lb)
Overall Length:	1230mm (48in)
Barrel Length:	520mm (20.5in)
Muzzle Velocity:	610m/sec (2000ft/sec)
Feed/Magazine:	20-round box magazine
Cyclic Rate:	475rpm
Range:	600m (1970ft)

The Breda Modello 30 was one of the least successful light machinegun designs. From 1930, it became the Italian Army's standard light machinegun, but it suffered from feed problems and was not robust enough to deal with the desert conditions of the North African campaign.

1930

Maschinengewehr MG34

The world's first true general-purpose machine gun, the MG34 was well suited to infantry support, anti-aircraft or vehicle-mounted deployments. Having one weapon for many roles simplified logistics, especially as it used the same ammunition as the infantry's rifles.

The distinctive saddle drum was more commonly used on mounted guns than infantry support weapons; the 250-round belt was preferred by infantry. The MG34 could get through a belt very quickly but produced devastatingly intense fire which nevertheless remained controllable.

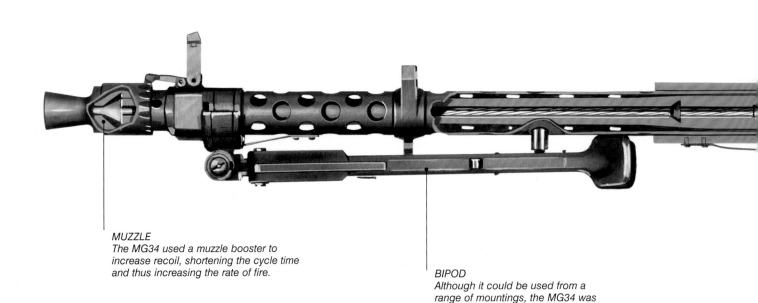

MUZZLE
The MG34 used a muzzle booster to increase recoil, shortening the cycle time and thus increasing the rate of fire.

BIPOD
Although it could be used from a range of mountings, the MG34 was primarily an infantry support weapon with its own lightweight bipod.

SPECIFICATIONS	
Country of Origin:	Germany
Date:	1936
Calibre:	7.92mm (.312in) Mauser
Operation:	Recoil, air-cooled
Weight:	12.1kg (26.67lb)
Overall Length:	1219mm (48in)
Barrel Length:	627mm (24.75in)
Muzzle Velocity:	762m/sec (2500ft/sec)
Feed/Magazine:	250-round belt or 75-round saddle drum magazine
Cyclic Rate:	800–900rpm
Range:	2000m (6560ft) +

The main drawback with the MG34, apart from its prodigious appetite for ammunition, was its complexity. It was expensive and time-consuming to manufacture, which were serious problems when vast numbers were needed for World War II.

In the heavy machinegun role (see right), the MG34 was mounted on a larger tripod and was belt-fed. It could be mounted on one of two tripods, a smaller one weighing 6.75kg (14.9lb), the larger 23.6kg (52lb). The larger tripod included extra features, such as a telescopic sight and sighting equipment for indirect fire.

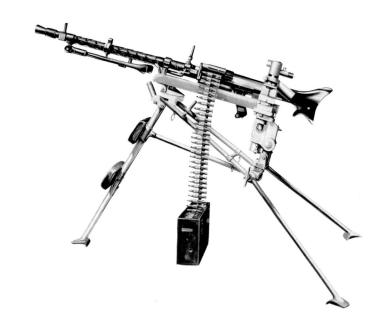

DRUM MAGAZINE
The saddle drum was convenient in some ways but was bulky to carry and offered relatively limited firepower.

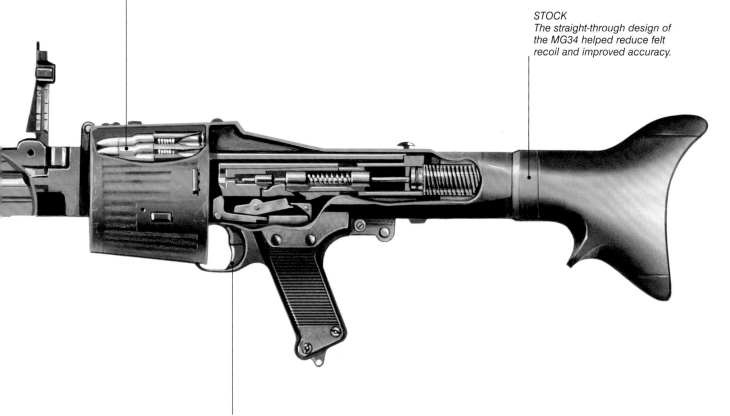

STOCK
The straight-through design of the MG34 helped reduce felt recoil and improved accuracy.

TRIGGER
The two-part trigger allowed semi-automatic or full-automatic fire to be selected simply by pulling the upper or lower part of the trigger, respectively.

BESAL Mk II and Vickers-Berthier

The Bren Gun and other top-loading machine guns were extremely successful in World War II. Indeed, Bren production was considered extremely important to the British war effort and there were concerns about the consequences if production, which was running at 1000 guns per week at one point, were to be disrupted by bombing.

The BESAL machine gun was designed as a cheaper version of the Bren Gun intended to be built in a relatively poorly equipped workshop. Although rather basic, it worked well and would have been a reasonable substitute had production of the Bren been seriously disrupted. The Vickers-Berthier was a pre-war rival to the Bren.

SPECIFICATIONS	
Country of Origin:	United Kingdom
Date:	1940
Calibre:	7.7mm (.303in)
Operation:	Gas-operated, air-cooled
Weight:	9.75kg (20.5lb)
Overall Length:	1185mm (46.75in)
Barrel Length:	558mm (22in)
Muzzle Velocity:	730m/sec (2300ft/sec)
Feed/Magazine:	225-round belt
Cyclic Rate:	600rpm
Range:	2000m (6560ft) +

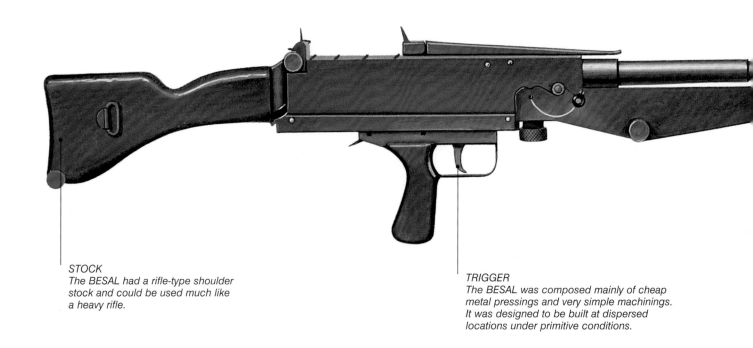

STOCK
The BESAL had a rifle-type shoulder stock and could be used much like a heavy rifle.

TRIGGER
The BESAL was composed mainly of cheap metal pressings and very simple machinings. It was designed to be built at dispersed locations under primitive conditions.

The Vickers-Berthier, designated Vickers G.O. (Gas-Operated), was brought out of storage in 1940 for security applications and airfield defence, and was used to arm the vehicles of the raiding forces that operated behind enemy lines in North Africa.

HANDLE
The carrying handle was added to the M3 version of the Vickers-Berthier, introduced in 1933.

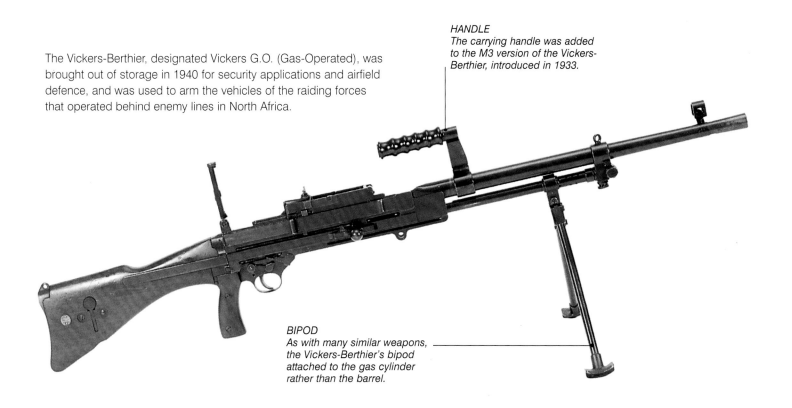

BIPOD
As with many similar weapons, the Vickers-Berthier's bipod attached to the gas cylinder rather than the barrel.

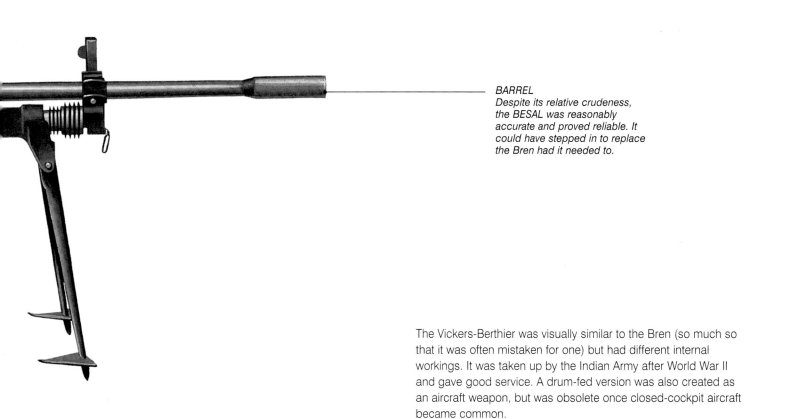

BARREL
Despite its relative crudeness, the BESAL was reasonably accurate and proved reliable. It could have stepped in to replace the Bren had it needed to.

The Vickers-Berthier was visually similar to the Bren (so much so that it was often mistaken for one) but had different internal workings. It was taken up by the Indian Army after World War II and gave good service. A drum-fed version was also created as an aircraft weapon, but was obsolete once closed-cockpit aircraft became common.

Heavy and Mounted Machine Guns

Heavy machine guns are generally used to arm aircraft and vehicles, or to provide defensive fire from a bunker or other fixed position. Their heavy rounds can endanger light vehicles and can penetrate most cover used by attacking enemy infantry.

Fiat Modello 35

Developed from the Modello 1914, the Modello 35 used a more powerful 8mm (.314in) round which should have increased its effectiveness. However, it was an unreliable weapon prone to overheating and 'running away': firing uncontrollably until its ammunition ran out.

SPECIFICATIONS	
Country of Origin:	Italy
Date:	1935
Calibre:	8mm (.314in)
Operation:	Gas-operated, air-cooled
Weight:	19.5kg (43lb)
Overall Length:	1270mm (50in)
Barrel Length:	680mm (26.75in)
Muzzle Velocity:	790m/sec (2600ft/sec)
Feed/Magazine:	50-round belt
Cyclic Rate:	450rpm
Range:	2000m (6560ft)

BESA

A Czech-designed machine gun designated ZB53 was put into production in Britain as the BESA as a dedicated weapon for armoured vehicles. The Mk 1 and 2 versions had a rate-of-fire selector; Mk 3 weapons had a fixed rate of fire.

SPECIFICATIONS	
Country of Origin:	United Kingdom/Czechoslovakia
Date:	1936
Calibre:	7.92mm (.312in) Mauser
Operation:	Gas-operated, air-cooled
Weight:	21.5kg (47lb)
Overall Length:	1105mm (43.5in)
Barrel Length:	736mm (29in)
Muzzle Velocity:	825m/sec (2700ft/sec)
Feed/Magazine:	225-round belt
Cyclic Rate:	750–850rpm
Range:	2000m (6560ft) +

TIMELINE   1935   1936   1938

DShK

Although the DShK machine gun of 1938 was somewhat lighter than previous Soviet heavy machine guns, this was offset by its heavy carriage. However, it was an effective weapon and became the standard Red Army vehicle-mounted machine gun.

SPECIFICATIONS

Country of Origin:	USSR
Date:	1938
Calibre:	12.7mm (.5in) Soviet
Operation:	Gas-operated, air-cooled
Weight:	35.5kg (78.5lb)
Overall Length:	1586mm (62.5in)
Barrel Length:	1066mm (42in)
Muzzle Velocity:	850m/sec (2788ft/sec)
Feed/Magazine:	50-round belt
Cyclic Rate:	550rpm
Range:	2000m (6560ft) +

Maschinengewehr MG42

The MG34 was a superb weapon but was expensive to produce. The MG42 was essentially a cheaper version, which nevertheless earned the respect of its users and their enemies. Its high rate of fire produced a distinctive and terrifying sound.

SPECIFICATIONS

Country of Origin:	Germany
Date:	1942
Calibre:	7.92mm (.312in) Mauser
Operation:	Short recoil, air-cooled
Weight:	11.5kg (25.35lb)
Overall Length:	1220mm (48in)
Barrel Length:	535mm (21in)
Muzzle Velocity:	800m/sec (2650ft/sec)
Feed/Magazine:	50-round belt
Cyclic Rate:	1200rpm
Range:	3000m (9842ft) +

Goryunov SG-43 (SGM)

A medium machine gun often mounted on a small two-wheeled carriage, the SG-43 was reliable and solidly constructed. It was the basis of an updated version (SGM) which was then adapted for use aboard armoured vehicles.

SPECIFICATIONS

Country of Origin:	USSR
Date:	1943
Calibre:	7.62mm (.3in) Soviet
Operation:	Gas-operated, air-cooled
Weight:	13.6kg (29.98lb)
Overall Length:	1120mm (44.1in)
Barrel Length:	719mm (28.3in)
Muzzle Velocity:	850m/sec (2788ft/sec)
Feed/Magazine:	250-round belt
Cyclic Rate:	650rpm
Range:	1000m (3280ft)

1942

1943

Anti-Tank Rifles

The anti-tank rifle was a World War I invention, which was more or less obsolete by 1939. In theory, a large-calibre armour-piercing bullet could damage a tank, but in practice these weapons were useful mainly against lighter vehicles.

Type 97

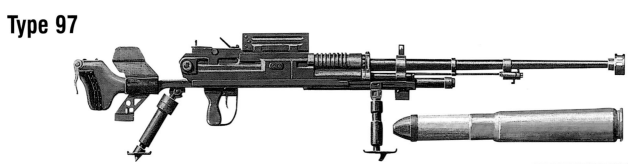

A 20mm (.78in) fully automatic anti-tank weapon, the Japanese Type 97 was fed from a seven-round magazine and was light enough to be moved through most terrain. It was extremely inaccurate due to its tremendous recoil.

SPECIFICATIONS	
Country of Origin:	Japan
Date:	1937
Calibre:	20mm (.78in)
Operation:	Gas-operated
Weight:	59kg (130lb)
Overall Length:	2060mm (81.1in)
Barrel Length:	1200mm (47.2in)
Muzzle Velocity:	750m/sec (2460 ft/sec)
Feed/Magazine:	7-round detachable box magazine
Range:	350m (1148ft) against 30mm (1.18in) armour; 700m (2296ft) against 20mm (.78in) armour

Panzerbüchse 39

A very long single-shot rifle firing a 7.92 x 94mm (.312 x 3.7in) cartridge, the Panzerbüchse 39 was given a new lease of life by the introduction of tungsten-cored ammunition copied from captured Polish weapons. It remained at best marginally effective, however.

SPECIFICATIONS	
Country of Origin:	Germany
Date:	1939
Calibre:	7.92mm (.312in)
Operation:	Bolt action
Weight:	11.6kg (25.57lb)
Overall Length:	1620mm (63.8in)
Barrel Length:	1085mm (42.7in)
Muzzle Velocity:	1265m/sec (4150ft/sec)
Feed/Magazine:	Single shot
Range:	300m (984ft) against 25mm (.98in) armour

TIMELINE   1937   1939

PTRD-41

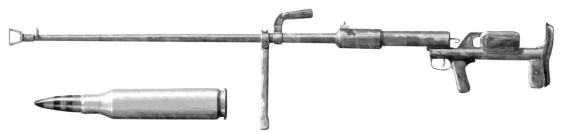

A very long rifle firing steel- or tungsten-cored ammunition, the PTRD was adopted by the Red Army at a time when other militaries were discarding their anti-tank rifles. Soviet troops often used their anti-tank rifles against enemy infantry positions.

SPECIFICATIONS	
Country of Origin:	USSR
Date:	1941
Calibre:	14.5mm (.57in)
Operation:	Single-fire
Weight:	17.3kg (38.1lb)
Overall Length:	2020mm (79.5in)
Barrel Length:	1350mm (53.14in)
Muzzle Velocity:	1114 m/sec (3655ft/sec)
Feed/Magazine:	Single shot
Range:	1000m (3280ft)

PTRS-41

The PTRS-41 was more complex and heavier than the PTRD-41 but was roughly equivalent in performance, other than possessing a 5-round magazine. It was easier to transport as the barrel was detachable, but also more prone to malfunction.

SPECIFICATIONS	
Country of Origin:	USSR
Date:	1941
Calibre:	14.5mm (.57in)
Operation:	Single-fire
Weight:	20.3kg (46lb)
Overall Length:	2100mm (83in)
Barrel Length:	1219mm (47in)
Muzzle Velocity:	1114m/sec (3655ft/sec)
Feed/Magazine:	5-round magazine
Range:	800m (2620ft)

Granatbüchse 39

A conversion of the Panzerbüchse 39, equipped with a grenade discharger, the Granatbüchse 39 could launch anti-armour grenades that might endanger a light tank. Its effective range was about 125m (410ft).

SPECIFICATIONS	
Country of Origin:	Germany
Date:	1942
Calibre:	N/A
Operation:	Bolt action
Weight:	Not known
Overall Length:	Not known
Barrel Length:	590mm (23.23in)
Muzzle Velocity:	N/A
Feed/Magazine:	Single shot
Range:	125m (410ft)

1941

1942

Boys Mk 1 Anti-Tank Rifle

Perhaps the definitive anti-tank rifle was the Boys Mk 1. A bolt action rifle firing a 3.97mm (.55in) round, the rifle was large and heavy with a bipod at the front and a separate grip below the padded butt. This capability was delivered in return for tremendous recoil and great weight: the barrel was mounted on a slide, and a shock absorber was fitted to the bipod.

RECEIVER
The Boys Mk 1 used a 5-round magazine but was not in any way intended for rapid fire. Its role was to take single powerful shots at hard targets, not to engage enemy infantry.

BARREL
A long barrel increased muzzle velocity, giving the heavy round a reasonable chance of penetrating a tank's armour.

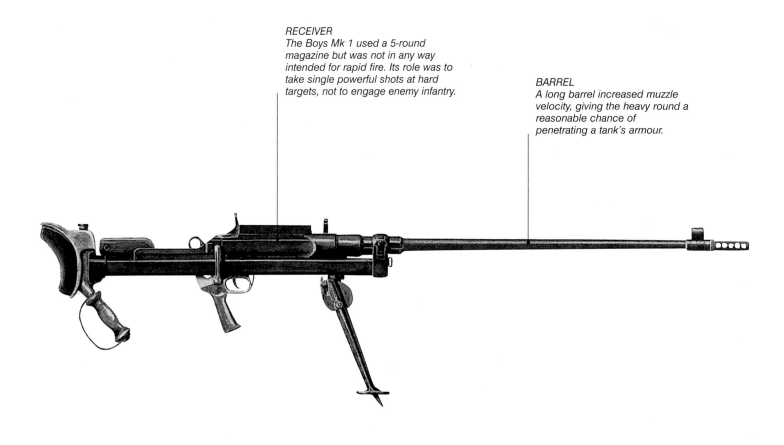

SPECIFICATIONS

Country of Origin:	United Kingdom
Date:	1937
Calibre:	13.97mm (.55in)
Operation:	Bolt action
Weight:	16kg (35lb)
Overall Length:	1575mm (62in)
Barrel Length:	910mm (36in); 762mm (30in) airborne version
Muzzle Velocity:	747m/sec (2450ft/sec)
Feed/Magazine:	5-round detachable box magazine
Range:	90m (295ft) against 16–19mm (.63–.75in) armour

The anti-tank rifle fell out of favour for the simple reason that it was no longer effective, but has recently returned to the battlefield in a new guise. As an 'anti-materiel rifle', the large-calibre rifle can be used to smash enemy communications equipment and support weapons and to disable the engines of light vehicles. It is also sometimes used as a super-long-range sniping weapon.

The Boys rifle was sometimes used to arm light vehicles, such as the Universal Carrier (right), where it was mounted in the hull. In the early 1930s it was considered an adequate anti-armour weapon. Advances in tank armour soon made it obsolete for its intended role, but it was still a useful weapon as it could punch through many objects that might be used as cover, or be fired at rocks to create a shower of splinters to injure concealed enemy troops.

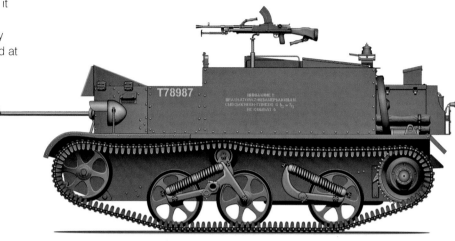

MUZZLE
A muzzle brake helped to control recoil somewhat and to reduce the weapon's 'signature', i.e. the amount of flash and the dust kicked up when firing.

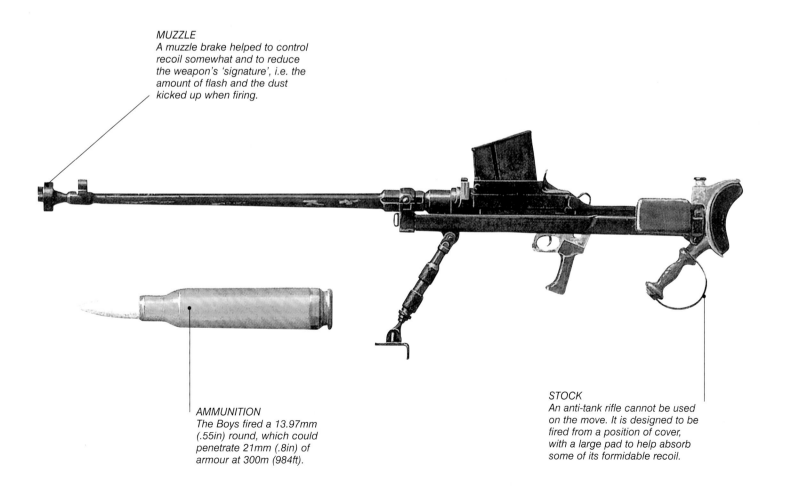

AMMUNITION
The Boys fired a 13.97mm (.55in) round, which could penetrate 21mm (.8in) of armour at 300m (984ft).

STOCK
An anti-tank rifle cannot be used on the move. It is designed to be fired from a position of cover, with a large pad to help absorb some of its formidable recoil.

Anti-Tank Weapons

The prevalence of armoured vehicles meant that infantry needed some means to disable them. Not all of the anti-tank weapons introduced during the war were particularly good, and some were virtually suicidal to use.

Northover Projector

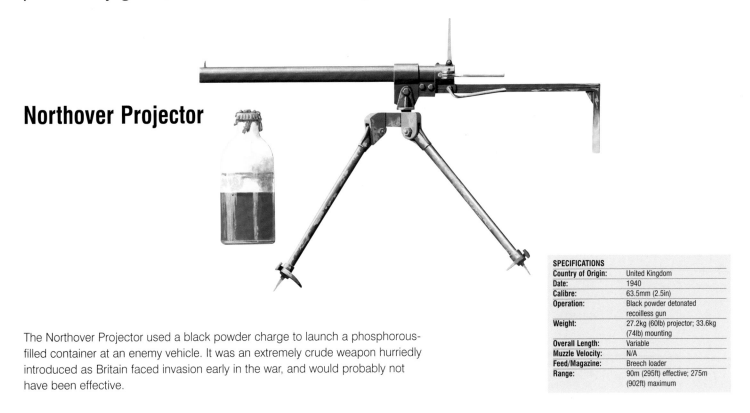

The Northover Projector used a black powder charge to launch a phosphorous-filled container at an enemy vehicle. It was an extremely crude weapon hurriedly introduced as Britain faced invasion early in the war, and would probably not have been effective.

SPECIFICATIONS	
Country of Origin:	United Kingdom
Date:	1940
Calibre:	63.5mm (2.5in)
Operation:	Black powder detonated recoilless gun
Weight:	27.2kg (60lb) projector; 33.6kg (74lb) mounting
Overall Length:	Variable
Muzzle Velocity:	N/A
Feed/Magazine:	Breech loader
Range:	90m (295ft) effective; 275m (902ft) maximum

PIAT (Projectile, Infantry, Anti-Tank)

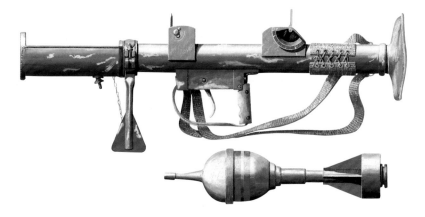

The PIAT was a spigot mortar, firing a shaped-charge warhead. It was hard to cock and bruising to fire, and not very effective even it if hit. PIATs were found to be useful against bunkers and other infantry positions.

SPECIFICATIONS	
Country of Origin:	United Kingdom
Date:	1942
Calibre:	89mm (3.5in)
Operation:	Firing spring
Weight:	14.51kg (32lb) launcher; 1.36kg (3lb) grenade
Overall Length:	990mm (3ft)
Muzzle Velocity:	76–137m/sec (250–450ft/sec)
Feed/Magazine:	Front loaded
Range:	100m (328ft) combat; 340m (1115ft) maximum

Panzerschreck (RPzB 54)

Developed from captured early-model M1 Bazookas, the Panzerschreck was a rather more effective weapon due to its larger warhead. Like the Bazooka, its large backblast pinpointed the firer's position and drew return fire.

SPECIFICATIONS	
Country of Origin:	Germany
Date:	1942
Calibre:	88mm (3.46in) high-explosive (HE) and high-explosive anti-tank (HEAT) warheads
Operation:	Solid rocket motor
Weight:	11kg (24.25lb) empty
Overall Length:	1640mm (64.5in)
Muzzle Velocity:	110m/sec (360ft/sec)
Feed/Magazine:	Breech loader
Range:	150m (492ft)

M9 Bazooka

The M9 Bazooka was a simple tubular launcher delivering a rocket-propelled shaped-charge warhead. It was at best marginally effective against well-armoured tanks, and had a short effective range, so was best used from the flanks or rear.

SPECIFICATIONS	
Country of Origin:	United States
Date:	1943
Calibre:	60mm (2.36in) high-explosive (HE) and high-explosive anti-tank (HEAT) warheads
Operation:	Solid rocket motor
Weight:	5.98kg (13.18lb)
Overall Length:	1545mm (61in)
Muzzle Velocity:	83m/sec (270ft/sec)
Feed/Magazine:	Breech loader
Range:	640m (2010ft)

Panzerfaust

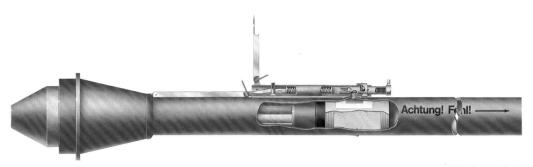

The Panzerfaust was a disposable weapon firing a rocket-propelled warhead from a very basic launcher. It had a short range but was surprisingly effective. More powerful versions were introduced as the war went on. The Panzerfaust often had warnings written in large red letters on the rear end of the tube: Achtung! Feuerstrahl! ('Attention! Fire Jet!').

SPECIFICATIONS	
Country of Origin:	Germany
Date:	1943
Calibre:	100mm (3.9in)
Operation:	Recoilless gun
Weight:	1.475kg (3.3lb) total
Overall Length:	1000mm (39.4in)
Muzzle Velocity:	30m/sec (98ft/sec)
Feed/Magazine:	N/A
Range:	30m (98ft)

1943

Flamethrowers

One of the most horrific weapons ever devised, the flamethrower not only burns its targets alive, it also consumes the oxygen in a confined space, suffocating defenders who are sheltered from the flames.

Model 93

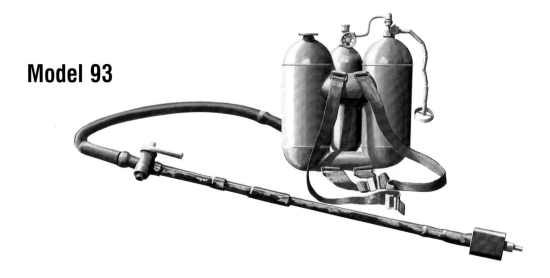

The Japanese Model 93 flamethrower was effective during the 1930s in China, but tended to fail to ignite in cold conditions. A redesigned version, designated Model 100, was introduced in 1940.

SPECIFICATIONS	
Country of Origin:	Japan
Date:	1933
Weight:	25kg (55lb)
Fuel Capacity:	14.7 litres (3.25 gallons)
Duration of Fire:	10 seconds
Range:	23–27m (75–89ft)

Flammenwerfer 41

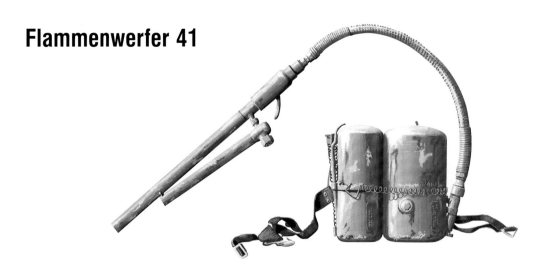

The Flammenwerfer 41 was a developed version of earlier German flame weapons, with an improved ignition system and side-by-side fuel and propellant tanks. It was the standard German flamethrower of the later war.

SPECIFICATIONS	
Country of Origin:	Germany
Date:	1941
Weight:	35.8kg (79lb)
Fuel Capacity:	11.8 litres (2.6 gallons)
Duration of Fire:	10 seconds
Range:	25–30m (82–98ft)

TIMELINE

1933    1941

Flame-Thrower M1A1

The M1 was developed from scratch to meet a US Army requirement. It was unreliable and was supplanted from 1943 by the M1A1, an improved but still flawed version, and then the much more effective M2.

SPECIFICATIONS	
Country of Origin:	United States
Date:	1942
Weight:	31.8kg (70lb)
Fuel Capacity:	18.2 litres (4 gallons)
Duration of Fire:	8–10 seconds
Range:	41–45m (135–148ft)

No 2 Flamethrower Mk 1 (Lifebuoy)

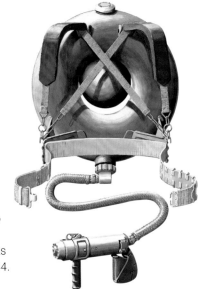

Nicknamed 'Lifebuoy' for its shape, which was designed to carry the most fuel possible in the tank, the No 2 Flamethrower suffered from too rapid development and was not effective until the Mk 2 version became available in 1944.

SPECIFICATIONS	
Country of Origin:	United Kingdom
Date:	1942
Weight:	29kg (64lb)
Fuel Capacity:	18.2 litres (4 gallons)
Duration of Fire:	10 seconds
Range:	27–36m (89–118ft)

ROKS-3 Flamethrower

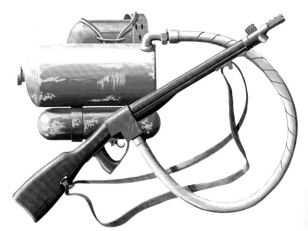

A simplified version of the ROKS-2 flamethrower, this weapon was a wartime expedient intended to be constructed in volume. Its effectiveness was increased when thicker fuel became available, increasing the weapon's range.

SPECIFICATIONS	
Country of Origin:	USSR
Date:	1943
Weight:	22.7kg (50lb)
Fuel Capacity:	9 litres (5 gallons)
Duration of Fire:	8–10 seconds
Range:	23–27m (75–89ft)

POST-WAR

Peace did not really break out at the end of World War II. Within a short period the combatant nations found themselves embroiled in the Korean War and the Malayan Emergency. Civil war in China, wars of independence in Southeast Asia and uprisings in Africa kept the major nations on a semi-war footing.

This era was also the beginning of the Cold War, with the great NATO/Warsaw Pact alliances forming and a real possibility that World War II might be continued with an East/West clash in Europe.

Left: British special forces struggle through thick jungle somewhere in Malaya, 1957. The man in the foreground is armed with a Lee-Enfield No 5 Mk 1 'Jungle Carbine', while his comrade behind carries an L1A1 SLR. In the background another soldier carries a Bren light machine gun.

Combat Revolvers

Although most militaries had replaced their service revolvers with semi-automatic pistols over the previous decades, the revolver remained a popular weapon for home defence and self-defence. Some law enforcement agencies continued to favour revolvers for many years.

Smith & Wesson 36 'Chief's Special'

The snub-nosed 'Chief's Special' was one of the most influential handguns ever made. As the name suggests, it was popular in the law enforcement marketplace but also saw considerable use by civilians and aircrew needing a small handgun for self-defence.

SPECIFICATIONS	
Country of Origin:	United States
Date:	1950
Calibre:	9.6mm (.38in) Special
Operation:	Revolver
Weight:	.553kg. (1.2lb)
Overall Length:	176mm (6.94in)
Barrel Length:	47.6mm (1.875in)
Muzzle Velocity:	Not known
Feed/Magazine:	5-round cylinder
Range:	23m (75ft)

Smith & Wesson Centennial

A small-frame double-action-only 9.6mm (.38in) or 9.1mm (.357in) revolver, the Centennial was marketed in several variants. Its main application was as a backup gun or a small, concealable weapon for self-defence.

SPECIFICATIONS	
Country of Origin:	United States
Date:	1952
Calibre:	9.6mm (.38in) .38 Special +P, 9.1mm (.357in) .357 Magnum
Operation:	Double-action only (DAO) revolver
Weight:	Not known
Overall Length:	Not known
Barrel Length:	50.8mm (2in) or 76mm (3in)
Muzzle Velocity:	Not known
Feed/Magazine:	5-round cylinder
Range:	50m (164ft)

TIMELINE

 1950

 1952

 1953

Colt Trooper Mk V

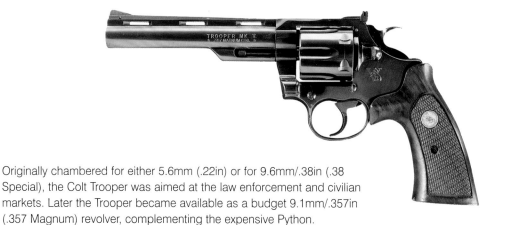

Originally chambered for either 5.6mm (.22in) or for 9.6mm/.38in (.38 Special), the Colt Trooper was aimed at the law enforcement and civilian markets. Later the Trooper became available as a budget 9.1mm/.357in (.357 Magnum) revolver, complementing the expensive Python.

SPECIFICATIONS	
Country of Origin:	United States
Date:	1953
Calibre:	9.1mm (.357in) .357 Magnum
Operation:	Double-action revolver
Weight:	1.2kg (2.62lb)
Overall Length:	260mm (10.24in)
Barrel Length:	203mm (8in)
Muzzle Velocity:	455m/sec (1500ft/sec)
Feed/Magazine:	6-round cylinder
Range:	50m (164ft)

Colt Python .357

The Python was developed from the more modest Colt Model 357 and completely supplanted it in the marketplace. Although heavy and expensive it is a very high-quality and durable weapon delivering impressive stopping power.

SPECIFICATIONS	
Country of Origin:	United States
Date:	1955
Calibre:	9.1mm (.357in) .357 Magnum
Operation:	Revolver
Weight:	1.08–1.2kg (2.37–2.62lb)
Overall Length:	235mm (9.25in)
Barrel Length:	102mm (4in) or 204mm (8in)
Muzzle Velocity:	455m/sec (1500ft/sec)
Cylinder capacity:	6-round cylinder
Range:	50m (164ft)

Smith & Wesson Model 29

The M29 was made famous in the 1970s by the 'Dirty Harry' movies, but had been available since 1955. Several versions exist today, mostly in the 629 series, with differing barrel lengths and finishes.

SPECIFICATIONS	
Country of Origin:	United States
Date:	1955
Calibre:	11.2mm (.44in) .44 Magnum
Operation:	Double-action revolver
Weight:	Variable, depending on barrel length
Overall Length:	Variable, depending on barrel length
Barrel Length:	102–270mm (4–10.6in)
Muzzle Velocity:	Variable, depending on barrel length
Feed/Magazine:	6-round cylinder
Range:	50m (164ft)

1955

Combat Semi-Automatics

A wide variety of semi-automatic handguns appeared in the post-war period. Some were entirely new, some were part of a long line of weapons. Many were simply copies of existing designs, often without regard to the niceties of patent law.

MAS 1950

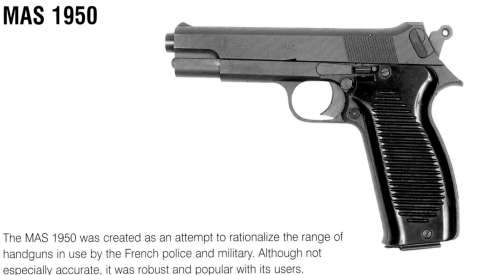

The MAS 1950 was created as an attempt to rationalize the range of handguns in use by the French police and military. Although not especially accurate, it was robust and popular with its users.

SPECIFICATIONS	
Country of Origin:	France
Date:	1950
Calibre:	9mm (.35in) Parabellum
Operation:	Short recoil, locked-breech
Weight:	860g (1.8lb)
Overall Length:	195mm (7.7in)
Barrel Length:	111mm (4.4in)
Muzzle Velocity:	315m/sec (1033ft/sec)
Feed/Magazine:	9-round detachable box magazine
Range:	50m (164ft)

Beretta M1951

The M951 was developed for the military market and went into service with the Egyptian and Israeli forces as well as the Italian Army. A full-automatic-capable version (sometimes fitted with a foregrip) was also developed.

SPECIFICATIONS	
Country of Origin:	Italy
Date:	1951
Calibre:	9mm (0.35in) Parabellum
Operation:	Short recoil, locked-breech
Weight:	0.87kg (1.92lb) empty
Overall Length:	203mm (8in)
Barrel Length:	114mm (4.5in)
Muzzle Velocity:	350m/sec (1148ft/sec)
Feed/Magazine:	8-round detachable box magazine
Range:	50m (164ft)

Helwan

A straight copy of the Beretta M951, the Helwan was produced under licence and went into service instead of the Tokagypt. Its performance was identical to the M1951 as it was essentially the same gun.

SPECIFICATIONS	
Country of Origin:	Egypt
Date:	1955
Calibre:	9mm (.35in) Parabellum
Operation:	Short recoil
Weight:	.89kg (1.96lb)
Overall Length:	203mm (8in)
Barrel Length:	114mm (4.5in)
Muzzle Velocity:	350m/sec (1148ft/sec)
Feed/Magazine:	8-round detachable box magazine
Range:	50m (164ft)

Astra Falcon

The Falcon was the last of Astra's 'water pistol' styled handguns. It is essentially a scaled-down Astra 400, creating a lighter and handier pistol that can still be found in service today.

SPECIFICATIONS	
Country of Origin:	Spain
Date:	1956
Calibre:	9mm (.35in) Short
Operation:	Blowback
Weight:	.646kg (1.4lb)
Overall Length:	164mm (6.4in)
Barrel Length:	98.5mm (3.8in)
Muzzle Velocity:	c.300m/sec (984ft/sec)
Feed/Magazine:	7-round detachable box magazine
Range:	30m (98ft)

Tokagypt 58

A copy of the Tokarev TT33 pistol, chambered for 9mm (.35in) Parabellum ammunition, the Tokagypt was manufactured in Hungary for the Egyptian Army (hence the name) but was not adopted and went to the police or the open market instead.

SPECIFICATIONS	
Country of Origin:	Egypt/Hungary
Date:	1958
Calibre:	9mm (.35in) Parabellum
Operation:	Short recoil
Weight:	0.91kg (2.01lb)
Overall Length:	194mm (7.65in)
Barrel Length:	114mm (4.5in)
Muzzle Velocity:	350m/sec (1150ft/sec)
Feed/Magazine:	7-round detachable box magazine
Range:	30m (98ft)

1956

1958

Alternative Propulsion: MBA Gyrojet

The Gyrojet pistol was an attempt to create a new kind of weapon, using a small rocket rather than a conventional bullet. In theory this offered advantages including low noise, reduced recoil and the ability to shoot underwater.

MUZZLE
The Gyrojet had a very low muzzle velocity, but increasing over trajectory up to about 1250 feet per second.

CARTRIDGE
Originally developed in a .51 (12.95mm) calibre, the cartridges were self-contained self-propelled rockets with calibers ranging from .49 (12.44mm) and 6–20mm (.23–.78in).

SPECIFICATIONS	
Country of Origin:	United States
Date:	1965
Calibre:	12.95mm (.51in) rocket
Operation:	Blow-forward
Weight:	.4 kg (.88lb)
Overall Length:	2760mm (10.88in)
Barrel Length:	127mm (5in)
Muzzle Velocity:	380m/sec (1250ft/sec)
Feed/Magazine:	6-round internal box magazine
Range:	50m (164ft)

The Gyrojet's ammunition used rocket propulsion, with angled vents to spin the projectile for stability. However, this meant that the round left the muzzle at fairly low speed and was both unstable and ineffective at this distance. Given time to get up to speed, lethality increased but accuracy became increasingly poor.

LOADING PORT
The Gyrojet was loaded through a port above the magazine. As the whole projectile was launched, there was no need for an ejection system.

COCKING
The Gyrojet was cocked by pushing this lever forward, chambering a round.

GRIP
The Gyrojet had an internal magazine inside the handgrip, making it very slow to reload compared with conventional semi-automatic pistols.

Semi-Automatic Rifles

Although the assault rifle was being developed in several countries, it did not immediately sweep all other weapons from the marketplace. Indeed, some nations (such as Britain) stayed with a semi-automatic service rifle for several decades.

Ljungman AG 42

A Swedish weapon issued in limited numbers during World War II and in use until the 1960s, the AG 42 used a 6.5 x 55mm (.256 x 2.16in) round. It was the basis for the Egyptian Hakim rifle and Rashid carbine.

SPECIFICATIONS	
Country of Origin:	Sweden
Date:	1941
Calibre:	6.5mm (.256in)
Operation:	Gas-operated
Weight:	4.7kg (10.36lb)
Overall Length:	1214mm (47.8in)
Barrel Length:	622mm (24.5in)
Muzzle Velocity:	Not known
Feed/Magazine:	10-round detachable box magazine
Range:	500m (1640ft)

Fusil Mitrailleur Modèle 49 (MAS 49)

Rearming after World War II, France sought to replace the assortment of older weapons then in service with a new semi-automatic rifle. The resulting MAS 49 rifle was highly reliable but was chambered for 7.5mm (.295in) instead of NATO-standard 7.62mm (.3in) ammunition.

SPECIFICATIONS	
Country of Origin:	France
Date:	1949
Calibre:	7.5mm (.295in)
Operation:	Gas-operated
Weight:	3.9kg (8.6lb)
Overall Length:	1010mm (39.76in)
Barrel Length:	521mm (20.51in)
Muzzle Velocity:	817m/sec (2680ft/sec)
Feed/Magazine:	10-round detachable box magazine
Range:	500m (1640ft)

TIMELINE

 1941

 1949

 1949

FN 1949 (FN AL, or SAFN)

Development of what became the FN 1949 began before World War II but was sufficiently disrupted that the weapon did not become available until 1949. It achieved good sales on the international market, notably in South America.

SPECIFICATIONS	
Country of Origin:	Belgium
Date:	1949
Calibre:	Various, including 8mm (.314in)
Operation:	Gas-operated
Weight:	4.31kg (9.5lb)
Overall Length:	1116mm (43.54in)
Barrel Length:	590mm (23.23in)
Muzzle Velocity:	710m/sec (2330ft/sec)
Feed/Magazine:	10-round fixed box magazine
Range:	500m (1640ft)

Samonabiject Puska vz52 (CZ52)

The vz52 was chambered for a short 7.62 x 45mm (.3 x 1.77in) round and featured a folding bayonet. After the Soviet takeover of Czechoslovakia, a less reliable version chambered for Warsaw Pact standard 7.62 x 39mm (.3 x 1.54in) appeared.

SPECIFICATIONS	
Country of Origin:	Czechoslovakia
Date:	1952
Calibre:	7.62mm (.3in) M52 or 7.62mm (.3in) Soviet M1943
Operation:	Gas-operated
Weight:	3.11kg (6.86lb)
Overall Length:	843mm (33.2in)
Barrel Length:	400mm (15.8in)
Muzzle Velocity:	710m/sec (2330ft/sec)
Feed/Magazine:	10-round detachable box magazine
Range:	500m (1640ft) +

Rashid

Tools for manufacturing the AG 42 were bought by Egypt, where the weapon was manufactured in 7.92 x 57mm (.312 x 2.24in) calibre as the Hakim rifle. This weapon was then developed into the Rashid carbine, firing Soviet 7.62 x 39mm (.3 x 1.54in) ammunition.

SPECIFICATIONS	
Country of Origin:	Egypt
Date:	1960
Calibre:	7.62mm (.3in)
Operation:	Gas-operated
Weight:	4.19kg (9.25lb)
Overall Length:	1035mm (40.75in)
Barrel Length:	520mm (20.5in)
Muzzle Velocity:	Not known
Feed/Magazine:	10-round detachable box magazine
Range:	300m (984ft)

1952   1960

The FN FAL Series

The Fabrique Nationale Fusil Automatique Léger (FN FAL) was developed to use the German 7.92 x 33mm (.312 x 1.3in) cartridge pioneered for the StG44, but NATO standardization resulted in a final chambering for 7.62 x 51mm (.3 x 2in) ammunition. Over 90 countries adopted this excellent weapon.

FN FAL

A heavy but very well designed rifle, the FN FAL proved itself to be extremely durable and effective in many different environments. Most FALs were capable of full-automatic fire, though recoil made controlling the weapon somewhat problematical.

SPECIFICATIONS	
Country of Origin:	Belgium
Date:	1954
Calibre:	7.62mm (.3in) NATO
Operation:	Gas-operated, self-loading
Weight:	4.31kg (9.5lb)
Overall Length:	1053mm (41.46in)
Barrel Length:	533mm (21in)
Muzzle Velocity:	853m/sec (2800ft/sec)
Feed/Magazine:	20-round detachable box magazine
Range:	800m (2625ft) +

L1A1 SLR

In British service, the FAL was designated L1A1 SLR (Self-Loading Rifle). It served from 1954 until it was replaced by the smaller-calibre L85A1 beginning in 1985.

SPECIFICATIONS	
Country of Origin:	United Kingdom
Date:	1954
Calibre:	7.62mm (.3in) NATO
Operation:	Gas-operated, self-loading
Weight:	4.31kg (9.5lb)
Overall Length:	1055mm (41.5in)
Barrel Length:	535mm (21.1in)
Muzzle Velocity:	853m/sec (2800ft/sec)
Feed/Magazine:	20-round detachable box magazine
Range:	800m (2625ft) +

TIMELINE

1954

FN Para

Most FN FALs had a solid stock, but variants with a lightweight folding stock were created for paratroops. Many paratroop variants used the standard-length barrel, but some were shortened to make exiting a plane easier.

SPECIFICATIONS	
Country of Origin:	Belgium
Date:	1954
Calibre:	7.62mm (.3in) NATO
Operation:	Gas-operated
Weight:	4.36kg (9.61lb)
Overall Length:	1020mm (40.15in) stock extended; 770mm (30.3in) stock folded
Barrel Length:	436mm (17.1in)
Muzzle Velocity:	853m/sec (2800ft/sec)
Feed/Magazine:	20-round detachable box magazine
Range:	500m (1640ft) +

FN FAL (Argentine)

During the 1982 Falklands War the Argentine Army used a full-automatic version of the FAL; their British opponents had opted for a semi-automatic variant of the same weapon.

SPECIFICATIONS	
Country of Origin:	Belgium
Date:	1958
Calibre:	7.62mm (.3in) NATO
Operation:	Gas-operated
Weight:	4.31kg (9.5lb)
Overall Length:	1053mm (41.46in)
Barrel Length:	533mm (21in)
Muzzle Velocity:	853m/sec (2800ft/sec)
Feed/Magazine:	20-round detachable box magazine
Range:	800m (2620ft) +

FN FNC

A variant of the FAL chambered for 5.56 x 45mm (.219 x 1.77in) ammunition, the FNC (or FN Carbine) can use standard M16 magazines. It achieved considerable international sales and remains in service today.

SPECIFICATIONS	
Country of Origin:	Belgium
Date:	1976
Calibre:	5.56mm (.219in) NATO
Operation:	Gas-operated
Weight:	3.8kg (8.38lb)
Overall Length:	997mm (39.25in) stock extended; 766mm (30.15in) stock folded
Barrel Length:	449mm (17.68in)
Muzzle Velocity:	965m/sec (3165ft/sec)
Feed/Magazine:	30-round detachable box magazine
Range:	500m (1640ft) +

1958 1976

L1A1 Self-Loading Rifle (SLR)

The L1A1 SLR adopted by the British Army was a 'battle rifle', i.e. it fired a large-calibre round. Even the full-automatic versions of the same weapon used by other nations cannot be considered to be assault rifles; they are too big and heavy, and they do not use a small-calibre round. The designation 'automatic rifle' serves as well as any other for these weapons.

However, the British decided that automatic fire was not desirable. The SLR's 20-round magazine would be quickly emptied and automatic fire with 7.62mm (.3in) ammunition would be hard to control. Marksmanship and quick semi-automatic fire was considered to be more effective.

FORESIGHT
The SLR was accurate out to about 800m (2625ft), much further than the average soldier can shoot accurately, and was well suited to an army that relied on marksmanship rather than volume of fire.

FLASH HIDER
Powerful rifles produce a considerable amount of flash and kick up dust that can betray the firer's location. A flash hider goes some way towards reducing the weapon's signature.

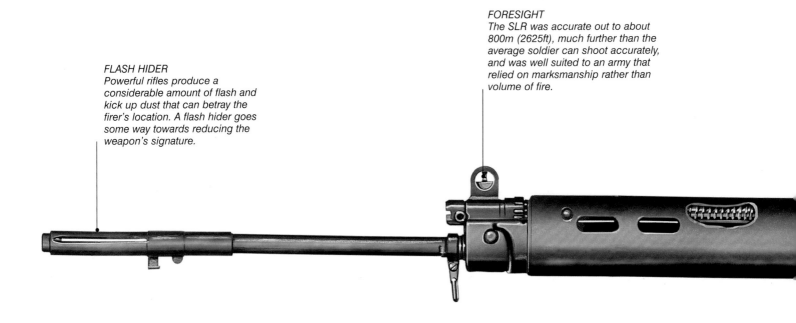

SPECIFICATIONS	
Country of Origin:	United Kingdom
Date:	1954
Calibre:	7.62mm (.3in) NATO
Operation:	Gas-operated, self-loading
Weight:	4.31kg (9.5lb)
Overall Length:	1055mm (41.5in)
Barrel Length:	535mm (21.1in)
Muzzle Velocity:	853m/sec (2800ft/sec)
Feed/Magazine:	20-round detachable box magazine
Range:	800m (2625ft) +

The 7.62mm (.3in) round offered a number of advantages. Its high velocity made accurate long-range shooting easier, and the heavy bullet would penetrate most cover – even something as solid as a brick wall was not necessarily adequate protection from rifle fire. Commonality of ammunition with the GPMGs used for support also simplified the support and logistics situation.

The SLR gave good service in environments as diverse as tropical jungles and arctic mountains, and also in urban terrain. However, it was eventually phased out in favour of a lighter, shorter weapon firing 5.56mm (.219in) ammunition. Other armies had adopted the assault rifle many years earlier, but the British kept their battle rifles right up to the middle of the 1980s.

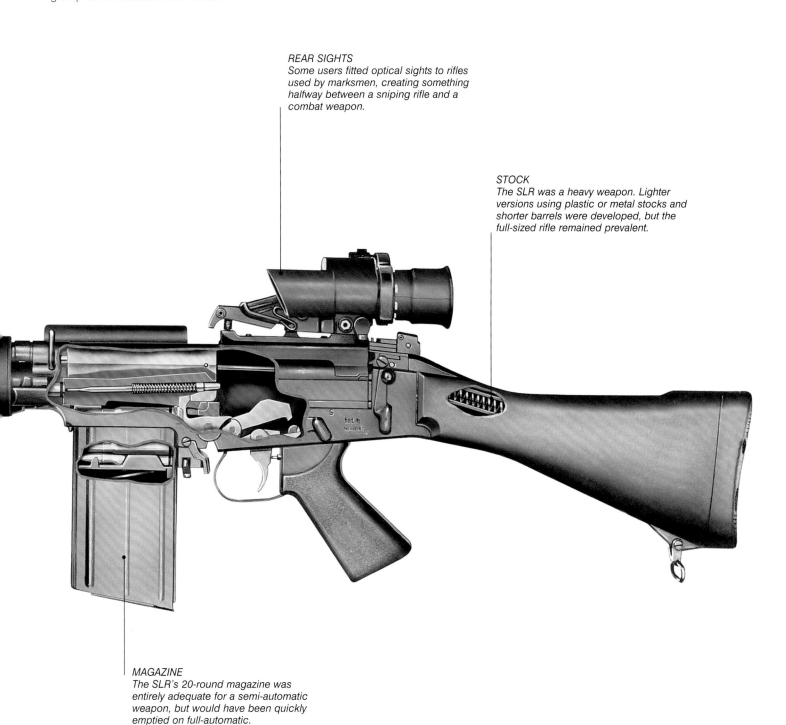

REAR SIGHTS
Some users fitted optical sights to rifles used by marksmen, creating something halfway between a sniping rifle and a combat weapon.

STOCK
The SLR was a heavy weapon. Lighter versions using plastic or metal stocks and shorter barrels were developed, but the full-sized rifle remained prevalent.

MAGAZINE
The SLR's 20-round magazine was entirely adequate for a semi-automatic weapon, but would have been quickly emptied on full-automatic.

Automatic Rifles

In the post-war period, several battle-rifle-calibre weapons capable of automatic fire appeared. In theory, the ability for any rifleman to lay down automatic suppressing fire seems worthwhile, but in practice not all such weapons were entirely successful.

M14

Developed from the M1 Garand, the M14 gained a detachable 20-round box magazine and automatic fire capability. Although tough and durable, the M14 was difficult to control under full-auto fire and tended to overheat.

SPECIFICATIONS	
Country of Origin:	United States
Date:	1957
Calibre:	7.62mm (.3in) NATO
Operation:	Gas-operated
Weight:	3.88kg (8.55lb)
Overall Length:	1117mm (44in)
Barrel Length:	558mm (22in)
Muzzle Velocity:	595m/sec (1950ft/sec)
Feed/Magazine:	20-round detachable box magazine
Range:	800m (2625ft) +

CETME M58

The CETME M58 was developed in Spain by a German-led team continuing their wartime work on the StG45 project. The result was a simple and easy-to-manufacture but effective automatic rifle.

SPECIFICATIONS	
Country of Origin:	Spain
Date:	1958
Calibre:	7.62mm (.3in) NATO
Operation:	Delayed blowback
Weight:	4.4kg (9.7lb)
Overall Length:	1015mm (40in)
Barrel Length:	450mm (17.72in)
Muzzle Velocity:	800m/sec (2625ft/sec)
Feed/Magazine:	20- or 30-round detachable box magazine
Range:	500m (1640ft) +

TIMELINE   1957   1958   1959

Beretta BM59

Another weapon derived from the M1 Garand, the BM59 differed mainly in its 20-round detachable magazine and selective-fire capability. As much as possible of the well-proven Garand was retained, gaining the BM59 a reputation as a 'breathed-on' Garand.

SPECIFICATIONS	
Country of Origin:	Italy
Date:	1959
Calibre:	7.62mm (.3in) NATO
Operation:	Gas-operated
Weight:	4.6kg (10.14lb)
Overall Length:	1095mm (43.11in)
Barrel Length:	490mm (19.29in)
Muzzle Velocity:	823m/sec (1700ft/sec)
Feed/Magazine:	20-round detachable box magazine
Range:	800m (2625ft)

M14A1

The full-automatic M14A1 was intended to act as a squad support weapon, and gained a bipod and pistol-style foregrip for this role. However, it still tended to overheat and the barrel could not be changed when hot.

SPECIFICATIONS	
Country of Origin:	United States
Date:	1963
Calibre:	7.62mm (.3in) NATO
Operation:	Gas-operated
Weight:	3.88kg (8.55lb)
Overall Length:	1117mm (44in)
Barrel Length:	558mm (22in)
Muzzle Velocity:	595m/sec (1950ft/sec)
Feed/Magazine:	20-round detachable box magazine
Range:	800m (2625ft) +

Ruger Mini-14

A quick glance at the Ruger Mini-14 shows that it is a more compact version of the M14 rifle, which in turn derives from the M1 Garand, the standard US rifle of World War II. The lightweight controllability of the Mini-14 has allowed its use by civilian, military and police customers, where it has proved popular.

SPECIFICATIONS	
Country of Origin:	United States
Date:	1973
Calibre:	5.56mm NATO or M193
Operation:	Gas-operated
Weight:	2.9kg (6.70lb)
Overall Length:	946mm (37.24in)
Barrel Length:	470mm (18.5in)
Muzzle Velocity:	1005m/sec (3297ft/sec)
Feed/Magazine:	5-, 10-, 20- or 30-round detachable box magazine
Range:	400m (1312ft)

1963

1973

M14 Carbine

The M14 can trace its lineage back to the M1 Garand rifle, which was at the time of its introduction an innovative weapon. Experimentation resulted in a range of variants and the emergence of an M1-based rifle fitted with a 20-round magazine. Conversion of this weapon to the new NATO 7.62 x 51mm (.3 x 2in) round created a weapon designated T44.

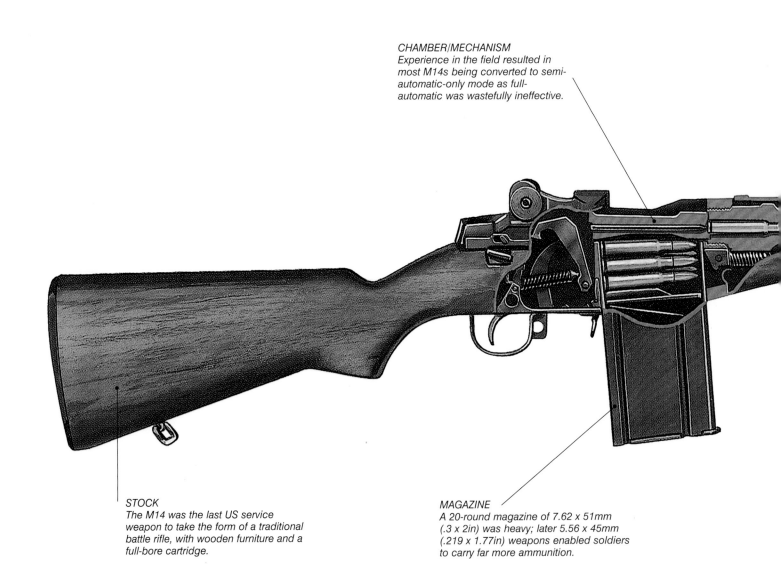

CHAMBER/MECHANISM
Experience in the field resulted in most M14s being converted to semi-automatic-only mode as full-automatic was wastefully ineffective.

STOCK
The M14 was the last US service weapon to take the form of a traditional battle rifle, with wooden furniture and a full-bore cartridge.

MAGAZINE
A 20-round magazine of 7.62 x 51mm (.3 x 2in) was heavy; later 5.56 x 45mm (.219 x 1.77in) weapons enabled soldiers to carry far more ammunition.

The main drawbacks of the M14 were its weight and that of its ammunition, which limited the amount that could be carried on a foot patrol. Although accurate and powerful, the M14 was also hard to control when conducting automatic fire. A variant, originally designated M14E2, was placed in service as a squad support weapon in 1963 and was redesignated M14A1 in 1966.

SIGHTS
The M14 was issued with standard iron sights, but 'accurized' sniper or marksman versions used a range of optical sights.

BARREL
Although variously referred to as a 'carbine' or a 'rifle', the M14 was quite a long weapon and could be difficult to handle in close urban or jungle terrain.

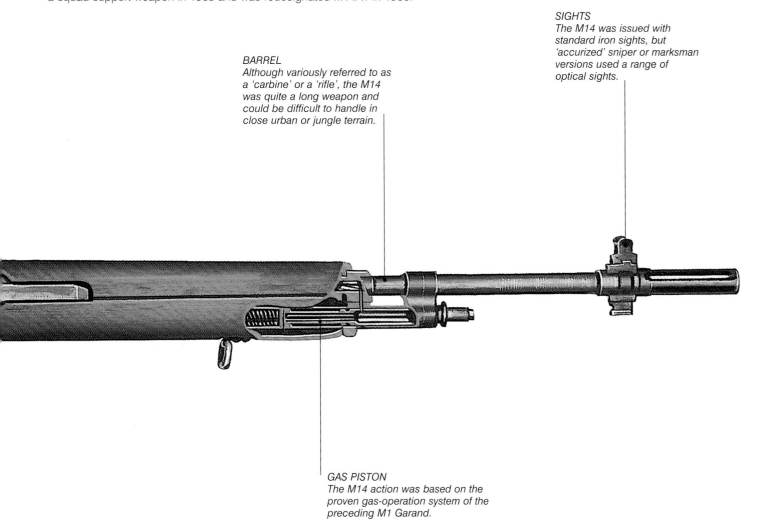

GAS PISTON
The M14 action was based on the proven gas-operation system of the preceding M1 Garand.

SPECIFICATIONS	
Country of Origin:	United States
Date:	1957
Calibre:	7.62mm (.3in) NATO
Operation:	Gas-operated
Weight:	3.88kg (8.55lb)
Overall Length:	1117mm (44in)
Barrel Length:	558mm (22in)
Muzzle Velocity:	595m/sec (1950ft/sec)
Feed/Magazine:	20-round detachable box magazine
Range:	800m (2625ft) +

The T44 entered US military service as the M14, starting in 1957, and saw action during the Vietnam War. It was the main US infantry rifle until the late 1960s when the lighter M16 began to enter service. Many M14s were later converted to M21 sniper/designated marksman rifles.

Post-War Submachine Guns

The submachine guns of the immediate post-war period were in most cases derived from wartime projects. Many of these weapons seem crude to the modern eye, but they were effective enough to be manufactured in numbers.

Carl Gustav M/45

More correctly designated Kulspruta Pistol M/45 ('Carl Gustav' was the name of the factory), the M/45 was adopted by the Swedish Army and US Special Forces. It was also licence-built overseas.

SPECIFICATIONS	
Country of Origin:	Sweden
Date:	1945
Calibre:	9mm (.35in) Parabellum
Operation:	Blowback
Weight:	3.9kg (8.6lb)
Overall Length:	808mm (31.81in)
Barrel Length:	213mm (8.38in)
Muzzle Velocity:	410m/sec (1345ft/sec)
Feed/Magazine:	36-round detachable box magazine
Range:	120m (394ft)

Madsen M1950

The Danish M1945 submachine gun borrowed concepts from wartime expedient weapons such as the Sten. Although it proved disappointing, it was developed into a series of weapons leading to the rather better M1950.

SPECIFICATIONS	
Country of Origin:	Denmark
Date:	1950
Calibre:	9mm (.35in) Parabellum
Operation:	Blowback
Weight:	3.17kg (6.99lb)
Overall Length:	800mm (31.5in) stock extended; 530mm (20.85in) stock folded
Barrel Length:	197mm (7.75in)
Muzzle Velocity:	380m/sec (1274ft/sec)
Feed/Magazine:	32-round detachable box magazine
Range:	150m (492ft) +

TIMELINE   1945   1950   1952

Vigneron

Belgian troops operating in the Congo were widely issued with the Vigneron SMG, and the weapon passed into use there when Congo became independent. Today, examples turn up all over Africa.

SPECIFICATIONS	
Country of Origin:	Belgium
Date:	1952
Calibre:	9mm (.35in) Parabellum
Operation:	Blowback
Weight:	3.29kg (7.25lb)
Overall Length:	890mm (35in) stock extended; 705mm (27.75in) stock folded
Barrel Length:	305mm (12in)
Muzzle Velocity:	365m/sec (1200ft/sec)
Feed/Magazine:	32-round detachable box magazine
Range:	200m (656ft) +

SIG MP310

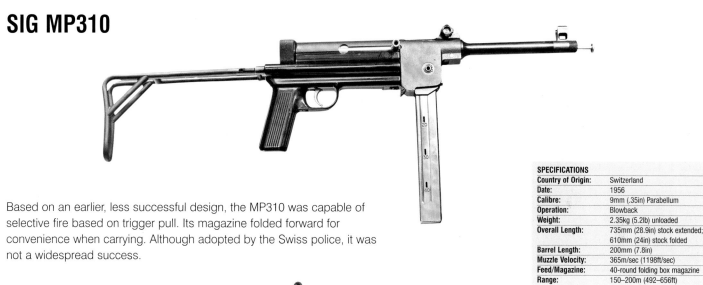

Based on an earlier, less successful design, the MP310 was capable of selective fire based on trigger pull. Its magazine folded forward for convenience when carrying. Although adopted by the Swiss police, it was not a widespread success.

SPECIFICATIONS	
Country of Origin:	Switzerland
Date:	1956
Calibre:	9mm (.35in) Parabellum
Operation:	Blowback
Weight:	2.35kg (5.2lb) unloaded
Overall Length:	735mm (28.9in) stock extended; 610mm (24in) stock folded
Barrel Length:	200mm (7.8in)
Muzzle Velocity:	365m/sec (1198ft/sec)
Feed/Magazine:	40-round folding box magazine
Range:	150–200m (492–656ft)

Erma MP58

Responding to a requirement from the German Federal Government for a cheap submachine gun design, the Erma company produced this well-made and reliable weapon. It was not adopted by the government and Erma eventually moved into the commercial market.

SPECIFICATIONS	
Country of Origin:	Germany
Date:	1958
Calibre:	9mm (.35in) Parabellum
Operation:	Blowback
Weight:	3.1kg (6.8lb)
Overall Length:	405mm (16in)
Barrel Length:	190mm (7.5in)
Muzzle Velocity:	395m/sec (1295ft/sec)
Feed/Magazine:	30-round detachable box magazine
Range:	70m (230ft)

1956 1958

The Sterling Family

The Patchett submachine gun was developed as a replacement for the rather crude Sten. It proved its worth in combat from 1944 onwards, and after the war it was the basis for the distinctive Sterling family of weapons.

Sterling L2A1

The Sterling was a simple blowback weapon based on a tubular receiver. In service, it quickly proved itself both effective and reliable. The L3A1 model was the first to enter service with the British Army.

SPECIFICATIONS	
Country of Origin:	United Kingdom
Date:	1953
Calibre:	9mm (.35in) Parabellum
Operation:	Blowback
Weight:	2.72kg (6lb)
Overall Length:	690mm (27.16in) stock extended; 483mm (19in) stock folded
Barrel Length:	198mm (7.8in)
Muzzle Velocity:	395m/sec (1295ft/sec)
Feed/Magazine:	34-round detachable box magazine
Range:	70m (230ft)

Sterling L2A3

The Sterling was refined through several models to the A3 (otherwise known as the Sterling Mk 4), the last to enter service. Despite its generally awkward shape, the Sterling proved effective and was adopted by the Canadian and Indian militaries.

SPECIFICATIONS	
Country of Origin:	United Kingdom
Date:	1956
Calibre:	9mm (.35in) Parabellum
Operation:	Blowback
Weight:	2.7kg (5.9lb) empty
Overall Length:	686mm (27in) stock extended; 481mm (18.9in) stock folded
Barrel Length:	196mm (7.7in)
Muzzle Velocity:	395m/sec (1295ft/sec)
Feed/Magazine:	34-round detachable box magazine
Range:	200m (656ft)

TIMELINE

 1953

 1956

 1967

Sterling L34A1

SPECIFICATIONS	
Country of Origin:	United Kingdom
Date:	1967
Calibre:	9mm (.35in) Parabellum
Operation:	Blowback
Weight:	3.6kg (7.94lb)
Overall Length:	864mm (34in) stock extended; 660mm (26in) stock folded
Barrel Length:	198mm (7.8in)
Muzzle Velocity:	300m/sec (984ft/sec)
Feed/Magazine:	34-round detachable box magazine
Range:	120m (394ft)

The silenced Sterling produced much lighter recoil than other versions, making it very manageable. Although the silencer reduced muzzle velocity, this did not greatly impair the weapon's effectiveness in a covert role.

Sterling Mk 7 'Para-Pistol'

SPECIFICATIONS	
Country of Origin:	United Kingdom
Date:	1960s
Calibre:	9mm (.35in)
Operation:	Blowback
Weight:	3kg (6.6lb)
Overall Length:	381mm (15in)
Barrel Length:	190.5mm (7.5in)
Muzzle Velocity:	300m/sec (984ft/sec)
Feed/Magazine:	10- or 15-round detachable box magazine
Range:	80m (262ft)

A shortened Sterling intended for use by paratroops and vehicle crews, the Mk 7 was not adopted for military service. Most of the weapons made were sold on the international commercial market.

SAF Carbine 1A (Indian)

SPECIFICATIONS	
Country of Origin:	India
Date:	1960s
Calibre:	9mm (.35in) Parabellum
Operation:	Blowback
Weight:	2.72kg (6lb)
Overall Length:	690mm (27.16in) stock extended; 483mm (19in) stock folded
Barrel Length:	198mm (7.8in)
Muzzle Velocity:	395m/sec (1295ft/sec)
Feed/Magazine:	34-round detachable box magazine
Range:	70m (230ft)

The Indian Army adopted a variant of the Sterling L2A1 for general issue, and produced a silenced version for covert operations. Both weapons are still manufactured.

1960s

Beretta Modello 12

An orthodox blowback weapon with a 'wraparound' bolt (i.e. one that partially wraps around the barrel) to reduce its length, the Modello 12 marked a departure from Beretta's previous designs. It used a tubular receiver, a popular design at the time, with a pistol-style foregrip for close-range combat.

Although the Modello 12 made extensive use of metal stampings to reduce costs, it was a very well-made weapon which was both durable and accurate. Available with either a fixed stock or a folding metal one, the Modello 12 could take 20-, 30- or 40-round magazines.

MAGAZINE
The weapon could be carried with a small magazine for convenience, switching to a larger one at the first reload or when combat is expected.

SPECIFICATIONS	
Country of Origin:	Italy
Date:	1959
Calibre:	9mm (.35in) Parabellum
Operation:	Blowback
Weight:	2.95kg (6.5lb)
Overall Length:	660mm (26in) wooden stock; 645mm (25.4in) metal stock extended; 416mm (16.4in) metal stock folded
Barrel Length:	203mm (8in)
Muzzle Velocity:	380m/sec (1247ft/sec)
Feed/Magazine:	20-, 30- or 40-round detachable box magazine
Range:	120m (394ft)

The Modello 12 achieved considerable international success, and was adopted by police and military units in South America and Africa as well as its native Italy. A slightly updated version, designated Modello 12S, was marketed in the late 1970s.

During the lifetime of this weapon, the submachine gun changed roles somewhat. It was eclipsed as a military weapon system by the more generally useful assault rifle, and moved more into an urban security role. Weapons like the Modello 12 are ideal for law enforcement and VIP protection applications, which take place largely in urban areas and where combat, if it occurs at all, requires the rapid elimination of threats through heavy and accurate short-range firepower.

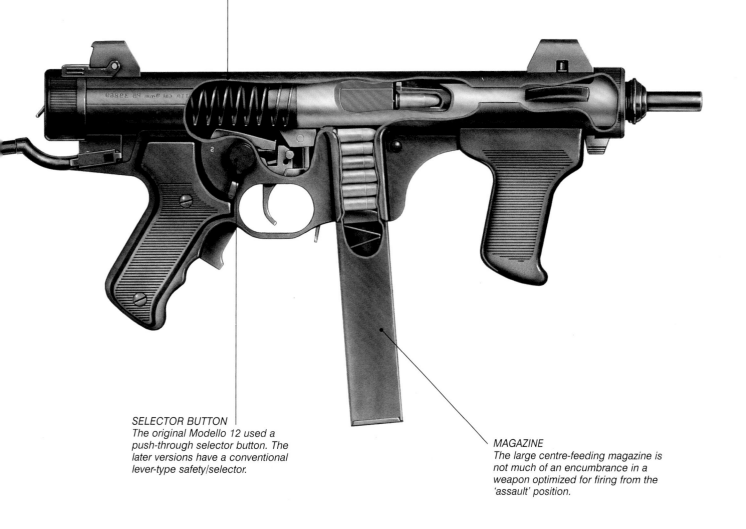

RECEIVER
The Modello 12 used stamped metal rather than machinings to reduce costs, but was still a well put together weapon.

SELECTOR BUTTON
The original Modello 12 used a push-through selector button. The later versions have a conventional lever-type safety/selector.

MAGAZINE
The large centre-feeding magazine is not much of an encumbrance in a weapon optimized for firing from the 'assault' position.

Versatile Support Weapons

Experience in World War II showed that it was desirable to have a single support weapon that could fit into several roles, rather than to try to build a different weapon for every application.

MAS AAT-52

Attempting to rationalize its infantry armament, France adopted the 7.5mm (.295in) AAT-52. This weapon was designed for mass production, using simple stamped and welded components as far as possible. Its main departure from the norm was the use of a delayed-blowback action.

SPECIFICATIONS	
Country of Origin:	France
Date:	1952
Calibre:	7.5mm (.295in)
Operation:	Lever-delayed blowback
Weight:	9.97kg (21.98lb) with bipod and light barrel; 11.37kg (25.07lb) with bipod and heavy barrel
Overall Length:	1080mm (42.5in)
Barrel Length:	500mm (16.69in) light barrel
Muzzle Velocity:	840m/sec (2756ft/sec)
Cyclic Rate:	700rpm
Feed/Magazine:	50-round metal-link belt
Range:	800m (2625ft)

MAS AAT-52 (tripod mounted)

The AAT-52 was designed to be used with a light barrel and bipod when in the light support role. For sustained fire, a heavier barrel which was better able to dissipate heat was used, along with a tripod mount.

SPECIFICATIONS	
Country of Origin:	France
Date:	1952
Calibre:	7.55mm (.295in)
Operation:	Lever-delayed blowback
Weight:	10.6kg (23.37lb)
Overall Length:	1080mm (42.5in)
Barrel Length:	600mm (23.62in)
Muzzle Velocity:	840m/sec (2756ft/sec)
Cyclic Rate:	700rpm
Feed/Magazine:	50-round metal-link belt
Range:	1200m (3937ft)

TIMELINE

 1952

 1952

 1955

NF-1 GPMG

In order to bring the French armed forces into line with NATO, their AAT-52 machine guns were modified to use 7.62 x 51mm (.3 x 2in) ammunition and redesignated NF-1. This had the effect of improving performance by adding 200–400m (656–1312ft) to the weapon's effective range.

SPECIFICATIONS	
Country of Origin:	France
Date:	1955
Calibre:	7.62mm (.3in) NATO
Operation:	Delayed blowback
Weight:	11.37kg (25lb)
Overall Length:	1245mm (49in)
Barrel Length:	600mm (23.62in)
Muzzle Velocity:	830m/sec (2723ft/sec)
Feed/Magazine:	Belt-fed
Cyclic Rate:	900rpm
Range:	1500m (4920ft) +

MG42/59

Derived from the excellent wartime MG42, one of the first true GPMGs, the German MG3 was a huge success. The MG42/59 was an export version of this weapon and was adopted by the Italian Army, among others.

SPECIFICATIONS	
Country of Origin:	West Germany
Date:	1959
Calibre:	7.62mm (.3in)
Operation:	Short recoil, air-cooled
Weight:	12kg (26.45lb)
Overall Length:	1220mm (48.03in)
Barrel Length:	531mm (20.9in)
Muzzle Velocity:	820m/sec (2690ft/sec)
Feed/Magazine:	Belt-fed
Cyclic Rate:	800rpm
Range:	3000m (9842ft) +

Lehky Kulomet vz59

Visually similar to the earlier vz52, the Czech vz59 was a much simpler weapon that used the best features of its predecessor. For the sustained-fire infantry support or vehicle-mounted role, it could be fitted with a heavy barrel.

SPECIFICATIONS	
Country of Origin:	Czechoslovakia
Date:	1959
Calibre:	7.62mm (.3in)
Operation:	Blowback
Weight:	8.67kg (19.1lb) with bipod and light barrel; 19.24kg (42.42lb) with tripod and heavy barrel
Overall Length:	1116mm (43.94in) light barrel; 1215mm (47.84in) heavy barrel
Barrel Length:	593mm (23.35in) light barrel; 693mm (27.28in) heavy barrel
Muzzle Velocity:	810m/sec (2657ft/sec) light barrel; 830m/sec (2723ft/sec) heavy barrel
Feed/Magazine:	Belt-fed
Cyclic Rate:	700–800rpm
Range:	800m (2620ft)

1959

L4 Bren Gun

Although it was very long in the tooth by the time that NATO standardized its ammunition, the Bren Gun was available in large numbers and was still widely respected as an excellent light support weapon. It was logical, therefore, for the British Army to convert its Brens to use the new ammunition rather than develop a new weapon that, quite possibly, might not be as good as the Bren.

Conversion to the new calibre was accompanied by few changes to a well-proven design, and the Bren continued its service under the new designation L4. It was eventually supplanted by the L7 GPMG, the British Army designation for the FN MAG-58.

BARREL
The L4 was given a chrome-plated barrel, which greatly reduced wear and overheating. Frequent barrel changes were less necessary, so spare barrels were rarely issued.

The final incarnation of the Bren in British Army service was the L4A4, which was primarily issued to units not expected to engage front-line enemy forces. L4A4s served out their final years mounted on various vehicles and defending airfields, artillery batteries and communications posts as well as in a light air-defence role. The RAF also took some L4A4s for similar purposes.

GAS PISTON
The gas-operated mechanism of the Bren was not changed during the conversion to NATO-standard ammunition.

SPECIFICATIONS	
Country of Origin:	United Kingdom
Date:	1958
Calibre:	7.62mm (.3in) NATO
Operation:	Gas-operated, air-cooled
Weight:	10.25kg (22.5lb)
Overall Length:	1150mm (45.25in)
Barrel Length:	625mm (25in)
Muzzle Velocity:	730m/sec (2400ft/sec)
Feed/Magazine:	30-round detachable box magazine
Range:	1000m (3280ft) +

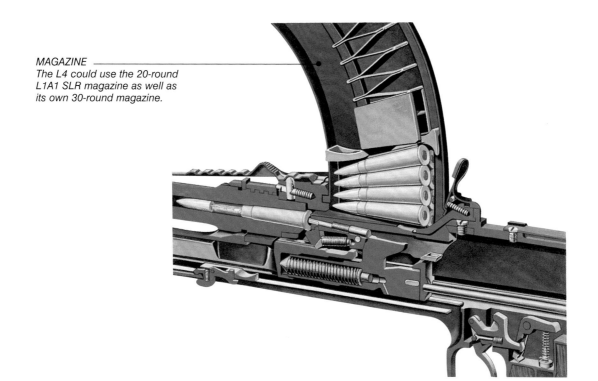

MAGAZINE
The L4 could use the 20-round
L1A1 SLR magazine as well as
its own 30-round magazine.

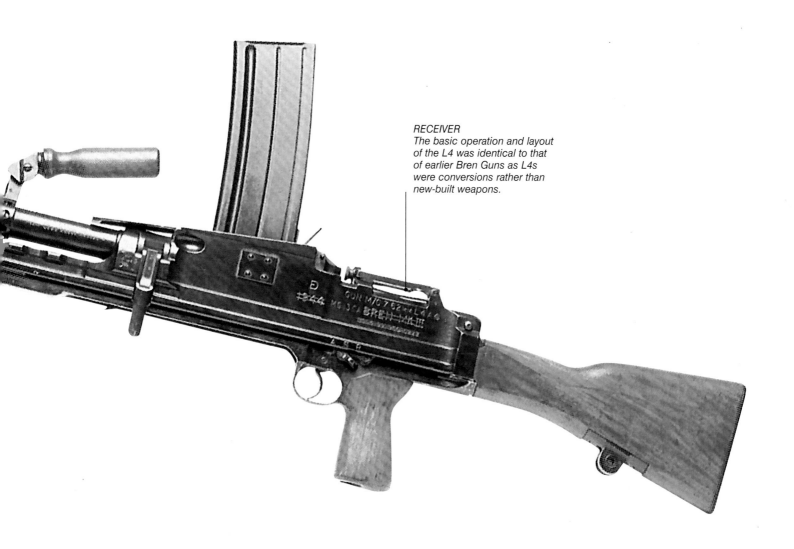

RECEIVER
The basic operation and layout
of the L4 was identical to that
of earlier Bren Guns as L4s
were conversions rather than
new-built weapons.

THE COLD WAR ERA

The period between 1960 and 1990 was greatly overshadowed by the Cold War between NATO and the Warsaw Pact.

Politics played a huge part in arms procurement, with weapons and military advisors offered to smaller states, usually with political strings attached. Thus many nations obtained their military equipment from either the West or from the Warsaw Pact. It was unusual for a nation to have a mix of weapon systems from the two major power blocs. The result was a considerable degree of polarization regarding weapon calibres and compatibilities.

Left: Iraqi soldiers armed with AK-47 assault rifles and a Soviet-made RPG-7 rocket-propelled grenade launcher undergo a training exercise.

Combat Handguns

A range of combat pistols emerged during the Cold War era. Many were developed from earlier, proven designs but used modern materials as well as some interesting new concepts.

Walther P1/P4

Based on the classic P38, the Walther P1 used the same mechanism but had a lightweight aluminium construction to save weight. The P4 was a short-barrelled version. Both were adopted by the German armed forces.

SPECIFICATIONS	
Country of Origin:	West Germany
Date:	1957
Calibre:	9mm (.35in) Parabellum
Operation:	Double-action blowback
Weight:	840g (1.9lb) steel frame; 770g (1.7lb) aluminium frame
Overall Length:	216mm (8.5in) P1; 19mm (7.8in) P4
Barrel Length:	125mm (4.9in) P1; 104mm (4.1in) P4
Muzzle Velocity:	365m/sec (1200ft/sec)
Feed/Magazine:	8-round magazine
Range:	50m (164ft)

Manurhin MR73

A very well-made French revolver available in a range of calibres and barrel lengths, the MR73 is capable of using 9mm (.35in) ammunition and found favour with police and civilian users alike. Competition versions are still popular today.

SPECIFICATIONS	
Country of Origin:	France
Date:	1973
Calibre:	9.6mm (.38in) .38 Special, 9.1mm (.357in) .357 Magnum, 9mm (.35in) Parabellum
Operation:	Revolver
Weight:	.88kg (1.94lb)
Overall Length:	195mm (7.67in)
Barrel Length:	63.5mm (2.5in)
Muzzle Velocity:	Variable, depending on cartridge
Feed/Magazine:	6-round cylinder
Range:	Variable, depending on cartridge

TIMELINE

 1957

 1973

MAB PA-15

After experimentation with smaller calibres, the PA-15 was manufactured in 9mm (.35in) Parabellum and was adopted by the French Army where it served from 1975 to 1990.

SPECIFICATIONS	
Country of Origin:	France
Date:	1975
Calibre:	9mm (.35in) Parabellum
Operation:	Delayed blowback
Weight:	1.07kg (2.36lb)
Overall Length:	203mm (8in)
Barrel Length:	114mm (4.5in)
Muzzle Velocity:	330m/sec (1100ft/sec)
Feed/Magazine:	15-round detachable box magazine
Range:	40m (131ft)

Walther P5

The P5 was another weapon based on the excellent mechanism of the P38, this one created for the German police. Their stringent safety requirements resulted in one of the most accidental-discharge-proof weapons available.

SPECIFICATIONS	
Country of Origin:	West Germany
Date:	1975
Calibre:	9mm (.35in) Parabellum
Operation:	Short recoil
Weight:	.79kg (1.75lb)
Overall Length:	180mm (7.08in)
Barrel Length:	90mm (3.54in)
Muzzle Velocity:	350m/sec (1150ft/sec)
Feed/Magazine:	8-round detachable box magazine
Range:	40m (131ft)

Steyr Model GB

Introduced in 1981, the Model GB was based on wartime experimentation and featured a large (18-round) magazine capacity. A promising weapon, its expected success was largely derailed by the appearance of the Glock 17 in the same market niche.

SPECIFICATIONS	
Country of Origin:	Austria
Date:	1981
Calibre:	9mm (.35in) Parabellum
Operation:	Gas-delayed blowback
Weight:	.845kg (1.9lb)
Overall Length:	216mm (8.5in)
Barrel Length:	136mm (5.4in)
Muzzle Velocity:	330m/sec (1100ft/sec)
Feed/Magazine:	18-round detachable box magazine
Range:	40m (131ft)

1975

1981

Beretta Semi-Automatics

The adoption of a Beretta handgun as the standard US Army sidearm in the 1990s, replacing the venerable Colt M1911A1, was a huge coup for the company, boosting sales to civilian users.

Beretta Cheetah (Beretta Series 81)

The Cheetah (or Series 80) was a compact semi-automatic available in a range of chamberings from 5.6mm/.22in '22LR' through 8.1mm (.32in) to 9.6mm (.38in). A target version became available in 2000.

SPECIFICATIONS	
Country of Origin:	Italy
Date:	1976
Calibre:	8.1mm (.32in) .32 ACP
Operation:	Blowback
Weight:	.68kg (1.49lb)
Overall Length:	172mm (6.77in)
Barrel Length:	97mm (3.8in)
Muzzle Velocity:	380m/sec (1247ft/sec)
Feed/Magazine:	12-round detachable box magazine
Range:	50m (164ft)

Beretta 92F

The Beretta 92 began life as an updated M1951 with a double-action trigger and increased magazine capacity. It was updated as the 92S to meet the needs of a number of law enforcement agencies.

SPECIFICATIONS	
Country of Origin:	Italy
Date:	1976
Calibre:	9mm (.35in) Parabellum
Operation:	Blowback
Weight:	.97kg (2.125lb))
Overall Length:	211mm (8.3in)
Barrel Length:	119mm (4.7in)
Muzzle Velocity:	380m/sec (1247ft/sec)
Feed/Magazine:	10-, 15-, 17-, 18- or 20-round detachable box magazine
Range:	50m (164ft)

TIMELINE

 1976   1981

Beretta 92SB

The 92SB, a further developed 92S, was the winning entry in the US Army pistol trials and was adopted for service after a primarily ergonomic upgrade which created the 92F. Its US military designation is M9.

SPECIFICATIONS	
Country of Origin:	Italy
Date:	1981
Calibre:	9mm (.35in) Parabellum
Operation:	Short recoil
Weight:	.98kg (2.16lb)
Overall Length:	197mm (7.76in)
Barrel Length:	109mm (4.29in)
Muzzle Velocity:	385m/sec (1263ft/sec)
Feed/Magazine:	13-round detachable box magazine
Range:	40m (131ft)

Beretta 93R

The 93R (R is for Raffica, or 'Burst') is a burst-capable version of the Beretta 92. It has a folding foregrip and an optional folding stock to improve controllability at a cyclic rate of 1100rpm.

SPECIFICATIONS	
Country of Origin:	Italy
Date:	1986
Calibre:	9mm (.35in) Parabellum
Operation:	Short recoil
Weight:	1.12kg (2.47lb)
Overall Length:	240mm (9.45in)
Barrel Length:	156mm (6.14in)
Muzzle Velocity:	375m/sec (1230ft/sec)
Feed/Magazine:	15- or 20-round detachable box magazine
Range:	40m (131ft)

Beretta 96

The 96 was essentially a 92 rechambered for 10.16mm (.4in) S&W ammunition. This calibre is favoured by some law enforcement agencies for its superior ballistic performance whilst retaining the characteristics of a 9mm (.35in) weapon.

SPECIFICATIONS	
Country of Origin:	Italy
Date:	1992
Calibre:	10.16mm (.4in) S&W
Operation:	Blowback
Weight:	.97kg (2.125lb)
Overall Length:	211mm (8.3in)
Barrel Length:	119mm (4.7in)
Muzzle Velocity:	380m/sec (1247ft/sec)
Feed/Magazine:	12-round detachable box magazine
Range:	50m (164ft)

1986

1992

Magnum Semi-Automatics: AMT AutoMag III

Creating a semi-automatic pistol to fire Magnum-calibre rounds presented a considerable challenge. Whereas a revolver has few moving parts during firing, a semi-automatic has many components that can fail or allow high-pressure gas to escape.

SIGHTS
Many AutoMags are fitted with a scope and used for hunting or specialist target-shooting competitions.

GRIP
One drawback of a large-calibre pistol is the limited ammunition capacity imposed by the bulk of its rounds.

SPECIFICATIONS	
Country of Origin:	United States
Date:	1966
Calibre:	7.62mm (.3in)
Operation:	Short recoil, locked-breech
Weight:	1.275kg (2.8lb)
Overall Length:	350mm (13.8in)
Barrel Length:	165mm (6.5in)
Muzzle Velocity:	Not known
Feed/Magazine:	8-round box magazine
Range:	50m (164ft)

A number of excessively powerful semi-automatics have appeared since the AutoMag demonstrated what was possible, but they remain minority weapons; most semi-automatics continue to use standard calibres.

CHAMBER
Magnum rounds create extremely high pressures and require a very securely sealed chamber to ensure the user's safety.

BARREL
Pistols using the AutoMag name have been offered in a range of powerful calibres since the 1970s.

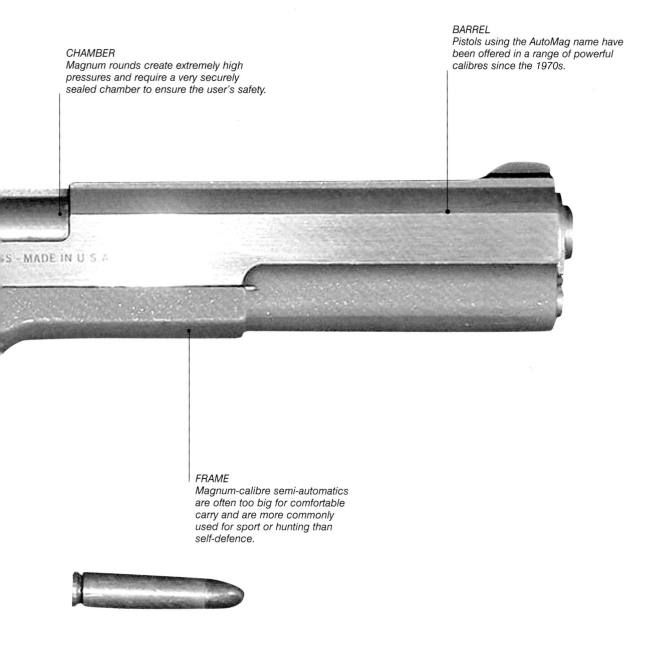

FRAME
Magnum-calibre semi-automatics are often too big for comfortable carry and are more commonly used for sport or hunting than self-defence.

The original Magnum-calibre semi-automatics began manufacture in 1971 with the AutoMag, which was chambered for an 11.2mm (.44in) round. Delivering similar performance to a .44 Magnum revolver but with somewhat less recoil and a larger capacity, the AutoMag found itself a niche with handgun hunters.

Compact Handguns

Small and light enough for habitual carry, compact handguns are ideal for users who feel they may need to have a weapon at some point in the future but do not expect imminent trouble.

Colt Defender Plus

The Colt Defender was a tough but lightweight aluminium-framed semi-automatic firing full-power 11.4mm/.45in (.45 ACP) cartridges. Despite its small size its magazine held a respectable seven rounds.

SPECIFICATIONS	
Country of Origin:	United States
Date:	1948
Calibre:	11.4mm (.45in) .45 ACP
Operation:	Single-action
Weight:	.63kg (1.38lb)
Overall Length:	171mm (6.75in)
Barrel Length:	76.2mm (3in)
Muzzle Velocity:	Not known
Feed/Magazine:	7-round magazine
Range:	20m (65ft)

Smith & Wesson Model 60

A compact five-shot revolver chambered for 9.6mm/.38in (.38 Special) or 9.1mm/.357in (.357 Magnum) ammunition, the short-barrel version of the Model 60 was an immediate success and remains a popular choice for concealed carry.

SPECIFICATIONS	
Country of Origin:	United States
Date:	1965
Calibre:	9.6mm (.38in) .38 Special, 9.1mm (.357in) .357 Magnum
Operation:	Double-action revolver
Weight:	.64kg (1.4lb)
Overall Length:	168mm (6.625in)
Barrel Length:	53.9mm (2.125in)
Muzzle Velocity:	Not known
Feed/Magazine:	5-round cylinder
Range:	23m (75ft)

TIMELINE

 1948

 1965

 1972

SIG-Sauer P-230

The P-230's small calibre makes for a very slim weapon, making it ideal for concealed carry or use as a backup gun. It is capable of firing either double-action or single-action.

SPECIFICATIONS	
Country of Origin:	Switzerland/West Germany
Date:	1972
Calibre:	9mm (.35in) Police
Operation:	Double action/single action (DA/SA)
Weight:	.5kg (1.1lb)
Overall Length:	68mm (6.61in)
Barrel Length:	91.4mm (3.6in)
Muzzle Velocity:	Not known
Feed/Magazine:	7- or 8-round magazine
Range:	20m (65ft)

Detonics Combat Master

Detonics made its name with the Combat Master, a compact 11.4mm (.45in) semi-automatic based on the M1911. Recoil is often a problem with small guns firing big cartridges, but the Combat Master's advanced mechanism helped counteract this.

SPECIFICATIONS	
Country of Origin:	United States
Date:	1975
Calibre:	11.4mm (.45in) .45 ACP
Operation:	Blowback
Weight:	.96kg (2.12lb)
Overall Length:	177mm (7in)
Barrel Length:	88.9mm (3.5in)
Muzzle Velocity:	390m/sec (1284ft/sec)
Feed/Magazine:	6-round magazine
Range:	20m (65ft)

COP .357 Derringer

Each of the COP derringer's four chambers had its own firing pin, activated in turn by a rotating striker. The weapon was double-action, allowing fast response to a threat, though this resulted in a heavy trigger pull.

SPECIFICATIONS	
Country of Origin:	United States
Date:	1978
Calibre:	9.1mm (.357in) .357 Magnum
Operation:	Double-action trigger with rotating firing-pin selector
Weight:	.8 kg (1.75lb)
Overall Length:	142mm (5.6in)
Barrel Length:	Not known
Muzzle Velocity:	Not known
Feed/Magazine:	Break-open, 4-round capacity
Range:	10m (32.8ft)

1975

1978

Ruger Revolvers

Sturm, Ruger & Co have produced a range of revolvers in addition to rifles, shotguns and semi-automatic pistols. They have produced some highly influential and distinctive designs, as well as weapons with a highly traditional appearance.

Ruger Single Six

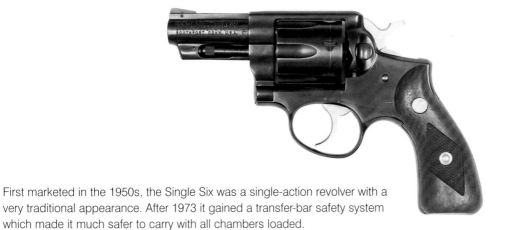

First marketed in the 1950s, the Single Six was a single-action revolver with a very traditional appearance. After 1973 it gained a transfer-bar safety system which made it much safer to carry with all chambers loaded.

SPECIFICATIONS	
Country of Origin:	United States
Date:	1953
Calibre:	5.6mm (.22in) LR
Operation:	Single-action revolver
Weight:	.9kg (2lb)
Overall Length:	259mm (10.2in)
Barrel Length:	116mm (4.6in)
Muzzle Velocity:	Not known
Feed/Magazine:	6-round cylinder
Range:	20m (66ft)

Ruger Security Six

Chambered for 9.1mm/.357in (.357 Magnum), the Security Six was aimed at the law enforcement marketplace. Its ability to penetrate cover that might defeat a 9.6mm (.38in) weapon or to disable a fleeing vehicle was well received.

SPECIFICATIONS	
Country of Origin:	United States
Date:	1972
Calibre:	9.1mm (.357in) .357 Magnum
Operation:	Revolver
Weight:	.95kg (2.09lb)
Overall Length:	235mm (9.25in)
Barrel Length:	102mm (4in)
Muzzle Velocity:	c.400m/sec (1312ft/sec)
Cylinder capacity:	6-round cylinder
Range:	40m (131ft) +

TIMELINE

 1953   1972    1979

Ruger Redhawk

The 11.2mm/.44in (.44 Magnum) Redhawk was aimed at the handgun hunting-market, where its long-barrel options proved popular. It has mounts for a telescopic sight cut into the barrel.

SPECIFICATIONS	
Country of Origin:	United States
Date:	1979
Calibre:	11.2mm (.44in) .44 Magnum
Operation:	Revolver
Weight:	1.5kg (3.37lb)
Overall Length:	165mm (6.5in)
Barrel Length:	190mm (7.48in)
Muzzle Velocity:	450m/sec (1475ft/sec)
Cylinder capacity:	6-round cylinder
Range:	50–100m (164–328ft)

Ruger Bisley (RB-44W)

The Bisley was a single-action revolver intended for target shooting and hunting. Its inspiration went all the way back the 1894-vintage Colt Bisley.

SPECIFICATIONS	
Country of Origin:	United States
Date:	1984
Calibre:	11.2mm (.44in) .44 Magnum
Operation:	Single-action revolver
Weight:	1.4kg (3.1lb)
Overall Length:	342mm (13.5in)
Barrel Length:	190mm (7.5in)
Muzzle Velocity:	Not known
Feed/Magazine:	6-round cylinder
Range:	50–100m (164–328ft)

Ruger GP100

Carrying on the tradition of the Security Six, Ruger's very robust GP100 is chambered for 9.1mm/.357in (.357 Magnum) or 9.6mm/.38in (.38 Special). A seven-shot version for 8.3mm/.327in .327 Federal Magnum is also available.

SPECIFICATIONS	
Country of Origin:	United States
Date:	1985
Calibre:	9.1mm (.357in) .357 Magnum
Operation:	Double-action revolver
Weight:	1kg (2.2lb)
Overall Length:	Not known
Barrel Length:	76mm (3in)
Muzzle Velocity:	c.400m/sec (1312ft/sec)
Feed/Magazine:	6-round cylinder
Range:	50–100m (164–328ft)

1984

1985

Magnum Handguns

9.1mm/.357in (.357 Magnum) weapons offer a good compromise between considerable stopping power and controllability. Their ability to shoot 9.6mm/.38in (.38 Special) ammunition for practice or reduced recoil is an additional advantage. Some users prefer the awesome power of an 11.2mm/.44in (.44 Magnum).

Korth Combat Magnum

Virtually handmade, the Korth 'Combat Magnum' is an expensive but highly accurate weapon. The 'combat' version was chambered for 9.1mm (.357in) with a 9mm (.35in) conversion available. 'Target' versions were available in other calibres.

SPECIFICATIONS	
Country of Origin:	West Germany
Date:	1965
Calibre:	9.1mm (.357in) .357 Magnum
Operation:	Double-action revolver
Weight:	1.133kg (2.4lb)
Overall Length:	240mm (9.4in)
Barrel Length:	100mm (4in)
Muzzle Velocity:	400m/sec (1300ft/sec)
Cylinder capacity:	6-round cylinder
Range:	50m (164ft) +

Astra .357 Police

Produced for the law enforcement market, the 9.1mm/.357in .357 Police was developed from the earlier Astra .357. A version chambered for 9mm (.35in) Parabellum was also marketed, but was not as popular.

SPECIFICATIONS	
Country of Origin:	Spain
Date:	1980
Calibre:	9.1mm (.357in) .357 Magnum
Operation:	Revolver
Weight:	1.04kg (2.29lb)
Overall Length:	212mm (8.34in)
Barrel Length:	77mm (3.03in)
Muzzle Velocity:	224m/sec (734ft/sec)
Feed/Magazine:	6-round cylinder
Range:	50m (164ft) +

TIMELINE			
	1965	1980	1983

IMI Desert Eagle

Developed in the United States but produced by Israeli Military Industries, the Desert Eagle was available in several calibres. Despite its power it was not adopted by the military.

SPECIFICATIONS	
Country of Origin:	United States/Israel
Date:	1983
Calibre:	12.7mm (.5in) .50in Action Express, 11.2mm (.44in) .44 Magnum, 9.1mm (.357in) .357 Magnum
Operation:	Gas-operated
Weight:	2.05kg (4.5lb) .50; 1.8kg (4.1lb) .44; 1.7kg (3.75lb) .357
Overall Length:	260mm (10.25in)
Barrel Length:	152mm (6in)
Muzzle Velocity:	c.457m/sec (1500ft/sec) .50; 448m/sec (1470ft/sec) .44; 436m/sec (1430ft/sec) .357
Feed/Magazine:	7-round (.50), 8-round (.44) or 9-round (.357) magazine
Range:	50m (164ft) +

Colt King Cobra

The King Cobra was developed from the Colt Trooper and was available with a range of barrel lengths. It was in production from 1986 to 1992 and again from 1994 to 1998.

SPECIFICATIONS	
Country of Origin:	United States
Date:	1986
Calibre:	9.6mm (.38in) .38 Special
Operation:	Double-action revolver
Weight:	.6kg (1.32lb)
Overall Length:	Variable depending on barrel
Barrel Length:	102mm (4in) or 152mm (6in)
Muzzle Velocity:	436m/sec (1430ft/sec)
Cylinder capacity:	6-round cylinder
Range:	50m (164ft) +

Colt Anaconda

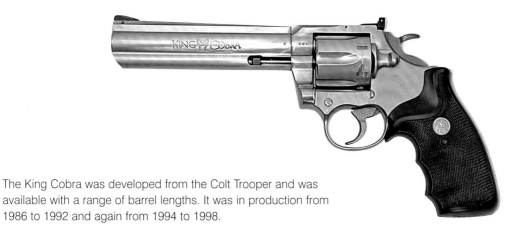

The Anaconda entered production in 1990, and despite initial problems with accuracy soon developed into an effective weapon. Too bulky for most people to carry around all day, it was primarily aimed at the hunting and sport market.

SPECIFICATIONS	
Country of Origin:	United States
Date:	1990
Calibre:	11.4mm (.45in) .45 Colt
Operation:	Double-action revolver
Weight:	1.5kg (3.3lb)
Overall Length:	280mm (11in)
Barrel Length:	152mm (6in)
Muzzle Velocity:	224m/sec (734ft/sec)
Feed/Magazine:	6-round cylinder
Range:	45.7m (150ft)

1986

1990

Smith & Wesson versus Colt

Smith & Wesson and Colt have competed for decades for pre-eminence in the military, law enforcement and private marketplaces. Both have produced some world-class handguns, not all of which have achieved the success they perhaps deserved.

Colt Cobra (Viper Variant)

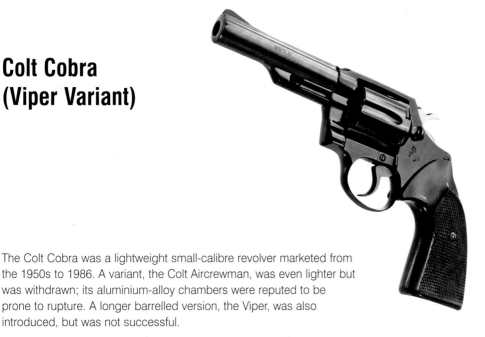

The Colt Cobra was a lightweight small-calibre revolver marketed from the 1950s to 1986. A variant, the Colt Aircrewman, was even lighter but was withdrawn; its aluminium-alloy chambers were reputed to be prone to rupture. A longer barrelled version, the Viper, was also introduced, but was not successful.

SPECIFICATIONS	
Country of Origin:	United States
Date:	1950
Calibre:	9.6mm (.38in) .38 Special (Viper variant)
Operation:	Revolver
Weight:	.425kg (.93lb)
Overall Length:	171mm (6.75in)
Barrel Length:	102mm (4in)
Muzzle Velocity:	240m/sec (787ft/sec)
Feed/Magazine:	6-round cylinder
Range:	40m (131ft)

Colt Lawman

At the end of the 1960s Colt discontinued many of its weapons and introduced the new 'J-frame' handguns, which used new manufacturing techniques. The Lawman was one of several new models aimed at the law enforcement marketplace.

SPECIFICATIONS	
Country of Origin:	United States
Date:	1970
Calibre:	9.1mm (.357in) .357 Magnum
Operation:	Double-action revolver
Weight:	.79kg (1.74lb)
Overall Length:	235mm (9in)
Barrel Length:	51mm (2in)
Muzzle Velocity:	436m/sec (1430ft/sec)
Feed/Magazine:	6-round cylinder
Range:	40m (131ft)

TIMELINE

 1950

 1970

 1980

S&W 459

The 459 was Smith & Wesson's entry in the US Army pistol trials. It was developed from the Model 39, through the high-capacity Model 59, specifically for the military market.

SPECIFICATIONS	
Country of Origin:	United States
Date:	1980
Calibre:	9mm (.35in) Parabellum
Operation:	DA/SA
Weight:	.73kg (1.6lb)
Overall Length:	175mm (6.89in)
Barrel Length:	89mm (3.5in)
Muzzle Velocity:	395m/sec (1295ft/sec)
Feed/Magazine:	14-round detachable box magazine
Range:	40m (131ft)

S&W 625

The 625 was unusual for a revolver, in that it was chambered for 11.4mm/.45in .45 ACP. This is traditionally a semi-automatic pistol calibre, and weapons that cross the traditional barriers in this manner are uncommon.

SPECIFICATIONS	
Country of Origin:	United States
Date:	1987
Calibre:	11.4mm (.45in) .45 ACP
Operation:	Double-action revolver
Weight:	1.13kg (2.5lb)
Overall Length:	238mm (9.38in)
Barrel Length:	102mm (4in)
Muzzle Velocity:	240m/sec (787ft/sec)
Feed/Magazine:	6-round cylinder
Range:	40m (131ft)

S&W 1006

Part of Smith & Wesson's 'Third Generation' of semi-automatic handguns, the 1006 was chambered for the powerful 10mm (.39in) Auto cartridge. It was developed in response to FBI interest in a 10mm (.39in) handgun.

SPECIFICATIONS	
Country of Origin:	United States
Date:	1989
Calibre:	10mm (.39in)
Operation:	Recoil DA/SA
Weight:	1.7kg (3.75lb)
Overall Length:	203mm (8in)
Barrel Length:	127mm (5in)
Muzzle Velocity:	395m/sec (1295ft/sec)
Feed/Magazine:	9- or 10-round magazine
Range:	50m (164ft) +

1987

1989

S&W Model 39 'Hush Puppy'

Special Forces troops often need to dispose of enemy sentries and guard dogs silently and at a distance. Silenced weapons are one answer, so in the Vietnam War era the US Navy SEAL teams requested a silenced handgun.

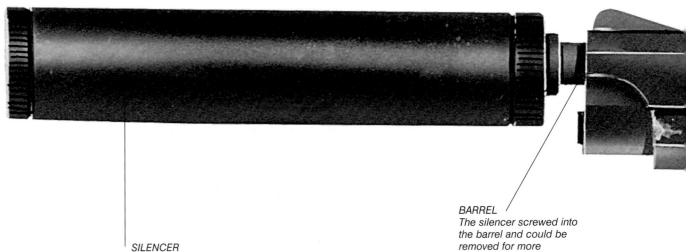

SILENCER
The nickname 'Hush Puppy' had nothing to do with the weapon's silencer; it referred to its use in eliminating enemy guard dogs.

BARREL
The silencer screwed into the barrel and could be removed for more convenient carry.

SPECIFICATIONS	
Country of Origin:	United States
Date:	1967
Calibre:	9mm (.35in) Parabellum
Operation:	Recoil, locked-breech
Weight:	.96kg (2.1lb)
Overall Length:	323mm (12.75in)
Barrel Length:	101mm (3.9in)
Muzzle Velocity:	274m/sec (900ft/sec)
Feed/Magazine:	8-round detachable box magazine
Range:	30m (98ft)

Various options were considered, including a suppressed Walther P38, but the eventual solution was to fit an extended barrel to a Smith & Wesson Model 39 and thread it for a silencer. With some other modifications, this weapon entered service in 1967 under the designation Mk 22 Model 0. It served until the 1980s.

The Model 39, with its eight-round magazine, was supplanted for general military use long before the 'Hush Puppy' was retired. This is not uncommon with specialist weapons; for example many bolt-action rifles remained in service as sniper weapons for decades after they had been replaced as infantry weapons by semi- or even full-automatic weapons.

SLIDE
The 'Hush Puppy' was fitted with a slide lock to reduce mechanical noise during firing.

GRIP
As a weapon intended for assassination of a target by stealth rather than sustained combat, the Hush Puppy's limited magazine capacity was not a drawback.

Heckler & Koch Semi-Automatics

H&K produced a range of advanced and, in some cases, unconventional handguns. Many of these were intended for law enforcement, a market where safety is a prime concern along with reliability and accuracy.

Heckler & Koch VP-70

The VP-70 was capable of firing single shots or three-round bursts at a cyclic rate of 2200rpm. It was the world's first polymer-framed pistol and could be converted to a carbine-like weapon by attaching a shoulder stock.

SPECIFICATIONS	
Country of Origin:	West Germany
Date:	1970
Calibre:	9mm (.35in) Parabellum
Operation:	Blowback
Weight:	.82kg (1.8lb)
Overall Length:	204mm (8in)
Barrel Length:	116mm (4.6in)
Muzzle Velocity:	350m/sec (1148ft/sec)
Feed/Magazine:	18-round box magazine
Range:	40m (131ft)

Heckler & Koch P9S

The standard P9 is a single-action semi-automatic pistol; the P9S is a double-action weapon. Both use H&K's roller-locked delayed blowback system. 11.4mm/.45in (.45 ACP) 9mm `(.35in), 7.65mm (.301in) and 5.6mm/.22in (.22 LR) versions are available.

SPECIFICATIONS	
Country of Origin:	West Germany
Date:	1970
Calibre:	11.4mm (.45in), 9mm (.35in), 7.65mm (.301in), 5.6mm (.22in)
Operation:	Double-action, delayed blowback
Weight:	.88kg (1.93lb)
Overall Length:	192mm (7.5in)
Barrel Length:	102mm (4in)
Muzzle Velocity:	c.350m/sec (1148ft/sec)
Feed/Magazine:	7-round (11.4mm/.45in), 9-round (9mm/.35in) detachable box magazine
Range:	30m (98ft)

TIMELINE

1970

Heckler & Koch P7

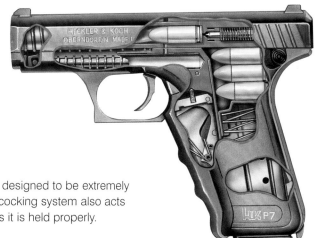

Developed for the Federal German Police, the P7 was designed to be extremely safe yet able to come into action quickly. Its squeeze-cocking system also acts as a safety device, preventing the weapon firing unless it is held properly.

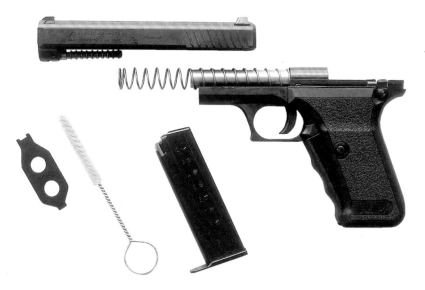

Unusually for a handgun, the P7 uses gas-actuated delayed-blowback operation. Gas channelled from the barrel resists slide recoil long enough for the round to leave the muzzle.

SPECIFICATIONS	
Country of Origin:	West Germany
Date:	1976
Calibre:	9mm (.35in) Parabellum
Operation:	Gas-actuated delayed blowback
Weight:	.8kg (1.76lb)
Overall Length:	171mm (6.73in)
Barrel Length:	105mm (4.13in)
Muzzle Velocity:	350m/sec (1150ft/sec)
Feed/Magazine:	13-round detachable box magazine
Range:	40m (131ft)

Heckler & Koch P11

The P11 was an underwater weapon developed in the 1970s for use by special forces personnel. Each of the five barrels held an electrically-ignited cartridge. Reloading required replacement of the entire barrel block.

SPECIFICATIONS	
Country of Origin:	West Germany
Date:	1976
Calibre:	7.6mm (.3in)
Operation:	Electric-actuated
Weight:	1.2kg (2.7lb) loaded
Overall Length:	200mm (7.87in)
Barrel Length:	N/A
Muzzle Velocity:	N/A
Feed/Magazine:	5 rounds in disposable barrel cluster
Range:	30m (98ft) in air; 10–15m (32.8–49ft) underwater

1976

Heckler & Koch USP

At the end of the 1980s, H&K began work on their USP (Universal Semi-Automatic Pistol). As its name suggests, this weapon was intended to create a single basic design from which a huge range of variants could be derived to suit the end user's needs. Available in 9mm (.35in), 10.16mm (.4in) and 11.4mm (.45in), the standard USP could be put together as a double- or single-action weapon and with a range of safety and decocking options, or in a 'US Law Enforcement' configuration with a modified double-action trigger.

Versions of the USP have been taken up by the German armed forces. The 'tactical' went into service with some elite units as the P12 while the army received the standard USP under the designation P8.

BARREL
The USP was developed around a 10.16mm (.4in) cartridge, but is also available in other popular chamberings.

SPECIFICATIONS

Country of Origin:	Germany
Date:	1990
Calibre:	11.4mm (.45in), 10.16mm (.4in), 9mm (.35in)
Operation:	Short recoil, DA/SA or DA/DAO
Weight:	.748kg (1.65lb)
Overall Length:	219mm (8.64in)
Barrel Length:	108mm (4.25in)
Muzzle Velocity:	350m/sec (1150ft/sec)
Feed/Magazine:	Detachable box magazine
Range:	30m (98ft) 11.4mm/.45in; 50m (164ft) 9mm/.35in

A match pistol and a 'tactical' variant, aimed at special forces and elite law enforcement units, followed the standard USP, along with a compact version of the standard and tactical models. All weapons used the proven Browning action rather than any of the innovative systems developed since.

FRAME
The USP uses advanced
synthetic materials for the
frame; metal parts are treated
to resist corrosion.

MECHANISM
The USP uses the breech-locking system
developed by John Browning, coupled to
a new recoil-reduction system.

SAFETY
Options include a manual safety and/or
decocking lever, ambidextrous controls
and a double-action-only trigger.

The High Power Family

At the time of his death, John Browning was working on a pistol design that arguably fathered all modern semi-automatic handguns. The 'High Power' name comes not from the 9mm (.35in) cartridge but from the weapon's 13-round magazine capacity.

FN/Browning GP Prototype 1924

Using Dieudonné Saive's staggered magazine concept, Browning and Saive created a prototype of what would become the 'Grande Puissance' or 'High Power' handgun. After Browning's death, Saive completed their work as a weapon designated GP-35 (or HP-35).

SPECIFICATIONS	
Country of Origin:	Belgium/United States
Date:	1924
Calibre:	9mm (.35in) Parabellum
Operation:	Short recoil
Weight:	1kg (2.19lb)
Overall Length:	197mm (7.8in)
Barrel Length:	118mm (4.7in)
Muzzle Velocity:	335m/sec (1100ft/sec)
Feed/Magazine:	13-round detachable box magazine
Range:	40–50m (131–164ft)

FN/Browning High Power (Hi-Power)

Produced by Fabrique Nationale d'Armes de Guerre (FN), the Browning High Power (HP-35 or GP-35) used a different locking system to Browning's earlier Colt M1911 design. It was an immense success and was taken into service by over 50 nations.

SPECIFICATIONS	
Country of Origin:	Belgium/United States
Date:	1935
Calibre:	9mm (.35in) Parabellum
Operation:	Short recoil
Weight:	.99kg (2.19lb)
Overall Length:	197mm (7.75in)
Barrel Length:	118mm (4.65in)
Muzzle Velocity:	335m/sec (1100ft/sec)
Feed/Magazine:	13-round detachable box magazine
Range:	30m (98ft)

TIMELINE

1924

1935

1962

L9A1

In British Army service, the Browning HP-35 was designated L9A1, though it was more commonly referred to as a 'Browning Nine-Millimetre'. Many other nations used the same weapon, often under local designations.

Browning Double Action

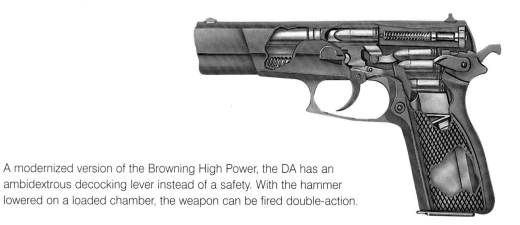

A modernized version of the Browning High Power, the DA has an ambidextrous decocking lever instead of a safety. With the hammer lowered on a loaded chamber, the weapon can be fired double-action.

Browning BDM

Developed at the end of the 1990s, the Browning Double (or Dual) Mode can be quickly adjusted with a screwdriver to switch between standard double-action and double-action-only mode to suit the user's preferences.

1983

1991

SIG-Sauer Semi-Automatics

When Swiss firm SIG moved into handgun manufacture, a foreign partner was necessary to enable overseas sales to be made. Sauer had made a previous foray into the field, without success, but together SIG-Sauer became a huge success.

SIG P210

Adopted for service with the Swiss Army in 1949, the P210 was phased out in the 1970s, with many examples going to sports shooters who valued its accuracy and high quality of manufacture.

SPECIFICATIONS	
Country of Origin:	Switzerland
Date:	1949
Calibre:	9mm (.35in) Parabellum
Operation:	Short recoil
Weight:	.9kg (1.98lb)
Overall Length:	215mm (8.5in)
Barrel Length:	120mm (4.7in)
Muzzle Velocity:	340m/sec (1115ft/sec)
Feed/Magazine:	8-round detachable box magazine
Range:	30m (98ft)

SIG-Sauer P220

The main drawback of the P210 was its price tag, which inhibited sales. Teaming up with Sauer of Germany, SIG produced and marketed a simplified handgun which still commanded respect for its quality.

SPECIFICATIONS	
Country of Origin:	Switzerland/West Germany
Date:	1975
Calibre:	9mm (.35in) Parabellum
Operation:	Recoil
Weight:	.8kg (1.7lb)
Overall Length:	198mm (7.79in)
Barrel Length:	112mm (4.4in)
Muzzle Velocity:	350m/sec (1148ft/sec)
Feed/Magazine:	7-, 9-, or 10-round magazine
Range:	30m (98ft)

TIMELINE

1949

1975

1978

SIG-Sauer P225

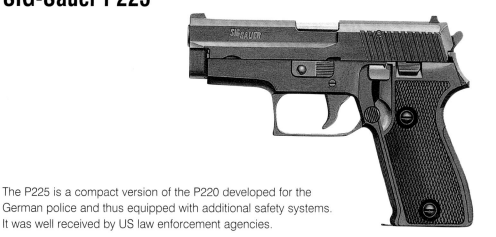

The P225 is a compact version of the P220 developed for the German police and thus equipped with additional safety systems. It was well received by US law enforcement agencies.

SPECIFICATIONS	
Country of Origin:	Switzerland/West Germany
Date:	1978
Calibre:	9mm (.35in) Parabellum
Operation:	Short recoil
Weight:	.74kg (1.63lb)
Overall Length:	180mm (7.08in)
Barrel Length:	98mm (3.85in)
Muzzle Velocity:	340m/sec (1115ft/sec)
Feed/Magazine:	8-round detachable box magazine
Range:	40m (131ft)

SIG-Sauer P226

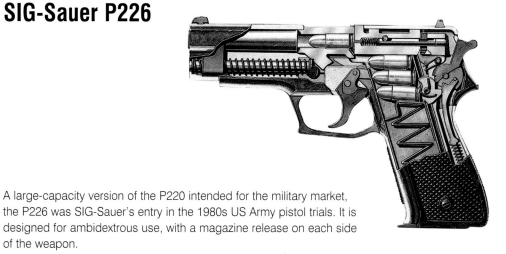

A large-capacity version of the P220 intended for the military market, the P226 was SIG-Sauer's entry in the 1980s US Army pistol trials. It is designed for ambidextrous use, with a magazine release on each side of the weapon.

SPECIFICATIONS	
Country of Origin:	Switzerland/West Germany
Date:	1981
Calibre:	9mm (.35in) Parabellum
Operation:	Mechanically locked, recoil-operated, DA/SA or DAO
Weight:	.75kg (1.65lb)
Overall Length:	196mm (7.71in)
Barrel Length:	112mm (4.4in)
Muzzle Velocity:	350m/sec (1148ft/sec)
Feed/Magazine:	15- or 20-round detachable box magazine
Range:	30m (98ft)

SIG-Sauer P245

Some handgun users, notably in the United States, will only consider a weapon chambered for 11.4mm/.45in (.45 ACP). SIG-Sauer responded with this version of the P220. It is intended primarily for concealed carry or as a police backup gun.

SPECIFICATIONS	
Country of Origin:	Switzerland/Germany
Date:	1998
Calibre:	11.4mm (.45in) .45 ACP
Operation:	Short recoil, DA/SA
Weight:	.815kg (1.79lb)
Overall Length:	185mm (7.28in)
Barrel Length:	99mm (3.89in)
Muzzle Velocity:	340m/sec (1115ft/sec)
Feed/Magazine:	6-round detachable box magazine
Range:	30m (98ft)

1981

1998

The Glock Family

When the first Glock handguns appeared in the 1980s, some people feared that these 'plastic guns' were invisible to security equipment. In fact they were not in any way 'stealth weapons' and polymer construction has since been widely accepted.

Glock 17

Developed in response to a request from the Austrian Army, the lightweight, high-capacity Glock 17 went on to achieve massive success with military, police and civilian users worldwide. Its 17-round magazine capacity is a major selling point.

SPECIFICATIONS	
Country of Origin:	Austria
Date:	1982
Calibre:	9mm (.35in) Parabellum
Operation:	Short recoil, locked-breech
Weight:	.65kg (1.43lb)
Overall Length:	188mm (7.5in)
Barrel Length:	114mm (4.49in)
Muzzle Velocity:	350m/sec (1148ft/sec)
Feed/Magazine:	17-round detachable box magazine
Range:	30m (98ft)

Glock 18

A fully automatic version of the 9mm (.35in) Glock 17, capable of 1300rpm, the Glock 18 uses a 19-round or 33-round magazine. Like all such weapons, it is hard to control under automatic fire.

SPECIFICATIONS	
Country of Origin:	Austria
Date:	1986
Calibre:	10mm (.39in)
Operation:	Short recoil, locked-breech
Weight:	.75kg (165lb)
Overall Length:	210mm (8.25in)
Barrel Length:	114mm (4.5in)
Muzzle Velocity:	375m/sec (1230ft/sec)
Feed/Magazine:	19-round detachable box magazine
Range:	50m (164ft)

TIMELINE

 1982

 1986

 1988

Glock 19

The Glock 19 is a compact version which normally uses a 15-round magazine. It can carry larger magazines, as well as a 10-round one for jurisdictions with restrictions on capacity. Most parts are compatible with the Glock 17.

SPECIFICATIONS	
Country of Origin:	Austria
Date:	1988
Calibre:	9mm (.35in) Parabellum
Operation:	Short recoil, locked-breech
Weight:	.6kg (1.31lb)
Overall Length:	174mm (6.85in)
Barrel Length:	102mm (4in)
Muzzle Velocity:	375m/sec (1230ft/sec)
Feed/Magazine:	15-round detachable box magazine
Range:	50m (164ft)

Glock 20

The Glock name was made with 9mm (.35in) pistols, but soon other calibres followed. The Glock 20 and 21 are chambered for the powerful 10mm (.39in) Auto round, with 10.16mm/.4in (.40 S&W) and 11.4mm/.45in (.45 ACP) models also available.

SPECIFICATIONS	
Country of Origin:	Austria
Date:	1990
Calibre:	10mm (.39in) Auto
Operation:	Short recoil, locked-breech
Weight:	.79kg (1.73lb)
Overall Length:	193mm (7.59in)
Barrel Length:	117mm (4.6in)
Muzzle Velocity:	350m/sec (1148ft/sec)
Feed/Magazine:	15-round detachable box magazine
Range:	50m (164ft)

Glock 26

The Glock 26 is a 'sub-compact' 9mm (.35in) weapon. Whereas the Glock 19 is simply a smaller 17, the 26 required extensive design work to make its mechanism fit into such a small package.

SPECIFICATIONS	
Country of Origin:	Austria
Date:	1995
Calibre:	9mm (.35in) Parabellum
Operation:	Short recoil, locked-breech
Weight:	.6kg (1.34lb) empty
Overall Length:	160mm (6.29in)
Barrel Length:	88mm (3.46in)
Muzzle Velocity:	350m/sec (1148ft/sec)
Feed/Magazine:	9-round detachable box magazine
Range:	50m (164ft)

1990   1995

Soviet and East European Handguns

The domination of Eastern Europe by the Warsaw Pact ensured that those countries that did not simply obtain their weapons from the Soviet Union followed Russian design practices and used standard Warsaw Pact ammunition in their weapons.

Stetchkin

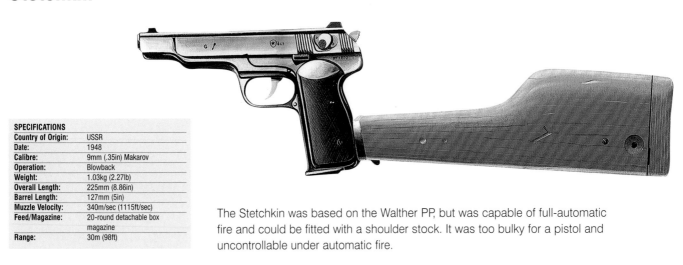

SPECIFICATIONS	
Country of Origin:	USSR
Date:	1948
Calibre:	9mm (.35in) Makarov
Operation:	Blowback
Weight:	1.03kg (2.27lb)
Overall Length:	225mm (8.86in)
Barrel Length:	127mm (5in)
Muzzle Velocity:	340m/sec (1115ft/sec)
Feed/Magazine:	20-round detachable box magazine
Range:	30m (98ft)

The Stetchkin was based on the Walther PP, but was capable of full-automatic fire and could be fitted with a shoulder stock. It was too bulky for a pistol and uncontrollable under automatic fire.

Pistole Makarov

Another derivative of the Walther PP, the Makarov was a workmanlike 9 x 18mm (.35 x .71in) calibre semi-automatic. It retained the Walther's double-action trigger and general reliability, and was adopted by China and East Germany, among other nations.

SPECIFICATIONS	
Country of Origin:	USSR/Russia
Date:	1951
Calibre:	9mm (.35in) Makarov
Operation:	Blowback
Weight:	.66kg (1.46lb)
Overall Length:	160mm (6.3in)
Barrel Length:	91mm (3.5in)
Muzzle Velocity:	315m/sec (1033ft/sec)
Feed/Magazine:	8-round detachable box magazine
Range:	40m (131ft)

TIMELINE  1948 1951 1965

P-64 (Polish)

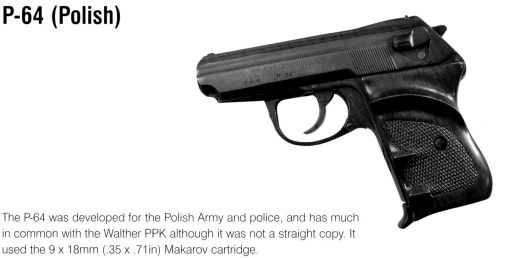

The P-64 was developed for the Polish Army and police, and has much in common with the Walther PPK although it was not a straight copy. It used the 9 x 18mm (.35 x .71in) Makarov cartridge.

SPECIFICATIONS	
Country of Origin:	Poland
Date:	1965
Calibre:	9mm (.35in) Makarov
Operation:	Blowback
Weight:	.62kg (1.36lb)
Overall Length:	160mm (6.3in)
Barrel Length:	84.6mm (3.3in)
Muzzle Velocity:	305m/sec (1001ft/sec)
Feed/Magazine:	6-round detachable box magazine
Range:	40m (131ft)

PSM (Military Model)

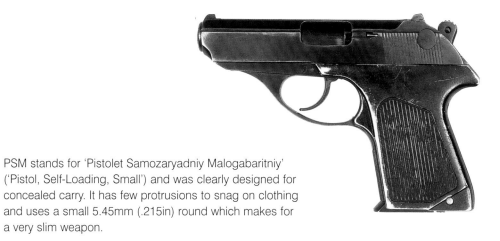

PSM stands for 'Pistolet Samozaryadniy Malogabaritniy' ('Pistol, Self-Loading, Small') and was clearly designed for concealed carry. It has few protrusions to snag on clothing and uses a small 5.45mm (.215in) round which makes for a very slim weapon.

SPECIFICATIONS	
Country of Origin:	USSR
Date:	1973
Calibre:	5.45mm (.215in) Soviet Pistol
Operation:	Blowback
Weight:	.46kg (1.01lb)
Overall Length:	160mm (6.3in)
Barrel Length:	85mm (3.35in)
Muzzle Velocity:	315m/sec (1033ft/sec)
Feed/Magazine:	8-round detachable box magazine
Range:	40m (131ft)

PSM (Security Forces Model)

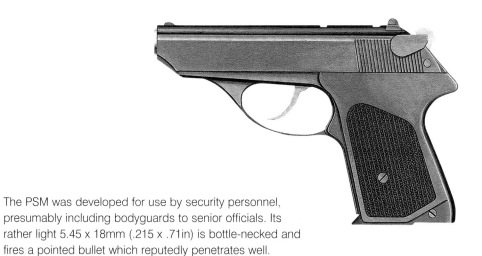

The PSM was developed for use by security personnel, presumably including bodyguards to senior officials. Its rather light 5.45 x 18mm (.215 x .71in) is bottle-necked and fires a pointed bullet which reputedly penetrates well.

SPECIFICATIONS	
Country of Origin:	USSR
Date:	1973
Calibre:	5.45mm (.215in) Soviet Pistol
Operation:	Blowback
Weight:	.46kg (1.01lb)
Overall Length:	160mm (6.3in)
Barrel Length:	85mm (3.35in)
Muzzle Velocity:	315m/sec (1033ft/sec)
Feed/Magazine:	8-round detachable box magazine
Range:	40m (131ft)

1973

Czech and Yugoslav Semi-Automatics

The Czech Republic has produced many excellent semi-automatic pistols, though until the thawing of East-West relations in recent years they were not common in Western nations.

CZ 52

A post-war single-action semi-automatic pistol chambered for 7.62 x 25mm (.3 x .98in) ammunition, the CZ 52 was notable for high felt recoil due to its high bore-axis, which caused the muzzle to flip up significantly.

SPECIFICATIONS	
Country of Origin:	Czechoslovakia
Date:	1952
Calibre:	7.62mm (.3in) Tokarev
Operation:	Recoil, roller-locked
Weight:	.95kg (2.09lb)
Overall Length:	209mm (8.2in)
Barrel Length:	120mm (4.7in)
Muzzle Velocity:	500m/sec (1640ft/sec)
Feed/Magazine:	8-round detachable box magazine
Range:	50m (164ft)

CZ 75

A high-quality double-action 9mm (.35in) semi-automatic, the CZ 75 achieved good market success and was widely copied, often without regard to the niceties of licensing. A full-automatic variant was also marketed.

SPECIFICATIONS	
Country of Origin:	Czechoslovakia
Date:	1976
Calibre:	9mm (.35in) Parabellum
Operation:	Short recoil
Weight:	.98kg (2.16lb)
Overall Length:	203mm (8in)
Barrel Length:	120mm (4.72in)
Muzzle Velocity:	338m/sec (1110ft/sec)
Feed/Magazine:	15-round detachable box magazine
Range:	40m (131ft)

TIMELINE

1952

1976

1982

CZ 82/83

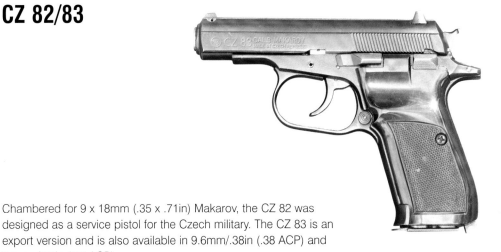

Chambered for 9 x 18mm (.35 x .71in) Makarov, the CZ 82 was designed as a service pistol for the Czech military. The CZ 83 is an export version and is also available in 9.6mm/.38in (.38 ACP) and 8.1mm/.32in (.32 ACP).

SPECIFICATIONS	
Country of Origin:	Czechoslovakia
Date:	1982
Calibre:	9mm (.35in) Makarov
Operation:	Blowback, double-action
Weight:	.92kg (2.02lb)
Overall Length:	172mm (6.8in)
Barrel Length:	96mm (3.7in)
Muzzle Velocity:	305m/sec (1001ft/sec)
Feed/Magazine:	12-round detachable box magazine
Range:	25m (82ft)

CZ 85

A modernized version of the CZ 75, the CZ 85 was given an ambidextrous safety catch. The subsequent CZ 85B version was further upgraded and is available in a variety of calibres.

SPECIFICATIONS	
Country of Origin:	Czechoslovakia
Date:	c.1986
Calibre:	9mm (.35in) Luger
Operation:	Blowback
Weight:	1kg (2.2lb)
Overall Length:	206mm (8.1in)
Barrel Length:	120mm (4.7in)
Muzzle Velocity:	370m/sec (1214ft/sec)
Feed/Magazine:	16-round detachable box magazine
Range:	40m (131ft)

CZ 99

The CZ 99 is a modern semi-automatic handgun, first developed in SFR Yugoslavia in 1989 by Zastava Arms. The CZ 99 was designed to replace the aging M57 TT pistol as the standard-issue handgun for the Serbian police and military ground forces.

SPECIFICATIONS	
Country of Origin:	Yugoslavia
Date:	1990
Calibre:	9mm (.35in) Parabellum, 10.16mm (.4in) .40 S&W
Operation:	Single- or double-action
Weight:	1.145kg (2.5lb)
Overall Length:	190mm (7.4in)
Barrel Length:	108mm (4.25in)
Muzzle Velocity:	300–457m/sec (985–1500ft/sec)
Feed/Magazine:	15- (9mm/.35in) or 10/12-round (10.16mm/.4in) magazine
Range:	40m (131ft)

1986

1990

The AK-47 and its Derivatives

The Kalashnikov AK-47 was manufactured in several variants by the nations of the Warsaw Pact. Its extremely robust and soldier-proof mechanism was also used as the basis of weapons outside the immediate Soviet sphere of influence.

AK-47

The AK-47 was inaccurate and suffered from high recoil, but this did not impair effectiveness over a combat range of about 400m (1312ft). Reliable and easy to use even for untrained militia, the AK-47 became hugely popular worldwide.

SPECIFICATIONS	
Country of Origin:	USSR
Date:	1947
Calibre:	7.62mm (.3in) Soviet M1943
Operation:	Gas-operated
Weight:	4.3kg (9.48lb)
Overall Length:	880mm (34.65in)
Barrel Length:	415mm (16.34in)
Muzzle Velocity:	600m/sec (1969ft/sec)
Feed/Magazine:	30-round detachable box magazine
Range:	400m (1312ft)

Chinese Type 56

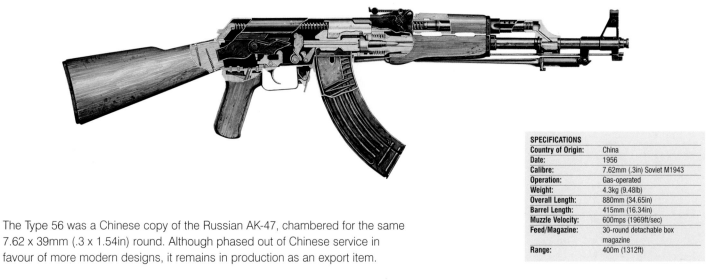

The Type 56 was a Chinese copy of the Russian AK-47, chambered for the same 7.62 x 39mm (.3 x 1.54in) round. Although phased out of Chinese service in favour of more modern designs, it remains in production as an export item.

SPECIFICATIONS	
Country of Origin:	China
Date:	1956
Calibre:	7.62mm (.3in) Soviet M1943
Operation:	Gas-operated
Weight:	4.3kg (9.48lb)
Overall Length:	880mm (34.65in)
Barrel Length:	415mm (16.34in)
Muzzle Velocity:	600mps (1969ft/sec)
Feed/Magazine:	30-round detachable box magazine
Range:	400m (1312ft)

TIMELINE   1947   1956   1972

Galil ARM

Based on the AK-47, the Galil was introduced to replace the FN FAL in Israeli service. The ARM was the standard model, with a short-barrel SAR (Short Assault Rifle) version also available.

SPECIFICATIONS	
Country of Origin:	Israel
Date:	1972
Calibre:	5.56mm (.219in) NATO
Operation:	Gas-operated, self-loading
Weight:	4.35kg (9.59lb)
Overall Length:	979mm (38.54in)
Barrel Length:	460mm (18.11in)
Muzzle Velocity:	990m/sec (3250ft/sec)
Feed/Magazine:	35- or 50-round box magazine
Range:	800m (2625ft) +

Valmet M76

A Finnish take on the AK-47 concept, the Valmet M76 was of generally higher quality than the AKM from which it was derived. A squad support version, designated M78, was also produced.

SPECIFICATIONS	
Country of Origin:	Finland
Date:	1976
Calibre:	7.62mm (.3in) Soviet M43, 5.56 (.219in)
Operation:	Gas-operated
Weight:	3.6kg (7.94lb)
Overall Length:	914mm (35.98in)
Barrel Length:	420mm (16.53in)
Muzzle Velocity:	720m/sec (2362ft/sec)
Feed/Magazine:	15-, 20- or 30-round detachable box magazine
Range:	500m (1640ft) +

Vektor R4

Derived from the Galil, the R4 was produced to arm the South African Defence Force. It included a built-in wire cutter and a bottle opener to prevent misuse of magazine lips for this purpose. Carbine versions were also manufactured.

SPECIFICATIONS	
Country of Origin:	South Africa
Date:	1982
Calibre:	5.56mm (.219in) M193
Operation:	Gas-operated
Weight:	4.3kg (9.48lb)
Overall Length:	1005mm (35.97in)
Barrel Length:	460mm (18.11in)
Muzzle Velocity:	980m/sec (3215ft/sec)
Feed/Magazine:	35- or 50-round detachable box magazine
Range:	500m (1640ft)

1976

1982

AKM: The World's Most Popular Assault Rifle

The AK-47 was modified several times during its early years of service, with many variants appearing. In 1959 the Soviet Army formally adopted a new model designated AKM (the M stood for *Modernizirovanniy*, or 'Modernized'), which incorporated many of these incremental modifications.

STOCK
The AKM was simply, indeed often crudely, made. It was intended to be put together in huge numbers to arm conscript armies.

SPECIFICATIONS	
Country of Origin:	USSR
Date:	1959
Calibre:	7.62mm (.3in) Soviet M1943
Operation:	Gas-operated
Weight:	4.3kg (9.48lb)
Overall Length:	880mm (34.65in)
Barrel Length:	415mm (16.34in)
Muzzle Velocity:	600m/sec (2350ft/sec)
Feed/Magazine:	30-round detachable box magazine
Range:	400m (1312ft)

Many weapons identified as AK-47s are in fact AKMs. The differences between the two are fairly small, though improvements over the original AK-47 include revised sights and a new trigger assembly. The AKM also uses a stamped rather than machined receiver.

ACTION
The Kalashnikov action is extremely robust and tolerant of the worst filth a soldier can manage to drop his rifle in.

BARREL
The interior of the barrel is chrome lined to resist the corrosive effects of propellant.

GAS PISTON
A long-stroke gas piston drives an action derived from Browning's work in the early twentieth century.

MAGAZINE
The design of AK-type magazines evolved over time, with an increased use of fluting to strengthen the thin metal walls.

The AKM was phased out of front-line service with the Russian Army in favour of the smaller-calibre AK-74. However, it was immensely popular on the export market, where its simple operation and rugged construction made it a favourite with conscript armies and militias worldwide. It remained in use with some Russian reserve and police units, and has attracted renewed interest in recent years as some militaries become less enthusiastic about small-calibre weapons.

Assault Rifle Lineage

Developing a good rifle is a difficult process. Some designers base their work on existing weapons; others go it alone. It is not always possible to determine a weapon's lineage just from its appearance.

Armalite AR-10

Although the innovative AR-10 lost out to the M14 in trials to become the US Army service weapon, it was the beginning of a line of weapons leading to the M16.

SPECIFICATIONS	
Country of Origin:	United States
Date:	1956
Calibre:	7.62mm (.3in) NATO
Operation:	Gas-operated, rotating bolt
Weight:	4.82kg (10.63lb)
Overall Length:	1029mm (40.5in)
Barrel Length:	508mm (20.0in)
Muzzle Velocity:	845m/sec (2772ft/sec)
Feed/Magazine:	20-round detachable box magazine
Range:	500m (1640ft) +

vz58

A Czech-designed weapon which outwardly resembled the AK-47, the vz58 used the same cartridge but was an entirely different design. Early models used a fixed plastic stock; later rifles had a folding metal stock.

SPECIFICATIONS	
Country of Origin:	Czechoslovakia
Date:	1958
Calibre:	7.62mm (.3in) Soviet M1943
Operation:	Gas-operated, falling breech-block
Weight:	2.91kg (6.42lb)
Overall Length:	845mm (33.3in)
Barrel Length:	390mm (15.4in)
Muzzle Velocity:	705m/sec (2313ft/sec)
Feed/Magazine:	30-round detachable box magazine
Range:	400m (1312ft)

TIMELINE   1956   1958   1966

Armalite AR-18

SPECIFICATIONS	
Country of Origin:	United States
Date:	1966
Calibre:	5.56mm (.219in) M109
Operation:	Gas-operated
Weight:	3.04kg (6.70lb)
Overall Length:	965mm (38in)
Barrel Length:	463mm (18.25in)
Muzzle Velocity:	990m/sec (2530ft/sec)
Feed/Magazine:	20-round detachable box magazine
Range:	500m (1640ft) +

Developed as a simplified version of the AR15 (M16 in US Army service), the AR-18 had significant internal differences. It was intended to appeal to armies needing cheap and simple weapons, but never achieved significant market success

Type 65

SPECIFICATIONS	
Country of Origin:	Taiwan
Date:	1976
Calibre:	5.56mm (.219in)
Operation:	Gas-operated
Weight:	3.31kg (7.29lb)
Overall Length:	990mm (38.9in)
Barrel Length:	508mm (20in)
Muzzle Velocity:	990m/sec (2530ft/sec)
Feed/Magazine:	Various STANAG magazines
Range:	500m (1640ft) +

Developed and manufactured in Taiwan, the Type 65 was based on the M16 but diverged from it during development. More recent models offer three-round burst fire in addition to full- or semi-automatic operation.

Fara 83

SPECIFICATIONS	
Country of Origin:	Argentina
Date:	1981
Calibre:	5.56mm (.219in) NATO
Operation:	Gas-operated, rotating bolt
Weight:	3.95kg (8.71lb)
Overall Length:	1000mm (39.4in) stock extended 745mm (29.3in) stock folded
Barrel Length:	452mm (17.8in)
Muzzle Velocity:	980m/sec (3215ft/sec)
Feed/Magazine:	30-round detachable box magazine
Range:	500m (1640ft) +

Developed in Argentina to replace the nation's licence-built FN FALs, the Fara 83 was a promising weapon based on the Galil. Relatively small numbers were built due to cuts in government funding for the project.

1976

1981

The M16 Family

The M16 was one of the most successful of all assault rifle designs. Futuristic-looking at the time of its introduction, it suffered from teething troubles but emerged as an effective and long-lived weapon system.

AR-15/M16

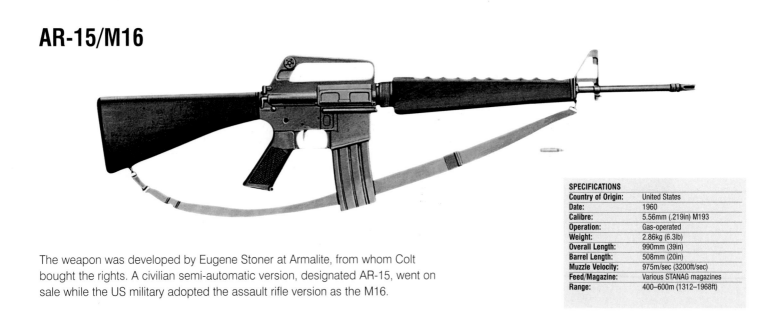

The weapon was developed by Eugene Stoner at Armalite, from whom Colt bought the rights. A civilian semi-automatic version, designated AR-15, went on sale while the US military adopted the assault rifle version as the M16.

SPECIFICATIONS	
Country of Origin:	United States
Date:	1960
Calibre:	5.56mm (.219in) M193
Operation:	Gas-operated
Weight:	2.86kg (6.3lb)
Overall Length:	990mm (39in)
Barrel Length:	508mm (20in)
Muzzle Velocity:	975m/sec (3200ft/sec)
Feed/Magazine:	Various STANAG magazines
Range:	400–600m (1312–1968ft)

M16A2

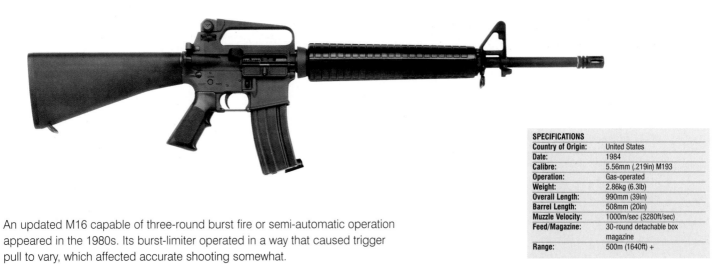

An updated M16 capable of three-round burst fire or semi-automatic operation appeared in the 1980s. Its burst-limiter operated in a way that caused trigger pull to vary, which affected accurate shooting somewhat.

SPECIFICATIONS	
Country of Origin:	United States
Date:	1984
Calibre:	5.56mm (.219in) M193
Operation:	Gas-operated
Weight:	2.86kg (6.3lb)
Overall Length:	990mm (39in)
Barrel Length:	508mm (20in)
Muzzle Velocity:	1000m/sec (3280ft/sec)
Feed/Magazine:	30-round detachable box magazine
Range:	500m (1640ft) +

TIMELINE

1960

1984

Diemaco C8

The C8 carbine is a Canadian 5.56mm (.219in) assault rifle based on the M16A2. Similar to the Colt M4, it has a shortened barrel and telescopic butt stock. The C8 is issued to Canadian special forces and armoured vehicle crews requiring a more compact weapon.

SPECIFICATIONS	
Country of Origin:	Canada
Date:	1994
Calibre:	5.56mm (.219in) NATO
Operation:	Gas-operated, rotating bolt
Weight:	3.3kg (7.3lb) unloaded
Overall Length:	1006mm (39.6in)
Barrel Length:	508mm (20in)
Muzzle Velocity:	900m/sec (3030ft/sec)
Feed/Magazine:	Various 30-round STANAG magazines
Range:	400m (1312ft)

Colt M4

A short, 'carbine' version of the M16 rifle, the M4 gradually replaced it in service. Capable of using the M203 under-barrel grenade launcher, the M4 offers all the M16's capabilities in a smaller package.

SPECIFICATIONS	
Country of Origin:	United States
Date:	1997
Calibre:	5.56mm (.219in) NATO
Operation:	Gas-operated
Weight:	2.88kg (6.36lb)
Overall Length:	838mm (33in)
Barrel Length:	368mm (14.5in)
Muzzle Velocity:	884m/sec (2900ft/sec)
Feed/Magazine:	30-round box magazine or other STANAG magazines
Range:	400m (1312ft)

Colt M4 Commando

The original 'Colt Commando' was a carbine version of the M16 produced by Colt. It was the progenitor of the M4 family, and today the 'Commando' name is applied to the shortest-barrel version of the M4.

SPECIFICATIONS	
Country of Origin:	United States
Date:	1997
Calibre:	5.56mm (.219in) NATO
Operation:	Gas-operated
Weight:	2.44kg (5.38lb)
Overall Length:	780mm (30.7in)
Barrel Length:	290mm (11.5in)
Muzzle Velocity:	796m/sec (2611ft/sec)
Feed/Magazine:	30-round box magazine
Range:	400m (1312ft)

1994   1997

M16A1

The M16 was rushed into service to replace the unsatisfactory M14, and not surprisingly fell short of the great things expected of it. Its main failing was its susceptibility to dirt, a problem compounded by the issue of weapons without cleaning kits to troops fighting in Vietnam. Not all of this was the fault of the weapon. Colt had promoted the M16 as a low-maintenance weapon when using their chosen ammunition. The US military issued different ammunition, which resulted in much greater fouling.

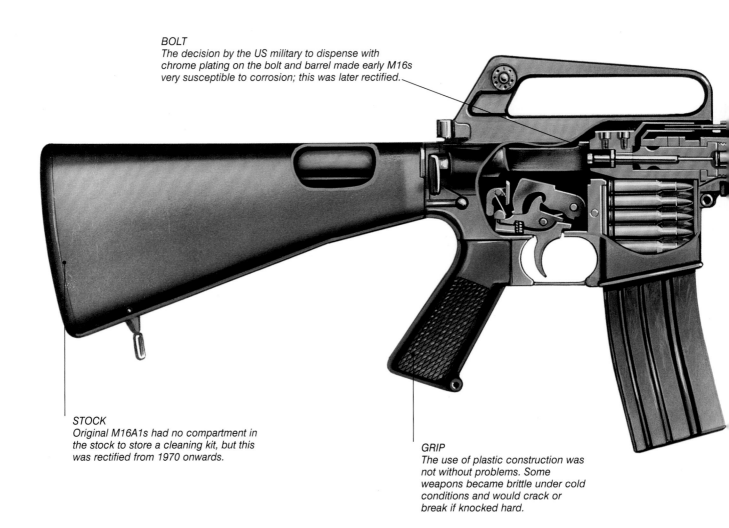

BOLT
The decision by the US military to dispense with chrome plating on the bolt and barrel made early M16s very susceptible to corrosion; this was later rectified.

STOCK
Original M16A1s had no compartment in the stock to store a cleaning kit, but this was rectified from 1970 onwards.

GRIP
The use of plastic construction was not without problems. Some weapons became brittle under cold conditions and would crack or break if knocked hard.

SPECIFICATIONS	
Country of Origin:	United States
Date:	1963
Calibre:	5.56mm (.219in) M193
Operation:	Gas-operated
Weight:	2.86kg (6.3lb)
Overall Length:	990mm (39in)
Barrel Length:	508mm (20in)
Muzzle Velocity:	1000m/sec (3280ft/sec)
Feed/Magazine:	30-round detachable box magazine
Range:	500m (1640ft) +

Despite having made a rather poor initial impression, the M16 turned out to be a serviceable weapon. The M16A1 eliminated some of its faults, including ammunition capacity: 30-round magazines became standard instead of the 20-round ones originally issued.

Although still not a truly great weapon, the M16A1 offered controllable automatic fire and permitted the user to carry far more ammunition than its predecessor. Developed versions continue to serve to this day.

BARREL
After a shaky start the M16 matured into an effective and accurate rifle capable of engaging targets out to 800m (2625ft) or beyond.

ACTION
The M16A1 was given a device named 'forward assist' to move the bolt in the event of a stoppage, improving the chances of quickly clearing a jammed weapon.

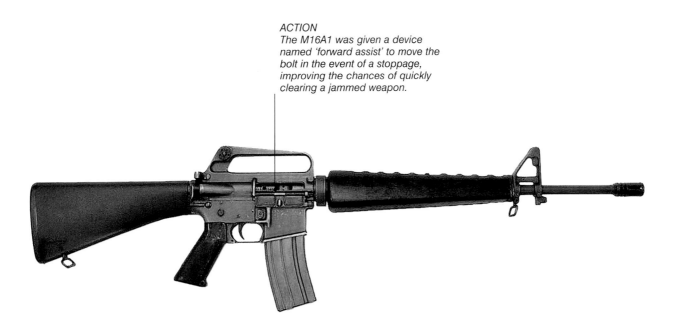

Assault Rifle Development

The move towards lightweight assault rifles seems almost inevitable; there are few armies today that do not use them. However, even a good design does not guarantee success in the marketplace, and improved, developed versions usually appear after a time.

AR 70/223

Seeking to standardize with the rest of NATO, Italy adopted the AR 70 as its service rifle. The initial design suffered from weaknesses in the receiver, which could lead to the bolt jamming. An upgraded AR 70/90 eliminated this flaw.

SPECIFICATIONS	
Country of Origin:	Italy
Date:	1972
Calibre:	5.56mm (.219in) NATO
Operation:	Gas-operated, self-loading
Weight:	3.8kg (8.37lb)
Overall Length:	995mm (39.1in)
Barrel Length:	450mm (17.7in)
Muzzle Velocity:	970m/sec (3182ft/sec)
Feed/Magazine:	30-round detachable box magazine
Range:	400m (1312ft)

SAR-80

Inspired by the M16, the SAR-80 was much cheaper to manufacture and, possibly, a superior weapon. It was capable of semi-automatic, full-automatic or burst fire and could launch rifle grenades without an adaptor.

SPECIFICATIONS	
Country of Origin:	Singapore
Date:	1976
Calibre:	5.56mm (.219in) NATO
Operation:	Gas-operated, self-loading
Weight:	3.17kg (7lb)
Overall Length:	970mm (38.18in)
Barrel Length:	459mm (18.07in)
Muzzle Velocity:	970m/sec (3182ft/sec)
Feed/Magazine:	30-round detachable box magazine
Range:	800m (2625ft) +

TIMELINE

1972

1976

1977

SIG SG540

A very reliable weapon, the SG540 could be adapted to other roles by changing its fittings. It was accurate enough to be a reasonable sniping weapon when fitted with a bipod and a telescopic sight.

SPECIFICATIONS	
Country of Origin:	Switzerland
Date:	1977
Calibre:	5.56mm (.219in) NATO
Operation:	Gas-operated, rotating bolt
Weight:	3.26kg (7.19lb)
Overall Length:	950mm (37in)
Barrel Length:	460mm (18in)
Muzzle Velocity:	980m/sec (3215ft/sec)
Feed/Magazine:	20- or 30-round detachable box magazine
Range:	800m (2625ft)

SR-88

Chartered Industries of Singapore (CIS) produced the SR-88 as an updated version of their SAR-80, which had performed disappointingly in the marketplace. It retained most of the features of the SAR-80.

SPECIFICATIONS	
Country of Origin:	Singapore
Date:	1984
Calibre:	5.56mm (.219in) NATO
Operation:	Gas-operated, rotating bolt
Weight:	3.68kg (8.11lb)
Overall Length:	960mm (37.7in)
Barrel Length:	460mm (18.1in)
Muzzle Velocity:	Not known
Feed/Magazine:	30-round detachable box magazine
Range:	800m (2625ft)

SR-88A

An improved SR-88, the SR-88A incorporated a number of changes including glass-fibre furniture and an aluminium lower receiver. A short-barrelled carbine variant was also introduced.

SPECIFICATIONS	
Country of Origin:	Singapore
Date:	1990
Calibre:	5.56mm (.219in) NATO
Operation:	Gas-operated, rotating bolt
Weight:	3.68kg (8.11lb)
Overall Length:	960mm (37.7in)
Barrel Length:	460mm (18.1in)
Muzzle Velocity:	Not known
Feed/Magazine:	30-round detachable box magazine
Range:	800m (2625ft)

The Heckler & Koch 33 Family

The Heckler & Koch HK33 is essentially a G3 rechambered for 5.56 x 45mm (.219 x 1.77in) ammunition, creating an assault rifle which was then used as the basis for a wide variety of models ranging from support weapons to sniper rifles.

Heckler & Koch G3

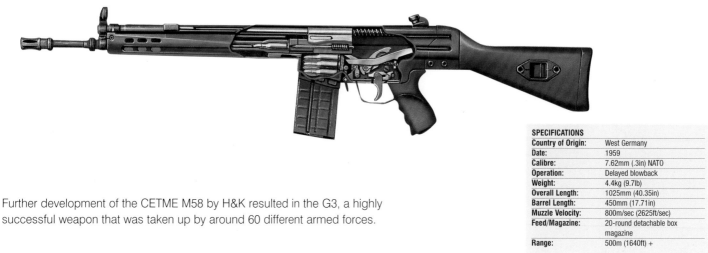

Further development of the CETME M58 by H&K resulted in the G3, a highly successful weapon that was taken up by around 60 different armed forces.

SPECIFICATIONS	
Country of Origin:	West Germany
Date:	1959
Calibre:	7.62mm (.3in) NATO
Operation:	Delayed blowback
Weight:	4.4kg (9.7lb)
Overall Length:	1025mm (40.35in)
Barrel Length:	450mm (17.71in)
Muzzle Velocity:	800m/sec (2625ft/sec)
Feed/Magazine:	20-round detachable box magazine
Range:	500m (1640ft) +

HK33

Heckler & Koch developed a family of small arms consisting of four types of firearms: the first chambered in 7.62mm (.3in) NATO, the second—using the Soviet 7.62mm (.3in) M43 round, the third—the intermediate 5.56mm (.219in) calibre and the fourth type—chambered for the 9mm (.354in) Parabellum pistol cartridge.

SPECIFICATIONS	
Country of Origin:	West Germany
Date:	1968
Calibre:	7.62mm (.3in) NATO
Operation:	Delayed blowback
Weight:	4.4kg (9.7lb)
Overall Length:	940mm (37.in)
Barrel Length:	332mm (13.1in)
Muzzle Velocity:	880m/sec (2887ft/sec)
Feed/Magazine:	20-round detachable box magazine
Range:	500m (1640ft) +

TIMELINE

1959

1968

HK33A2

SPECIFICATIONS	
Country of Origin:	West Germany
Date:	1968
Calibre:	5.56mm (.219in) NATO
Operation:	Roller-delayed blowback
Weight:	3.65kg (8.05lb)
Overall Length:	920mm (36.2in)
Barrel Length:	390mm (15.4in)
Muzzle Velocity:	950msec (3117ft/sec)
Feed/Magazine:	25-, 30-, or 40-round detachable box magazine
Range:	100–400m (328–1312ft)

The A2 model was a fairly standard 5.56mm (.219in) assault rifle with a fixed stock of synthetic material. It was capable of semi-automatic operation or full-automatic fire with a cyclic rate of 750rpm.

HK33A3

SPECIFICATIONS	
Country of Origin:	West Germany
Date:	1968
Calibre:	5.56mm (.219in) NATO
Operation:	Gas-operated
Weight:	3.98kg (8.8lb)
Overall Length:	940mm (37.in)
Barrel Length:	332mm (13.1in)
Muzzle Velocity:	880m/sec (2887ft/sec)
Feed/Magazine:	25-, 30-, 40-round detachable box magazine
Range:	100–400m (328–1312ft)

The A3 variant was given a folding metal stock and a shortened barrel to create a carbine version which otherwise was very similar to the standard assault rifle.

HK93

SPECIFICATIONS	
Country of Origin:	West Germany
Date:	1974
Calibre:	5.56mm (.219in) .223 Remington
Operation:	Roller-delayed blowback
Weight:	3.8kg (8.4lb)
Overall Length:	920mm (36.2in)
Barrel Length:	431mm (16.9in)
Muzzle Velocity:	880m/sec (2887ft/sec)
Feed/Magazine:	5-, 20-, 25-, 30-, 40-round double column, detachable box magazine
Range:	100–400m (328–1312ft)

The HK93 is a semi-automatic version of the HK33, intended for the civilian market. Its roller-locking system imparts a smoothness of operation uncommon in semi-automatic rifles, making it popular among target shooters.

1974

Heckler & Koch G41

Standardization of ammunition within the NATO alliance meant that weapons not chambered for 5.56 x 45mm (.219 x 1.77in) or 7.62 x 51mm (.3 x 2in) stood little chance in the marketplace. Some designs, built around a particular cartridge, fared badly and fell by the wayside. Others were readily adapted and were highly successful in their new calibre.

BOLT
The G41 uses the G3's roller-locking system and fires from a closed bolt, which improves accuracy.

STOCK
The folding stock allows the weapon to be used as a rifle-calibre submachine gun if desired, and makes movement in vehicles or urban terrain easier.

SPECIFICATIONS	
Country of Origin:	Germany
Date:	1987
Calibre:	5.56mm (.219in) NATO
Operation:	Roller-delayed blowback
Weight:	4.1kg (9.04lb)
Overall Length:	997mm (39.3in)
Barrel Length:	450mm (17.7in)
Muzzle Velocity:	920m/sec (3018ft/sec) SS109 cartridge; 950m/sec (3117ft/sec) M193 cartridge
Feed/Magazine:	Various STANAG magazines
Range:	100–400m (328–1312ft)

The H&K G41 uses a low-noise bolt and has a device to hold the bolt open when the magazine become empty, in much the same way that the slide of some semi-automatic pistols locks open to facilitate rapid reloading. As with many other H&K weapons, a range of variants has been marketed.

RECEIVER
the G41's modular construction allows it to
be configured as a range of variants and to
take a number of accessories including
grenade launchers and many different
types of optical and electronic sights.

MAGAZINE
The G41 was designed to take all
STANAG (NATO-standard)
magazines. These can be made to
almost any capacity, though those
used for military service usually hold
20 or 30 rounds of 5.56 x 45mm
(.219 x 1.77in) NATO ammunition.

BARREL
The barrel is equipped
with a flash suppressor
that is also designed to
launch rifle grenades.

Some weapons were specifically designed to use NATO standard
ammunition. Among them is the G41, essentially an improved G33.
Like many contemporary weapons, it was designed not merely to
take standard ammunition but to be able to use M16 magazines.
Standardisation of magazines greatly simplified the logistics
process and made arms procurement cheaper.

Bullpup Assault Rifles

The term 'bullpup' refers to a weapon that has its action located behind the trigger group. This allows the weapon as a whole to be made much shorter whilst retaining the same barrel length.

Enfield EM-2

Developed after World War II, the EM-2 was an innovative weapon using a short 7mm (.275in) round. It was well regarded and might have become the standard British service weapon but for the decision to standardize calibres throughout NATO.

SPECIFICATIONS	
Country of Origin:	United Kingdom
Date:	1951
Calibre:	7mm (.275in)
Operation:	Gas-operated
Weight:	3.41kg (7.52lb)
Overall Length:	889mm (35in)
Barrel Length:	623mm (24.5in)
Muzzle Velocity:	771m/sec (2530ft/sec)
Feed/Magazine:	20-round detachable box magazine
Range:	400m (1312ft) +

Steyr-Mannlicher AUG

Although flimsy-looking, the AUG is an extremely robust weapon. Twisting the handgrip allows the barrel to be quickly removed and replaced with a heavier or shorter one for the support or carbine role.

SPECIFICATIONS	
Country of Origin:	Austria
Date:	1978
Calibre:	5.56mm (.219in) M198 or NATO
Operation:	Gas-operated
Weight:	3.6kg (7.93lb)
Overall Length:	790mm (31.1in)
Barrel Length:	508mm (20in)
Muzzle Velocity:	970m/sec (3182ft/sec)
Feed/Magazine:	30- or 42-round detachable box magazine
Range:	500m (1640ft) +

TIMELINE

1951

1978

FAMAS F1

Known as Le Clarion ('The Trumpet'), the FAMAS is a very short weapon which nevertheless has a barrel only marginally shorter than a standard assault rifle. It is capable of burst fire as well as full- and semi-automatic operation.

SPECIFICATIONS	
Country of Origin:	France
Date:	1978
Calibre:	5.56mm (.219in)
Operation:	Gas-operated
Weight:	3.61kg (7.96lb)
Overall Length:	757mm (29.8in)
Barrel Length:	488mm (19.2in)
Muzzle Velocity:	960m/sec (3100ft/sec)
Feed/Magazine:	25-round box magazine
Range:	300m (984ft)

Norinco Type 86S

The Norinco Type 86S is an AKM-type bullpup rifle. It operates the same way as other AKM-type rifles with a few exceptions: the trigger-sear-hammer group is housed in a rear extension of the receiver, well behind the pistol grip. The Type 86S was once imported to the United States by China Sports, intended for the civilian market.

SPECIFICATIONS	
Country of Origin:	China
Date:	1980
Calibre:	7.62mm (.3in)
Operation:	Gas-operated
Weight:	3.59kg (7.91lb)
Overall Length:	667mm (26.25in)
Barrel Length:	438mm (17.2in)
Muzzle Velocity:	710m/sec (2429ft/sec)
Feed/Magazine:	30-round box magazine
Range:	300m (984ft)

L85A1 Carbine (L22)

A shortened version of the L85A1 intended to be used by vehicle crews, the L22 reduced the length of an already compact rifle. A short weapon is an asset when moving in and out of vehicles.

SPECIFICATIONS	
Country of Origin:	United Kingdom
Date:	1985
Calibre:	5.56mm (.219in) NATO
Operation:	Gas-operated
Weight:	3.71kg (8.1lb)
Overall Length:	709mm (27.9in)
Barrel Length:	442mm (17.4in)
Muzzle Velocity:	940m/sec (3084ft/sec)
Feed/Magazine:	30-round detachable box magazine
Range:	300m (984ft)

1980

1985

Enfield Individual Weapon L85A1 (SA 80)

Adopted to replace the L1A1 SLR, the L85A1 suffered from a number of serious defects at first. These included a tendency for the cocking handle to come off and magazines to fall out. Later versions were rather better.

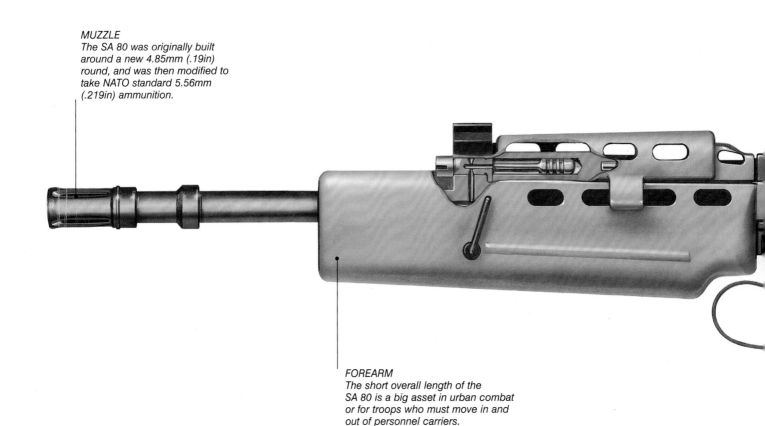

MUZZLE
The SA 80 was originally built around a new 4.85mm (.19in) round, and was then modified to take NATO standard 5.56mm (.219in) ammunition.

FOREARM
The short overall length of the SA 80 is a big asset in urban combat or for troops who must move in and out of personnel carriers.

SPECIFICATIONS	
Country of Origin:	United Kingdom
Date:	1985
Calibre:	5.56mm (.219in) NATO
Operation:	Gas-operated
Weight:	3.71kg (8.1lb)
Overall Length:	709mm (27.9in)
Barrel Length:	442mm (17.4in)
Muzzle Velocity:	940m/sec (3084ft/sec)
Feed/Magazine:	30-round detachable box magazine
Range:	500m (1640ft)

After years of damning reports cataloguing the weapon's failings, it was decided in 1997 to implement an upgrade programme. This was completed by 2002 and dealt with most of the SA 80's faults, though some personnel still found their weapons unsatisfactory in Afghanistan and Iraq.

The SA 80 shares its main drawback with other bullpup weapons: it cannot be fired left-handed. However, this is counterbalanced by its short, handy length and accuracy when used with the standard-issue 4X optical sight.

SCOPE
The 4X sight allows accurate fire out to 500m (1640ft) or so, and can be used for reconnaissance/surveillance purposes.

STOCK
The SA 80's mechanism is fairly typical of bullpup rifles, making use of the stock to house some of the moving parts.

The AK-74 Family

In the mid-1970s the Soviet Army switched over to using 5.45 x 39mm (.215 x 1.54in) ammunition and introduced a new rifle to fire it. The AK-74 was developed from the AKM and gave rise to a large number of variants and derivatives.

AK-74

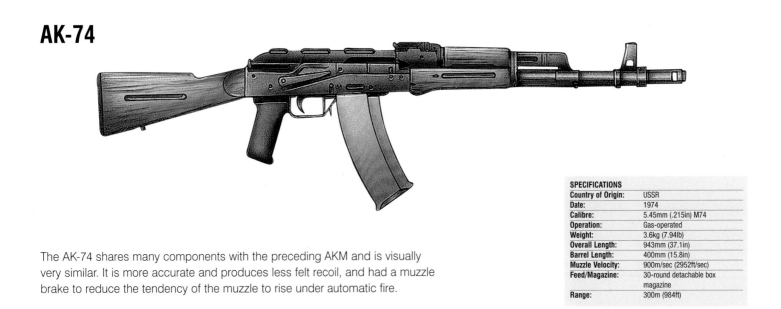

The AK-74 shares many components with the preceding AKM and is visually very similar. It is more accurate and produces less felt recoil, and had a muzzle brake to reduce the tendency of the muzzle to rise under automatic fire.

SPECIFICATIONS	
Country of Origin:	USSR
Date:	1974
Calibre:	5.45mm (.215in) M74
Operation:	Gas-operated
Weight:	3.6kg (7.94lb)
Overall Length:	943mm (37.1in)
Barrel Length:	400mm (15.8in)
Muzzle Velocity:	900m/sec (2952ft/sec)
Feed/Magazine:	30-round detachable box magazine
Range:	300m (984ft)

AKS-74

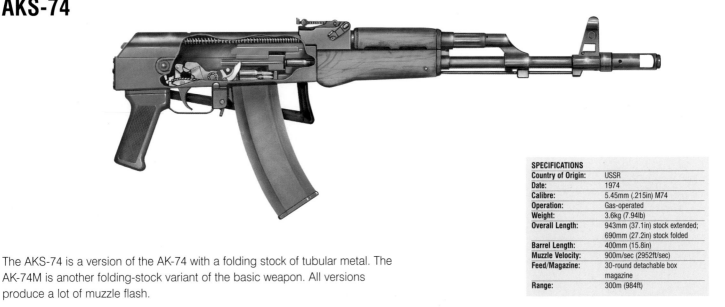

The AKS-74 is a version of the AK-74 with a folding stock of tubular metal. The AK-74M is another folding-stock variant of the basic weapon. All versions produce a lot of muzzle flash.

SPECIFICATIONS	
Country of Origin:	USSR
Date:	1974
Calibre:	5.45mm (.215in) M74
Operation:	Gas-operated
Weight:	3.6kg (7.94lb)
Overall Length:	943mm (37.1in) stock extended; 690mm (27.2in) stock folded
Barrel Length:	400mm (15.8in)
Muzzle Velocity:	900m/sec (2952ft/sec)
Feed/Magazine:	30-round detachable box magazine
Range:	300m (984ft)

TIMELINE

1974

RPK-74

The RPK-74 is a squad support version of the AK-74, with a longer and heavier barrel. It can use 45-round magazines or standard 30-round AK-74 magazines. Experiments with larger-capacity drums did not achieve much success.

SPECIFICATIONS	
Country of Origin:	USSR
Date:	1974
Calibre:	5.45mm (.215in)
Operation:	Gas-operated, air-cooled
Weight:	9kg (19.84lb)
Overall Length:	1160mm (45.67in)
Barrel Length:	658mm (25.9in)
Muzzle Velocity:	800m/sec (2600ft/sec)
Feed/Magazine:	30- or 45-round detachable box magazine
Range:	2000m (6560ft) + .

AKSU-74

The AKSU-74 is a smaller variant of the AK-74 intended for special forces and vehicle crews. Its small size and folding stock take it into submachine gun territory, though it retains a rifle-calibre capability.

SPECIFICATIONS	
Country of Origin:	USSR
Date:	1974
Calibre:	5.45mm (.215in) M74
Operation:	Gas-operated
Weight:	3.2kg (7lb)
Overall Length:	730mm (28in)
Barrel Length:	390mm (15.3in)
Muzzle Velocity:	900m/sec (2952ft/sec)
Feed/Magazine:	30-round detachable box magazine
Range:	600m (1968ft)

RPKS-74

A variant of the RPK-74 with a folding stock, the RPKS-74 was introduced for use by paratroops and other personnel likely to operate in confined spaces. It is otherwise unchanged from the standard weapon.

SPECIFICATIONS	
Country of Origin:	USSR
Date:	1974
Calibre:	5.45mm (.215in)
Operation:	Gas-operated
Weight:	4.6kg (10.1lb)
Overall Length:	1060mm (41.7in)
Barrel Length:	616mm (24.2in)
Muzzle Velocity:	800m/sec (2600ft/sec)
Feed/Magazine:	30-round detachable box magazine
Range:	800m (2625ft)

Bolt-Action Accuracy

Long after semi- and full-automatic rifles came to dominate the battlefield, most sniping weapons used bolt action. Many sniping rifles were based on obsolete service weapons; others were developed or simply redesignated from civilian designs.

M40A1

Adapted from the civilian Remington Model 700, the M40 used a Mauser-type action which was retained by the upgraded M40A1. The A1 used a stainless steel barrel and fibre-glass furniture rather than more traditional materials such as wood.

SPECIFICATIONS	
Country of Origin:	United States
Date:	1966
Calibre:	7.62mm (.3in) NATO
Operation:	Bolt action
Weight:	6.57kg (14.48lb)
Overall Length:	1117mm (43.98in)
Barrel Length:	610mm (24in)
Muzzle Velocity:	777m/sec (2550ft/sec)
Feed/Magazine:	5-round integral box magazine
Range:	800m (2625ft) +

FR-F1

Developed from the MAS 36, the FR-F1 was given a longer barrel with flash hider and a pistol grip. It used 7.5mm (.295in) ammunition, however, at a time when the rest of Europe was standardizing on 7.62 x 51mm (.3 x 2in).

SPECIFICATIONS	
Country of Origin:	France
Date:	1966
Calibre:	7.5mm (.295in)
Operation:	Bolt action
Weight:	5.2kg (11.46lb)
Overall Length:	1138mm (44.8in)
Barrel Length:	552mm (21.37in)
Muzzle Velocity:	852m/sec (2795ft/sec)
Feed/Magazine:	10-round integral box magazine
Range:	800m (2625ft)

TIMELINE

1966

RSAF L42A1

Long after bolt-action Lee-Enfields were phased out by the British Army, this 7.62 x 51mm (.3 x 2in) conversion of the Rifle No 4 continued to serve as a sniping weapon. The main difference was an improved barrel for greater long-range accuracy.

SPECIFICATIONS	
Country of Origin:	United Kingdom
Date:	1970
Calibre:	7.62mm (.3in) NATO
Operation:	Bolt action
Weight:	4.43kg (9.76lb)
Overall Length:	1181mm (46.5in)
Barrel Length:	699mm (27.5in)
Muzzle Velocity:	838m/sec (2750ft/sec)
Feed/Magazine:	10-round detachable box magazine
Range:	1000m (3280ft) +

Enfield Enforcer

The Enforcer was developed from the Enfield Envoy match rifle, which was in turn derived from the SMLE Rifle No 4. Intended for law enforcement use, it had a different stock and grip to the L42A1.

SPECIFICATIONS	
Country of Origin:	United Kingdom
Date:	1970
Calibre:	7.62mm (.3in) NATO
Operation:	Bolt action
Weight:	4.42kg (9.7lb)
Overall Length:	1180mm (46.4in)
Barrel Length:	700mm (27in)
Muzzle Velocity:	744m/sec (2441ft/sec)
Feed/Magazine:	10-round detachable box magazine
Range:	500m (1640ft)

Mauser SP66

The SP66 uses a variation on the proven Mauser action: a short-action bolt that allowed the user to continue aiming the weapon whilst reloading. A very fine weapon, it is also very expensive.

SPECIFICATIONS	
Country of Origin:	West Germany
Date:	1976
Calibre:	7.62mm (.3in) NATO
Operation:	Bolt action
Weight:	6.12kg (13.5lb) with telescopic sight
Overall Length:	1210mm (47.64in)
Barrel Length:	650mm (25.59in)
Muzzle Velocity:	868m/sec (2848ft/sec)
Feed/Magazine:	3-round integral box magazine
Range:	1000m (3280ft)

1970

1976

Bolt-Action Sniper Rifles

Bolt-action rifles are generally more accurate than semi-automatic weapons, largely due to the lack of moving internal parts as the round travels down the barrel. Rate of fire is not a problem for a well set up, precise shot.

Steyr SSG69

The SSG69 was developed to fulfil the need for a sniper weapon that was robust enough for use by mountain troops. It uses a rear-locking Mannlicher-type bolt rather than the more usual front-locking Mauser type.

SPECIFICATIONS	
Country of Origin:	Austria
Date:	1969
Calibre:	7.62mm (.3in) NATO
Operation:	Bolt action
Weight:	3.9kg (8.6lb)
Overall Length:	1140mm (44.8in)
Barrel Length:	650mm (25.6in)
Muzzle Velocity:	860m/sec (2820ft/sec)
Feed/Magazine:	5-round rotary or 10-round box magazine
Range:	1000m (3280ft)

FN 30-11 Sniping Rifle

Using a Mauser-type action, the FN 30-11 is a fairly conventional sniping weapon developed for the Belgian Army. It used the bipod and flash hider from the FN MAG-58 general purpose machine gun.

SPECIFICATIONS	
Country of Origin:	Belgium
Date:	1976
Calibre:	7.62mm (.3in) NATO
Operation:	Bolt action
Weight:	4.85kg (10.6lb)
Overall Length:	1117mm (43.9in)
Barrel Length:	502mm (19.7in)
Muzzle Velocity:	850m/sec (2789 ft/sec)
Feed/Magazine:	10-round internal box magazine
Range:	1000m (3280ft)

TIMELINE

1969

1976

1985

Beretta 501 Sniper

Entering production in 1985, this rifle was of conventional design in most ways, but featured a counterweight in the forestock to help counter barrel vibrations during firing. It served mainly with the Italian Army.

SPECIFICATIONS	
Country of Origin:	Italy
Date:	1985
Calibre:	7.62mm (.3in) NATO
Operation:	Bolt action
Weight:	5.55kg (12.23lb)
Overall Length:	1165mm (45.87in)
Barrel Length:	586mm (23.07in)
Muzzle Velocity:	840m/sec (2755ft/sec)
Feed/Magazine:	5-round detachable box magazine
Range:	1000m (3280ft) +

Parker-Hale Model 85

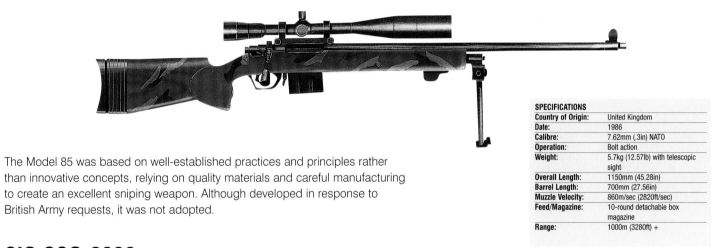

The Model 85 was based on well-established practices and principles rather than innovative concepts, relying on quality materials and careful manufacturing to create an excellent sniping weapon. Although developed in response to British Army requests, it was not adopted.

SPECIFICATIONS	
Country of Origin:	United Kingdom
Date:	1986
Calibre:	7.62mm (.3in) NATO
Operation:	Bolt action
Weight:	5.7kg (12.57lb) with telescopic sight
Overall Length:	1150mm (45.28in)
Barrel Length:	700mm (27.56in)
Muzzle Velocity:	860m/sec (2820ft/sec)
Feed/Magazine:	10-round detachable box magazine
Range:	1000m (3280ft) +

SIG SSG-2000

Developed from a civilian target rifle, the SSG-2000 entered production in 1989. Like many dedicated sniping weapons, it has no iron sights but can take a wide variety of telescopic sights.

SPECIFICATIONS	
Country of Origin:	Switzerland
Date:	1989
Calibre:	7.62mm (.3in) NATO
Operation:	Bolt action
Weight:	6.6kg (14.5lb)
Overall Length:	1210mm (47.6in)
Barrel Length:	610mm (24in)
Muzzle Velocity:	860m/sec (2820ft/sec)
Feed/Magazine:	4-round internal box magazine
Range:	1000m (3280ft)

1986

1989

Semi-Automatic Sniper Rifles

Although 'one shot, one kill' is a famous sniper creed, a semi-automatic weapon allows rapid engagement of several targets. It also enables the sniper to defend himself better if caught out of his element by conventionally armed hostiles.

Dragunov SVD

Although it resembles the AK series of assault rifles in many ways, the Dragunov SVD is a separate design. It is a very robust and reliable semi-automatic weapon, accurate out to well over a kilometre (3280ft), but it is not a sniper rifle as such. Instead, it is more equivalent to a 'designated marksman's rifle'.

SPECIFICATIONS	
Country of Origin:	USSR
Date:	1963
Calibre:	7.62mm (.3in) Soviet
Operation:	Gas-operated
Weight:	4.31kg (9.5lb)
Overall Length:	1225mm (48.2in)
Barrel Length:	610mm (24in)
Muzzle Velocity:	828m/sec (2720ft/sec)
Feed/Magazine:	10-round detachable box magazine
Range:	1000m (3280ft)

Galil Sniper

Based on the Galil assault rifle, the Galil Sniper was built for reliability and toughness first and foremost. While not as precise as some 'true' sniping weapons, the Galil can withstand considerable abuse and still shoot accurately.

SPECIFICATIONS	
Country of Origin:	Israel
Date:	1972
Calibre:	7.62mm (.3in) NATO
Operation:	Gas-operated, self-loading
Weight:	6.4kg (14.11lb)
Overall Length:	1115mm (43.89in)
Barrel Length:	508mm (20in)
Muzzle Velocity:	815m/sec (2675ft/sec)
Feed/Magazine:	20-round detachable box magazine
Range:	800m (2625ft) +

TIMELINE

1963

1972

Heckler & Koch PSG1

Developed (though extensively redesigned) from the G3 assault rifle, the PSG has a longer barrel with polygonal rifling. It has no iron sights but comes with a telescopic sight mounting as standard.

SPECIFICATIONS	
Country of Origin:	West Germany
Date:	1972
Calibre:	7.62mm (.3in) NATO
Operation:	Roller-locked delayed blowback
Weight:	8.1kg (17.86lb)
Overall Length:	1208mm (47.56in)
Barrel Length:	650mm (25.6in)
Muzzle Velocity:	815m/sec (2675ft/sec)
Feed/Magazine:	5- or 20-round detachable box magazine
Range:	600m (1968ft)

Mauser M86

The M86 is produced by Mauser as a less expensive alternative to the SP66 rifle. A conventional weapon, it uses a new bolt design based on Mauser's proven double front lug system. The intended buyers are mainly law enforcement agencies.

SPECIFICATIONS	
Country of Origin:	Germany
Date:	1990
Calibre:	7.62mm (.3in) NATO
Operation:	Bolt action
Weight:	5.9kg (13lb)
Overall Length:	1270mm (50in)
Barrel Length:	730mm (28.7in)
Muzzle Velocity:	Not known
Feed/Magazine:	9-round detachable box magazine
Range:	800m (2625ft) +

Heckler & Koch MSG90

Clearly of PSG1 lineage, the MSG90 is lighter and also cheaper to manufacture. Replacement of the trigger assembly allows the weapon to be converted to a fully automatic light support weapon.

SPECIFICATIONS	
Country of Origin:	Germany
Date:	1997
Calibre:	7.62mm (.3in) NATO
Operation:	Roller-delayed blowback
Weight:	6.4kg (14.1lb)
Overall Length:	1165mm (45.8in)
Barrel Length:	600mm (23.6in)
Muzzle Velocity:	815m/sec (2675ft/sec)
Feed/Magazine:	5- or 20-round detachable box magazine
Range:	600m (1968ft)

1990

1997

M21 Sniper Rifle

An 'accurized' version of the M14 rifle, the M21 continued to serve long after its parent weapon went out of use. One of its advantages is the ability to use a suppressor for near-silent shooting. The M21 has seen service from the Vietnam War right up to the present day, with snipers in the recent conflicts in Iraq and Afghanistan using the weapon.

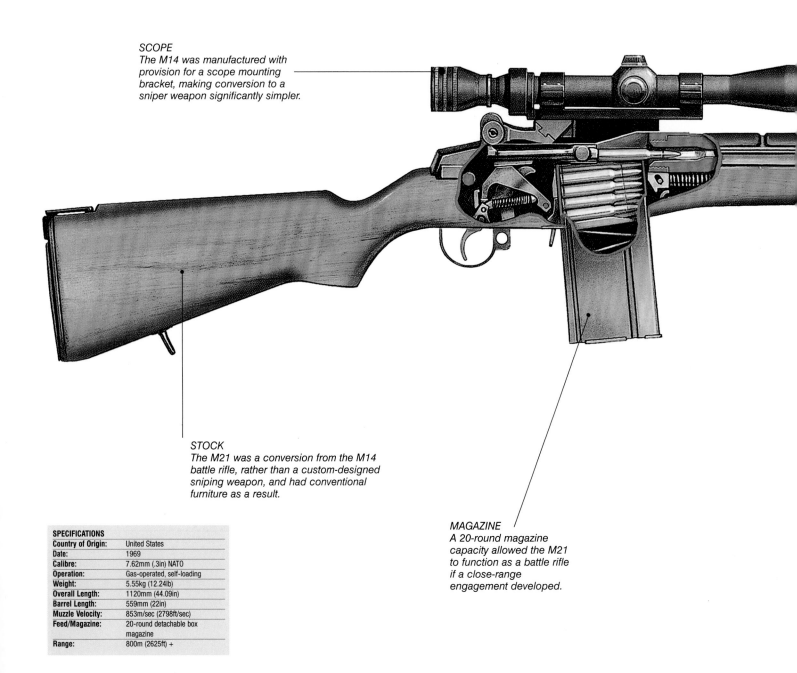

SCOPE
The M14 was manufactured with provision for a scope mounting bracket, making conversion to a sniper weapon significantly simpler.

STOCK
The M21 was a conversion from the M14 battle rifle, rather than a custom-designed sniping weapon, and had conventional furniture as a result.

MAGAZINE
A 20-round magazine capacity allowed the M21 to function as a battle rifle if a close-range engagement developed.

SPECIFICATIONS	
Country of Origin:	United States
Date:	1969
Calibre:	7.62mm (.3in) NATO
Operation:	Gas-operated, self-loading
Weight:	5.55kg (12.24lb)
Overall Length:	1120mm (44.09in)
Barrel Length:	559mm (22in)
Muzzle Velocity:	853m/sec (2798ft/sec)
Feed/Magazine:	20-round detachable box magazine
Range:	800m (2625ft) +

The M21 entered service in 1969 and served until 1988, and recently gained a new lease of life. The need to engage at longer ranges during operations in Afghanistan resulted in many M21s being reissued to front-line troops.

MUZZLE/FORESIGHT
The original foresight of the M14 was retained, though a telescopic sight was issued with the M21 as standard.

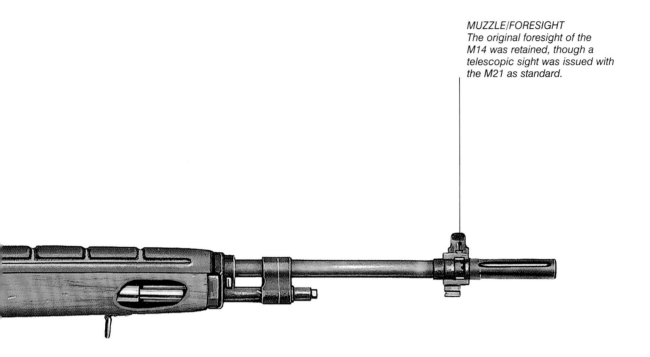

BARREL
The M21 retains the short-stroke gas-operation system first used in the M1 Garand, using propellant gas tapped off near the muzzle.

Walther WA2000

The WA2000 is one of the most accurate rifles ever made, but such precision does not come cheap. Its high cost suits this weapon to low-volume purchasers such as elite police sniper units, rather than to military users. It is better suited to law enforcement use than the rigours of life in the field with the army.

STOCK
The bullpup configuration allows the WA2000 to have a long barrel, necessary for accuracy, but a relatively short overall length.

SPECIFICATIONS	
Country of Origin:	West Germany
Date:	1982
Calibre:	7.62mm (.3in) .300 Winchester Magnum
Operation:	Gas-operated
Weight:	8.31kg (18.32lb)
Overall Length:	905mm (35.63in)
Barrel Length:	650mm (25.59in)
Muzzle Velocity:	c.800m/sec (2624ft/sec)
Feed/Magazine:	6-round detachable box magazine
Range:	1000m (3280ft) +

The WA2000 represented an innovative approach to sniper rifles and is an extremely well-made bullpup weapon. The barrel is clamped at front and rear but has no other contact with the rifle's furniture, and is fluted to reduce vibration.

The WA2000 uses a bullpup configuration and semi-automatic operation, both of which are highly unusual in a sniper weapon. Like other precision weapons, it has an adjustable stock and cheek-piece, and the trigger can be fine-tuned to the user's preferences.

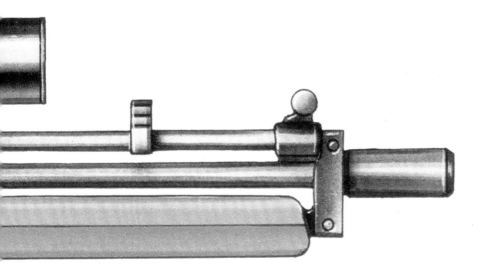

SCOPE
The WA2000 has no iron sights; it is intended to be used with a scope or not at all. It can mount a variety of sighting devices.

BARREL
The barrel is free-floating, i.e. it does not touch the forearm of the weapon. This allows the user to support the rifle without placing any tension on the barrel which could reduce accuracy.

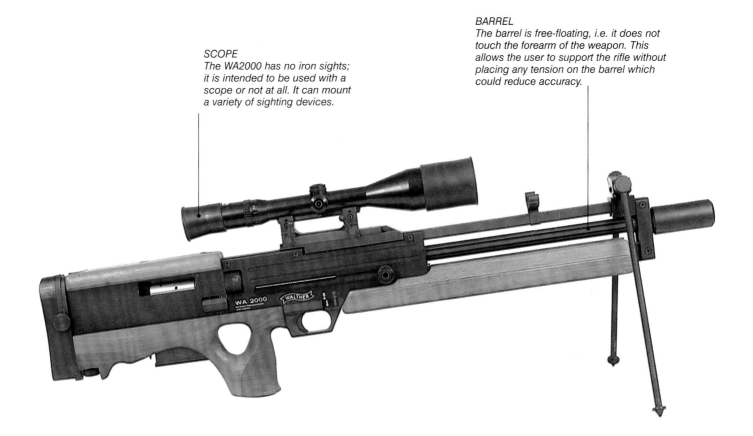

Centre Magazine Submachine Guns

Placing the magazine-well in the handgrip of a submachine gun is a logical choice. It makes 'hand-finds-hand' instinctive reloading possible and shortens the overall weapon. This configuration began to gain popularity after World War II.

CZ Model 25

The Model 25 was part of a series of weapons that began with the CZ 23, a post-war weapon which saw the first use of a telescoping bolt that wraps partially around the chamber when closed.

SPECIFICATIONS	
Country of Origin:	Czechoslovakia
Date:	1949
Calibre:	9mm (.35in) Parabellum, 7.62mm (.3in) Tokarev
Operation:	Blowback
Weight:	3kg (6.75lb)
Overall Length:	686mm (27in)
Barrel Length:	284mm (11.2in)
Muzzle Velocity:	395m/sec (1300ft/sec)
Feed/Magazine:	24-, 40- round (9mm/.35in), or 32-round (7.62mm/.3in) detachable box magazine
Range:	120m (394ft)

MAT 49

A post-war weapon that served well into the Cold War era, the MAT 49 was a rather basic but solid and dependable weapon. It saw extensive service during the conflicts in Indochina and Algeria.

SPECIFICATIONS	
Country of Origin:	France
Date:	1949
Calibre:	9mm (.35in) Parabellum
Operation:	Blowback
Weight:	3.5kg (7.72lb)
Overall Length:	720mm (28.35in)
Barrel Length:	228mm (8.98in)
Muzzle Velocity:	390m/sec (1280ft/sec)
Feed/Magazine:	20- or 32-round detachable box magazine
Range:	70m (230ft)

TIMELINE   1949   1970

Ingram M10

A compact and concealable submachine gun with a very high rate of fire, the M10 is normally chambered for 9mm (.35in) but is also available in 11.4mm/.45in .45 ACP. The M11 variant uses 9mm (.35in) Short (.380) ammunition and a Sionics suppressor.

SPECIFICATIONS	
Country of Origin:	United States
Date:	1970
Calibre:	11.4mm (.45in) .45 ACP, 9mm (.35in) Parabellum
Operation:	Blowback
Weight:	2.84kg (6.25lb)
Overall Length:	548mm (21.57in)
Barrel Length:	146mm (5.75in)
Muzzle Velocity:	366m/sec (1200ft/sec)
Feed/Magazine:	32-round detachable box magazine
Range:	70m (230ft)

FMK-3

Developed for the Argentine Army, the FMK entered production in 1974. It is a simple but reliable weapon and is surprisingly accurate even under full-automatic fire. One-handed shooting is less accurate but still controllable.

SPECIFICATIONS	
Country of Origin:	Argentina
Date:	1974
Calibre:	9mm (.35in) Parabellum
Operation:	Blowback, closed bolt
Weight:	3.4kg (7.49lb)
Overall Length:	693mm (27.2in)
Barrel Length:	290mm (11.4in)
Muzzle Velocity:	400m/sec (1312ft/sec)
Feed/Magazine:	25- 32- or 40-round detachable box magazine
Range:	100m (328ft)

BXP

The South African BXP was designed to be able to use a silencer or, curiously, a rifle grenade launcher. The folding stock creates a foregrip when it is not deployed.

SPECIFICATIONS	
Country of Origin:	South Africa
Date:	1988
Calibre:	9mm (.35in) Parabellum
Operation:	Blowback
Weight:	2.5kg (5.5lb)
Overall Length:	607mm (23.9in)
Barrel Length:	208mm (8.2in)
Muzzle Velocity:	370m/sec (1214ft/sec)
Feed/Magazine:	22- or 32-round detachable box magazine
Range:	80m (262ft) +

1974

1988

Cold War Submachine Guns

The Cold War era saw submachine gun design leap forward, with World War II-type weapons disappearing in favour of a range of innovative light automatic weapons designed to fulfil a particular need or tactical role.

Dux Model 59

SPECIFICATIONS	
Country of Origin:	West Germany/Spain
Date:	1959
Calibre:	9mm (.35in) Parabellum
Operation:	Blowback
Weight:	3.49kg (7.69lb)
Overall Length:	825mm (32.48in)
Barrel Length:	248mm (9.75in)
Muzzle Velocity:	390m/sec (1280ft/sec)
Feed/Magazine:	50-round detachable box magazine
Range:	70m (230ft)

The DUX Model 53 submachine gun had its roots in the Soviet Sudaev PPS-43 submachine gun. A few of these were tested by the West German border guard service and subsequently adopted. The Model 59 was a later development. DUX submachine guns are simple blowback-operated, full-automatic only weapons that fire from an open bolt.

vz61 Skorpion

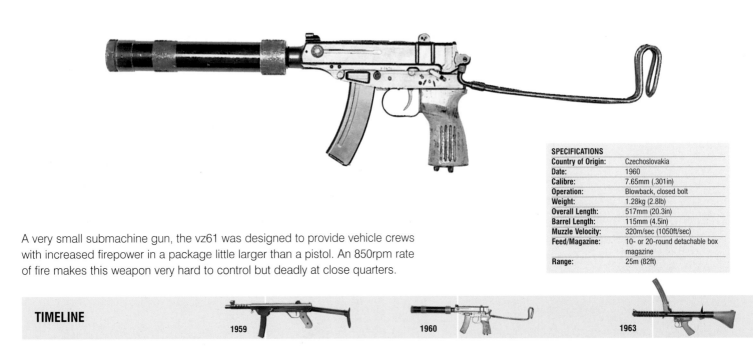

SPECIFICATIONS	
Country of Origin:	Czechoslovakia
Date:	1960
Calibre:	7.65mm (.301in)
Operation:	Blowback, closed bolt
Weight:	1.28kg (2.8lb)
Overall Length:	517mm (20.3in)
Barrel Length:	115mm (4.5in)
Muzzle Velocity:	320m/sec (1050ft/sec)
Feed/Magazine:	10- or 20-round detachable box magazine
Range:	25m (82ft)

A very small submachine gun, the vz61 was designed to provide vehicle crews with increased firepower in a package little larger than a pistol. An 850rpm rate of fire makes this weapon very hard to control but deadly at close quarters.

TIMELINE			
	1959	1960	1963

F1 SMG

The F1 was a Sterling-type submachine gun with a top-mounted magazine, a feature that suited its Australian users. It made its combat debut in Vietnam where it proved reliable and effective.

SPECIFICATIONS	
Country of Origin:	Australia
Date:	1963
Calibre:	9mm (.35in)
Operation:	Blowback
Weight:	3.26kg (7.1lb)
Overall Length:	715mm (28.1in)
Barrel Length:	203mm (8in)
Muzzle Velocity:	365m/sec (1200ft/sec)
Feed/Magazine:	34-round magazine
Range:	100–200m (328–656ft)

vz82 Skorpion

Adoption of the Russian 9 x 18mm (.35 x .71in) pistol cartridge by the Czech Army prompted development of this new version of the Skorpion. A 9.6mm/.38in (.380 ACP) variant was also produced for export.

SPECIFICATIONS	
Country of Origin:	Czechoslovakia
Date:	1982
Calibre:	9mm (.35in) Makarov
Operation:	Blowback, closed bolt
Weight:	1.28kg (2.8lb)
Overall Length:	517mm (20.3in)
Barrel Length:	115mm (4.5in)
Muzzle Velocity:	320m/sec (1050ft/sec)
Feed/Magazine:	10- or 20-round magazine
Range:	25m (82ft)

Steyr AUG Para

An adapted version of the AUG rifle, with a short barrel and chambered for 9mm (.35in) Parabellum, the AUG Para was, as its name suggests, intended for use by paratroops. This was one of the first assault-rifle-to-submachine-gun conversions.

SPECIFICATIONS	
Country of Origin:	Austria
Date:	1988
Calibre:	9mm (.35in) Parabellum
Operation:	Gas-operated, rotating bolt
Weight:	3.6kg (7.9lb)
Overall Length:	665mm (26.2in)
Barrel Length:	420mm (16.5in)
Muzzle Velocity:	970m/sec (3182ft/sec)
Feed/Magazine:	25- or 32-round detachable box magazine
Range:	300m (984ft)

1982

1988

The Influential Uzi

Designed by (and named for, against his wishes) Uziel Gal, the Uzi submachine gun may have been influenced by the CZ 25 series of weapons, but certainly surpassed them. It made popular the handgrip-magazine configuration and influenced SMG design for decades.

Uzi

The original Uzi design used a fixed wooden stock, but a folding metal one was soon found to be superior, especially in the Uzi's intended role as a weapon for vehicle crews and other non-infantry troops.

SPECIFICATIONS	
Country of Origin:	Israel
Date:	1953
Calibre:	9mm (.35in) Parabellum
Operation:	Blowback
Weight:	3.7kg (8.15lb)
Overall Length:	650mm (25.6in)
Barrel Length:	260mm (10.23in)
Muzzle Velocity:	400m/sec (1312ft/sec)
Feed/Magazine:	25- or 32-round detachable box magazine
Range:	120m (394ft)

Steyr MPi69

The MPi69 used an unusual trigger system: pulling halfway back fired a single shot, whilst full travel initiated automatic fire. The weapon's sling was attached to the cocking handle, with the user pulling on it to cock the weapon.

SPECIFICATIONS	
Country of Origin:	Austria
Date:	1969
Calibre:	9mm (.35in)
Operation:	Blowback
Weight:	3.13kg (6.9lb)
Overall Length:	670mm (26.3in)
Barrel Length:	260mm (10.2in)
Muzzle Velocity:	381m/sec (1250ft/sec)
Feed/Magazine:	25- or 32-round detachable box magazine
Range:	100–150m (328–492ft)

1953

1969

1971

Star Z70B

The Z70 initially used a two-part trigger. The top section was pulled for automatic fire and the bottom half for single shots. This proved to be unreliable, so was replaced with a more conventional system to create the Z70B.

SPECIFICATIONS	
Country of Origin:	Spain
Date:	1971
Calibre:	9mm (.35in) Parabellum
Operation:	Blowback
Weight:	2.87kg (6.33lb)
Overall Length:	700mm (27.56in)
Barrel Length:	200mm (7.87in)
Muzzle Velocity:	380m/sec (1247ft/sec)
Feed/Magazine:	20-, 30-, or 40-round detachable box magazine
Range:	50m (164ft) +

Mini-Uzi

The Mini-Uzi is exactly what it claims to be – a smaller version of the Uzi. Its shorter bolt results in an increased rate of fire, from 600rpm to 950rpm. An even smaller version, named the Micro-Uzi, appeared in 1986.

SPECIFICATIONS	
Country of Origin:	Israel
Date:	1980
Calibre:	9mm (.35in) Parabellum
Operation:	Blowback
Weight:	2.7kg (5.95lb)
Overall Length:	600mm (23.62in)
Barrel Length:	197mm (7.76in)
Muzzle Velocity:	352m/sec (1155ft/sec)
Feed/Magazine:	20-, 25- or 32-round detachable box magazine
Range:	50m (164ft)

Star Z84

Constructed of stamped metal and with few moving parts, the Z84 was a light but robust and reliable weapon. It was well balanced, making accurate one-handed fire a reasonably effective option.

SPECIFICATIONS	
Country of Origin:	Spain
Date:	1985
Calibre:	9mm (.35in)
Operation:	Blowback, open bolt
Weight:	3kg (6.61lb)
Overall Length:	615mm (24.2in)
Barrel Length:	215mm (8.4in)
Muzzle Velocity:	399m/sec (1312ft/sec)
Feed/Magazine:	25- or 30-round detachable box magazine
Range:	150–200m (492–656ft)

1980

1985

The Uzi

The main advantage of the Uzi is its relative shortness, which was somewhat wasted on early models by fitting a fixed stock to create an automatic carbine. With a folding stock the Uzi really came into its own as a lightweight, handy but reliable and accurate weapon.

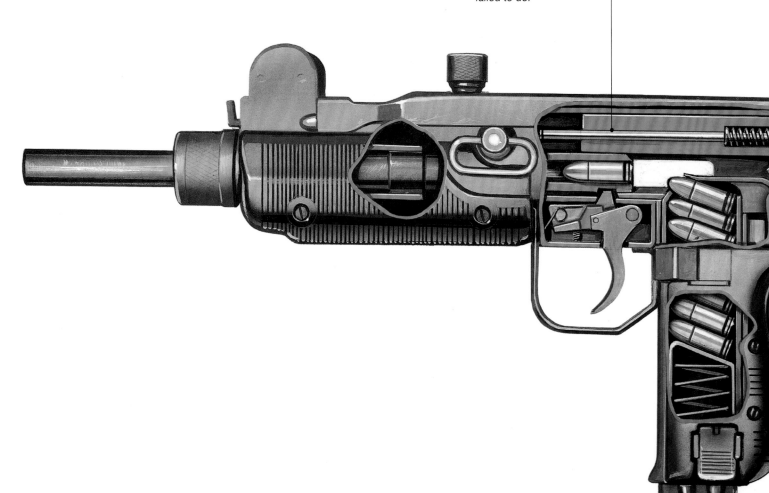

WRAPAROUND BOLT
The Uzi was not the first submachine gun to use a wraparound bolt, but its enormous success popularized the system in a way that previous weapons failed to do.

SPECIFICATIONS	
Country of Origin:	Israel
Date:	1953
Calibre:	9mm (.35in) Parabellum
Operation:	Blowback
Weight:	3.7kg (8.15lb)
Overall Length:	650mm (25.6in)
Barrel Length:	260mm (10.23in)
Muzzle Velocity:	400m/sec (1312ft/sec)
Feed/Magazine:	25- or 32-round detachable box magazine
Range:	120m (394ft)

The development of the Mini- and Micro-Uzi variants made the Uzi more concealable. Not all that much larger than a handgun, these versions offer far more firepower and, whilst too short-ranged for the battlefield, they are prized by VIP protection teams and other personnel who may need to carry a potent weapon discreetly.

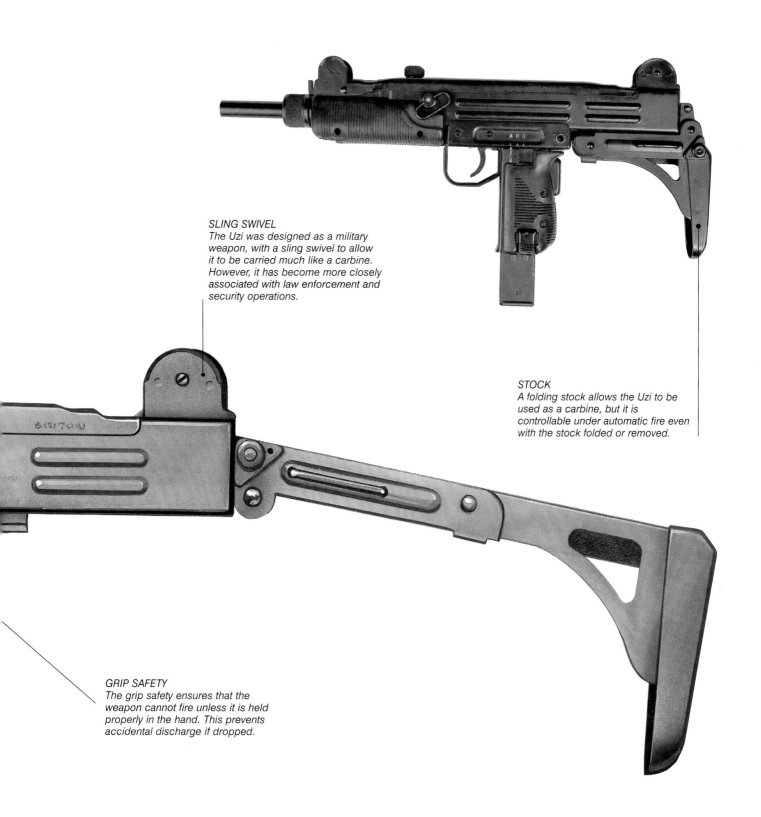

SLING SWIVEL
The Uzi was designed as a military weapon, with a sling swivel to allow it to be carried much like a carbine. However, it has become more closely associated with law enforcement and security operations.

STOCK
A folding stock allows the Uzi to be used as a carbine, but it is controllable under automatic fire even with the stock folded or removed.

GRIP SAFETY
The grip safety ensures that the weapon cannot fire unless it is held properly in the hand. This prevents accidental discharge if dropped.

The Uzi achieved its small size by the use of a 'wraparound' or 'telescoping' bolt, which overlaps the barrel. This allows the bolt to be heavy enough to keep the rate of fire to a manageable level, but short enough not to require a large weapon to contain it.

Heckler & Koch Submachine Guns

The H&K MP5 achieved enormous market success, with a huge range of specialist variants produced. All share the MP5's excellent quality and impressive accuracy, making these weapons a popular choice with law enforcement agencies.

HK MP5

Using the roller-delayed blowback system developed for the wartime MG42, the MP5 fires from a closed bolt, making it more accurate than most submachine guns. Later models have burst capability in addition to semi- and full-automatic fire.

SPECIFICATIONS	
Country of Origin:	West Germany
Date:	1966
Calibre:	9mm (.35in) Parabellum
Operation:	Roller-delayed blowback, closed bolt
Weight:	2.55kg (5.62lb)
Overall Length:	680mm (26.77in)
Barrel Length:	225mm (8.85in)
Muzzle Velocity:	400m/sec (1312ft/sec)
Feed/Magazine:	15- or 30-round detachable box magazine
Range:	70m (230ft)

HK MP5A2

With a fixed, solid plastic stock the MP5A2 can be considered to be the 'standard' MP5, if such a thing exists. Its plastic furniture is robust but lightweight, and well designed from an ergonomic point of view.

SPECIFICATIONS	
Country of Origin:	West Germany
Date:	1966
Calibre:	9mm (.35in) Parabellum
Operation:	Roller-delayed blowback, closed bolt
Weight:	2.55kg (5.62lb)
Overall Length:	680mm (26.77in)
Barrel Length:	225mm (8.85in)
Muzzle Velocity:	400m/sec (1312ft/sec)
Feed/Magazine:	15-, 30-, 32-round detachable box or 100-round Beta C-Mag drum magazine
Range:	200m (656ft)

TIMELINE

1966

HK MP5A3

The MP5A3 has a retractable metal stock, creating a very compact weapon for all-day carry by security personnel but retaining the ability to shoot accurately from the shoulder.

SPECIFICATIONS	
Country of Origin:	West Germany
Date:	1966
Calibre:	9mm (.35in) Parabellum
Operation:	Roller-delayed blowback, closed bolt
Weight:	3.08kg (6.8lb)
Overall Length:	700mm (27.6in) stock extended; 550mm (21.7in) stock retracted
Barrel Length:	225mm (8.9in)
Muzzle Velocity:	400m/sec (1312ft/sec)
Feed/Magazine:	15-, 30-, 32-round detachable box or 100-round Beta C-Mag drum magazine
Range:	200m (656ft)

HK MP5SD

The MP5SD is a suppressed version, and is available in configurations that mirror most of the other variants, i.e. folding stock, fixed stock, foregrip and so forth. Users include various special forces units.

SPECIFICATIONS	
Country of Origin:	West Germany
Date:	1970
Calibre:	9mm (.35in) Parabellum
Operation:	Roller-delayed blowback, closed bolt
Weight:	2.9kg (6.39lb)
Overall Length:	550mm (21.65in)
Barrel Length:	146mm (5.75in)
Muzzle Velocity:	285m/sec (935ft/sec)
Feed/Magazine:	15- or 30-round detachable box magazine
Range:	50m (164ft)

1970

Submachine Guns for VIP Protection

Submachine guns are a popular choice for security details. They are light and easy to carry yet offer very significant firepower. The ability to stop an assailant rapidly at short range is often more important than long-range accuracy.

Franchi LF-57

A blowback-operated, full-automatic-only weapon, the LF-57 was adopted by the Italian Navy. However, it sold in only limited numbers overseas, losing out to Beretta and H&K designs.

SPECIFICATIONS	
Country of Origin:	Italy
Date:	1956
Calibre:	9mm (.35in)
Operation:	Blowback
Weight:	3.17kg (6.9lb)
Overall Length:	686mm (27in)
Barrel Length:	200mm (7.8in)
Muzzle Velocity:	365m/sec (1200ft/sec)
Feed/Magazine:	20- or 40-round detachable box magazine
Range:	150–200m (492–656ft)

Walther MPK/MPL

These two high-quality submachine guns are identical but for their barrel lengths. The MPL is the long-barrel version; the MPK is the shorter variant. Various European police forces adopted these weapons during the 1960s.

SPECIFICATIONS	
Country of Origin:	West Germany
Date:	1963
Calibre:	9mm (.35in)
Operation:	Blowback
Weight:	3.kg (6.61lb) MPL; 2.83kg (6.23lb) MPK
Overall Length:	746mm (29.3in) MPL; 659mm (25.9in) MPK
Barrel Length:	260mm (10.2in) MPL; 173mm (6.8in) MPK
Muzzle Velocity:	395m/sec (1299ft/sec) MPL; 355m/sec (1167ft/sec) MPK
Feed/Magazine:	32-round detachable box magazine
Range:	200m (656ft) MPL; 100m (328ft) MPK

TIMELINE

 1956  1963  1975

HK53 KL

The HK53 is a smaller version of the HK33 rifle. Although it is chambered for 5.56mm (.219in) rifle ammunition, it can fulfil a submachine gun role and offers the additional advantages of better penetration and long-range accuracy.

SPECIFICATIONS	
Country of Origin:	Germany
Date:	1975
Calibre:	5.56mm (.219in) NATO
Operation:	Blowback
Weight:	2.54kg (5.6lb)
Overall Length:	680mm (26.8in)
Barrel Length:	225mm (8.85in)
Muzzle Velocity:	400m/sec (1312ft/sec)
Feed/Magazine:	25 or 30-round detachable box magazine
Range:	400m (1312ft)

Spectre

With a 50-round magazine and the ability to cock the weapon by pulling the trigger, the Spectre offers a rapid and effective response to a short-range threat. It has proved popular in the security market.

SPECIFICATIONS	
Country of Origin:	Italy
Date:	1983
Calibre:	9mm (.35in) Parabellum
Operation:	Blowback
Weight:	2.9kg (6.39lb)
Overall Length:	580mm (22.83in)
Barrel Length:	130mm (5.12in)
Muzzle Velocity:	400m/sec (1312ft/sec)
Feed/Magazine:	30- or 50-round detachable box magazine
Range:	50m (164ft)

Jatimatic

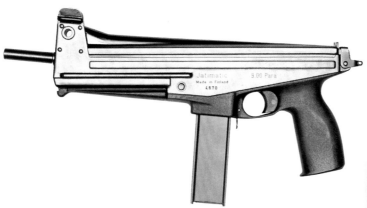

The Jatimatic's curious appearance comes from the fact that the bolt recoils slightly upwards, allowing the handgrip to be set higher. This helps counteract muzzle climb. Originally marketed in the 1980s, it reappeared in 1993.

SPECIFICATIONS	
Country of Origin:	Finland
Date:	1984
Calibre:	9mm (.35in)
Operation:	Straight blowback
Weight:	1.65kg (3.63lb)
Overall Length:	400mm (15.7in)
Barrel Length:	203mm (8in)
Muzzle Velocity:	360m/sec (1181ft/sec)
Feed/Magazine:	20- or 40-round magazine
Range:	100m (328ft)

1983

1984

Light Support Weapons

Many of the light support weapons that appeared in the Cold War era were based on assault rifle concepts, or were purposely designed to complement them, sharing components as well as ammunition.

Stoner M63 Light Machine Gun

Part of Eugene Stoner's weapon system, the M63 LMG configuration used a 150-round belt held in a box under the weapon. This enabled the LMG to be used as a high-firepower assault weapon.

SPECIFICATIONS	
Country of Origin:	United States
Date:	1963
Calibre:	5.56mm (.219in)
Operation:	Gas-operated, air-cooled
Weight:	5.3kg (11.68lb)
Overall Length:	1022mm (40.25in) standard barrel
Barrel Length:	508mm (20in) standard 399mm (15.7in) short
Muzzle Velocity:	1000m/sec (3280ft/sec)
Feed/Magazine:	150-round disintegrating-link boxed belt or a detachable box magazine
Range:	1000m (3280ft)

Steyr AUG/HB

Fitting a heavy barrel and bipod to the AUG assault rifle converts it into a light support weapon which can be modified to fire from an open bolt. This aids cooling at the price of reduced accuracy.

SPECIFICATIONS	
Country of Origin:	Austria
Date:	1980
Calibre:	9mm (.35in) Parabellum, 5.56mm (.219in) NATO
Operation:	Gas-operated, rotating bolt
Weight:	3.6kg (7.9lb)
Overall Length:	790mm (31.1in)
Barrel Length:	508mm (20in)
Muzzle Velocity:	970m/sec (3182ft/sec)
Feed/Magazine:	25-, 32-round (9mm/.35in) or 30-, 42-round (5.56mm/.219in) detachable box magazine
Range:	2700m (8858ft)

TIMELINE

 1963

 1980

 1982

CETME AMELI

Although it resembles the MG42, the AMELI uses a blowback mechanism derived from the CETME rifle. It is a very lightweight and compact weapon capable of being set to fire at 1200rpm or 850rpm.

SPECIFICATIONS	
Country of Origin:	Spain
Date:	1982
Calibre:	5.56mm (.219in) NATO
Operation:	Gas operated, air-cooled
Weight:	6.35kg (14lb) standard; 5.2kg (11.46lb) lightweight
Overall Length:	970mm (38.19in)
Barrel Length:	400mm (15.75in)
Muzzle Velocity:	875m/sec (2870ft/sec)
Feed/Magazine:	100- or 200-round boxed belt
Range:	1000m (3280ft) +

Light Support Weapon L86A1

The LSW is essentially an L85A1 rifle with a longer, heavier barrel and bipod. It also has a rear grip for sustained fire, but lacking a quick-change barrel and with limited ammunition, its capability in this area is limited.

SPECIFICATIONS	
Country of Origin:	United Kingdom
Date:	1985
Calibre:	5.56mm (.219in) NATO
Operation:	Gas-operated, air-cooled
Weight:	5.4kg (11.9lb)
Overall Length:	900mm (35.43in)
Barrel Length:	646mm (25.43in)
Muzzle Velocity:	970m/sec (3182ft/sec)
Feed/Magazine:	30-round detachable box magazine
Range:	1000m (3280ft)

Negev

The Israeli Negev LMG was designed from the outset as a multipurpose weapon. It can launch rifle grenades and, with a short barrel and the bipod removed, can be used as a high-capacity assault rifle.

SPECIFICATIONS	
Country of Origin:	Israel
Date:	1988
Calibre:	5.56mm (.219in) NATO
Operation:	Gas-operated, rotating bolt
Weight:	7.4kg (16.3lb)
Overall Length:	1020mm (40.2in)
Barrel Length:	460mm (18.1in)
Muzzle Velocity:	915m/sec (3002ft/sec)
Feed/Magazine:	150-round M27 ammunition belt or 35-round box magazine
Range:	300–1000m (984–3280ft)

1985

1988

Heckler & Koch Support Weapons

Within this family of weapons, the first digit of the designation is the weapon type (1 for magazine-fed, 2 for belt-fed); the second indicates calibre (1 is 7.62 x 51mm/.3 x 2in, 2 is 7.62 x 39mm/.3 x 1.54in, 3 is 5.56 x 45mm/.219 x 1.77in).

HK21

Beginning with the belt-fed 7.62mm (.3in) HK21, H&K created a family of support weapons using a common receiver and interchangeable parts. It was adopted for police service in Germany, under the designation G8.

SPECIFICATIONS	
Country of Origin:	West Germany
Date:	1970
Calibre:	7.62mm (.3in) NATO
Operation:	Delayed blowback
Weight:	7.92kg (17.46lb)
Overall Length:	1021mm (40.2in)
Barrel Length:	450mm (17.72in)
Muzzle Velocity:	800m/sec (2625ft/sec)
Feed/Magazine:	Belt-fed
Range:	2000m (6560ft)

HK11

The HK11 is a magazine-fed version of the HK21. It normally uses a 30-round magazine but can take a 20-round G3 magazine. An 'assault' foregrip is available and fits all members of the weapon family.

SPECIFICATIONS	
Country of Origin:	West Germany
Date:	1970
Calibre:	7.62mm (.3in) NATO
Operation:	Delayed blowback, selective fire
Weight:	8.15kg (17.97lb)
Overall Length:	1030mm (40.55in)
Barrel Length:	450mm (17.72in)
Muzzle Velocity:	800m/sec (2625ft/sec)
Feed/Magazine:	20-round detachable box or 80-round drum magazine
Range:	1000m (3280ft) +

TIMELINE

1970   1981

HK13

Essentially the same weapon as the HK11, the HK13 is chambered for 5.56 x 45mm (.219 x 1.77in) ammunition. H&K manufactured very few weapons in 7.62 x 39mm (.3 x 1.54in) but theoretically this weapon can be converted to that calibre, making it an HK12.

SPECIFICATIONS	
Country of Origin:	West Germany
Date:	1972
Calibre:	5.56mm (.219in) NATO
Operation:	Roller-locked delayed blowback, air-cooled
Weight:	8kg (17.64lb)
Overall Length:	1030mm (40.55in)
Barrel Length:	450mm (17.72in)
Muzzle Velocity:	925m/sec (3035ft/sec)
Feed/Magazine:	20- or 30-round detachable box magazine or belt fed
Range:	1000m (3280ft) +

HK21E

The basic HK21 was developed through the 21A1 and, later, the 21E models. The '21E' designation stands for 'export'. By changing the barrel, the weapon can be converted to 7.62 x 39mm/.3 x 1.54in (HK22) or 5.56 x 45mm/.219 x 1.77in (HK23).

SPECIFICATIONS	
Country of Origin:	West Germany
Date:	1981
Calibre:	7.62mm (.3in) NATO
Operation:	Gas-operated, air-cooled
Weight:	9.3kg (20.5lb)
Overall Length:	1140mm (44.88in)
Barrel Length:	560mm (22.04in)
Muzzle Velocity:	840m/sec (2755ft/sec)
Feed/Magazine:	Belt-fed
Range:	1000m (3280ft) +

HK23

When a member of this weapon family is converted to a different feed system or calibre, its designation should change, but this practice is not always followed. Thus an HK23 converted to magazine feed might still retain its original designation.

SPECIFICATIONS	
Country of Origin:	West Germany
Date:	1981
Calibre:	5.56mm (.219in) NATO
Operation:	Delayed blowback
Weight:	8.7kg (19.18lb) on bipod
Overall Length:	1030mm (40.5in)
Barrel Length:	450mm (17.71in)
Muzzle Velocity:	925m/sec (3035ft/sec)
Feed/Magazine:	20- or 30-round box magazine, 100-round drum magazine or 50- or 100-round belt
Range:	1000m (3280ft) +

1981

Squad Automatic Weapons

Most modern armies build their infantry formations around a group of riflemen and a support weapon. Some make the automatic weapon the focus of the unit; others focus on the rifles and treat the automatic weapon as a support system.

Valmet M78

A heavy-barrelled, light-support version of the Valmet M76 rifle using a heavier receiver, the M78 was normally chambered for 7.62 x 39mm (.3 x 1.54in) but was also offered in 7.62mm (.3in) and 5.56mm (.219in) NATO calibres.

SPECIFICATIONS	
Country of Origin:	Finland
Date:	1976
Calibre:	7.62mm (.3in) NATO, 5.56mm (.219in) NATO
Operation:	Gas-operated, rotating bolt
Weight:	4.76kg (10.5lb)
Overall Length:	1095mm (43.125in)
Barrel Length:	612mm (24.125in)
Muzzle Velocity:	718m/sec (2355ft/sec)
Feed/Magazine:	30-round detachable box magazine
Cyclic Rate:	650rpm
Range:	800m (2625ft)

FN Minimi

The FN Minimi is chambered for 5.56 x 45mm (.219 x 1.77in) assault rifle ammunition and can use a standard M16 magazine instead of its more normal belt feed. A short barrel/telescoping stock version is also available for special-forces applications.

SPECIFICATIONS	
Country of Origin:	Belgium
Date:	1982
Calibre:	5.56mm (.219in) NATO
Operation:	Gas-operated, air-cooled
Weight:	6.83kg (15.05lb)
Overall Length:	1040mm (40.56in)
Barrel Length:	466mm (18.34in)
Muzzle Velocity:	915m/sec (3000ft/sec)
Feed/Magazine:	30-round STANAG magazine or 100-round belt
Cyclic Rate:	750–1100rpm
Range:	2000m (6560ft) +

TIMELINE

1976

FN Minimi (tripod)

Although it is normally used for mobile fire support of a rifle squad, the Minimi can function in the sustained-fire support role using a tripod. It has proven itself extremely reliable under combat conditions.

SPECIFICATIONS	
Country of Origin:	Belgium
Date:	1982
Calibre:	5.56mm (.219in) NATO
Operation:	Gas-operated, air-cooled
Weight:	6.83kg (15.05lb)
Overall Length:	1040mm (40.56lb)
Barrel Length:	466mm (18.34in)
Muzzle Velocity:	915m/sec (3000ft/sec)
Feed/Magazine:	30-round STANAG magazine or 100-round belt
Cyclic Rate:	750–1100rpm
Range:	2000m (6560ft) +

M249

The M249 Squad Automatic Weapon (SAW) is a slightly modified FN Minimi. It has a perforated steel heat shield above the barrel which helps prevent optical distortion caused by heated air rising from the barrel.

SPECIFICATIONS	
Country of Origin:	United States
Date:	1982
Calibre:	5.56mm (.219in)
Operation:	Gas-operated, open bolt
Weight:	7.5kg (17lb)
Overall Length:	1041mm (41in)
Barrel Length:	521mm (21in)
Muzzle Velocity:	915m/sec (3000ft/sec)
Feed/Magazine:	30-round STANAG magazine or 200-round belt
Cyclic Rate:	750–1000rpm
Range:	910m (2985ft)

CIS Ultimax

The Ultimax achieved modest success in the marketplace and might have done much better had it emerged before the FN Minimi, but instead it was launched into a market niche that was already filled by an excellent weapon.

SPECIFICATIONS	
Country of Origin:	Singapore
Date:	1982
Calibre:	5.56mm (.219in) NATO
Operation:	Gas-operated, rotating bolt
Weight:	4.9kg (10.80lb)
Overall Length:	1024mm (40.3in)
Barrel Length:	330mm (13in)
Muzzle Velocity:	970m/sec (3182ft/sec)
Feed/Magazine:	30-round STANAG box magazine or 100-round drum
Cyclic Rate:	400–600rpm
Range:	460–1300m (1509–4265ft) depending on cartridge

  1982

General-Purpose Machine Guns

General-purpose machine guns (GPMGs) are chambered for a more powerful cartridge than light machine guns. Usually this is a 'battle rifle' calibre which is also used by sniper weapons and is a holdover from a previous generation of larger-calibre infantry rifles.

FN MAG/L7A1

One of the finest machine guns of all time, the FN MAG was taken into British service as the L7A1, and under other designations with over 80 other forces. Its gas regulator allows the rate of fire to be quickly adjusted.

SPECIFICATIONS	
Country of Origin:	Belgium
Date:	1955
Calibre:	7.62mm (.3in) NATO
Operation:	Gas-operated, air-cooled
Weight:	10.15kg (22.25lb)
Overall Length:	1250mm (49.2in)
Barrel Length:	546mm (21.5in)
Muzzle Velocity:	853m/sec (2800ft/sec)
Feed/Magazine:	Belt-fed
Cyclic Rate:	600–1000rpm
Range:	3000m (9842ft)

M60

The M60 incorporated some good ideas, such as a Stellite lining on the barrel which allowed firing even when white hot, but overall it was a mediocre design with an awkward barrel change and a tendency to jam.

SPECIFICATIONS	
Country of Origin:	United States
Date:	1960
Calibre:	7.62mm (.3in) NATO
Operation:	Gas-operated, air-cooled
Weight:	10.4kg (23lb)
Overall Length:	1110mm (43.75in)
Barrel Length:	560mm (22.05in)
Muzzle Velocity:	855m/sec (2805ft/sec)
Feed/Magazine:	Belt-fed
Cyclic Rate:	600rpm
Range:	3000m (9842ft) +

TIMELINE   1955   1960   1966

Maschinengewehr 3 (MG3)

Derived from the wartime MG42, the MG3 is a slightly modified version chambered for 7.62mm (.3in) NATO ammunition. It retains the MG42's high rate of fire, but this can be reduced by using a heavier bolt if desired.

SPECIFICATIONS	
Country of Origin:	West Germany
Date:	1966
Calibre:	7.62mm (.3in) NATO
Operation:	Short recoil, air-cooled
Weight:	11.5kg (25.35lb)
Overall Length:	1220mm (48in)
Barrel Length:	531mm (20.9in)
Muzzle Velocity:	820m/sec (2690ft/sec)
Feed/Magazine:	50- or 100-round belt (50-round belt may be contained in drum)
Cyclic Rate:	950–1300rpm depending on bolt
Range:	3000m (9842ft) +

M240

The M240 is essentially an FN MAG. It was originally adopted by US forces as a vehicular armament, but gradually supplanted the M60 as an infantry support weapon.

SPECIFICATIONS	
Country of Origin:	Belgium
Date:	1977
Calibre:	7.62mm (.3in) NATO
Operation:	Gas-operated, open bolt
Weight:	11.79kg (26lb)
Overall Length:	1263mm (49.7in)
Barrel Length:	630mm (24.8in)
Muzzle Velocity:	853m/sec (2800ft/sec)
Feed/Magazine:	Belt-fed
Cyclic Rate:	650–1000rpm
Range:	800m (2625ft)

M60E3

Many variants of the M60 appeared during its career. The M60E3 was a redesigned model which was lighter and more user-friendly. It marked a real improvement but still retained some of the weaknesses of the original design.

SPECIFICATIONS	
Country of Origin:	United States
Date:	1994
Calibre:	7.62mm (.3in) NATO
Operation:	Gas-operated, air-cooled
Weight:	8.61kg (18.98lb)
Overall Length:	1067mm (42in)
Barrel Length:	560mm (22.04in)
Muzzle Velocity:	860m/sec (2821ft/sec)
Feed/Magazine:	Belt-fed
Cyclic Rate:	550rpm
Range:	1100m (3609ft) +

1977   1994

FN MAG 58

As the name suggests, a GPMG must be able to operate in a variety of roles at least passably well. It is not a precision weapon nor a one-trick pony; its task is to deliver automatic fire support wherever and however it is needed – be that as infantry support, from a mount on a vehicle or in the light anti-aircraft role.

GAS PISTON
The MAG 58 uses a long-stroke gas-operated piston to drive its action, a well-proven system.

SPECIFICATIONS	
Country of Origin:	Belgium
Date:	1955
Calibre:	7.62mm (.3in) NATO
Operation:	Gas-operated, air-cooled
Weight:	10.15kg (22.25lb)
Overall Length:	1250mm (49.2in)
Barrel Length:	546mm (21.5in)
Muzzle Velocity:	853m/sec (2800ft/sec)
Feed/Magazine:	Belt-fed
Cyclic Rate:	600–1000rpm
Range:	3000m (9842ft)

A good GPMG must be capable of sustained fire, which requires the ability to dissipate heat and to change a hot barrel efficiently under combat conditions. At the same time it must not be so heavy that the crew cannot keep up with the riflemen they are supposed to be supporting.

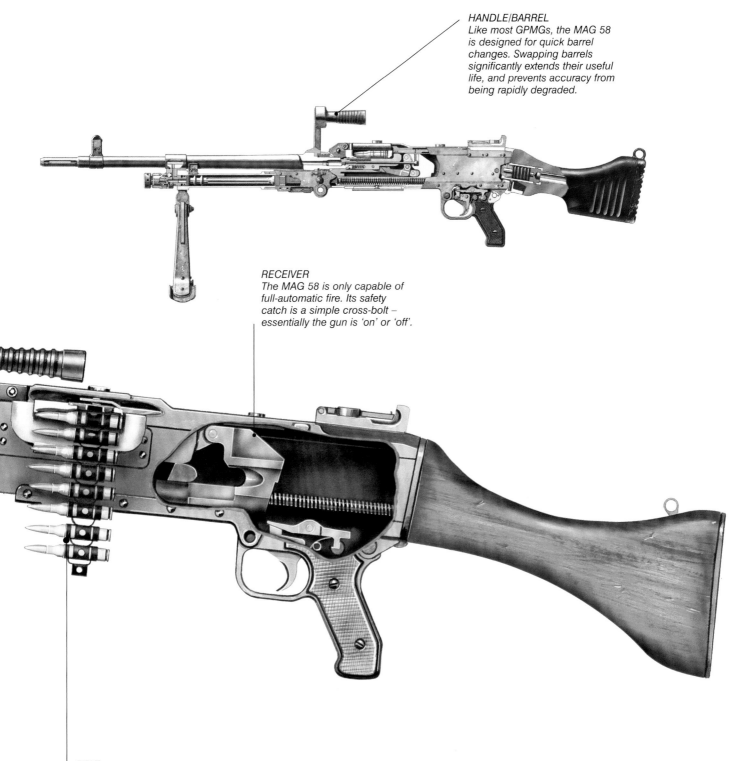

HANDLE/BARREL
Like most GPMGs, the MAG 58 is designed for quick barrel changes. Swapping barrels significantly extends their useful life, and prevents accuracy from being rapidly degraded.

RECEIVER
The MAG 58 is only capable of full-automatic fire. Its safety catch is a simple cross-bolt – essentially the gun is 'on' or 'off'.

BELT
The MAG 58 uses a disintegrating-link ammunition belt. This can be left free or can be contained in a box to facilitate firing on the move.

The immense success of the FN MAG is largely due to the fact that it got the job done – whatever the job happened to be. Tough and reliable, it is also accurate enough for long-range fire. This owes as much to the quality of its construction as to its design.

Eastern Machine Guns

Soviet weapon design not only influenced the nations of the Warsaw Pact, but also the Communist nations of North Korea and China. Although the political wind has changed, North Korean and Chinese weapons continue to have a strong Soviet influence.

RPK

The RPK is an AKM assault rifle with a longer, heavier barrel. Although this method does not create an excellent machine gun, it does mean that any solider can operate the support weapon, and makes spares procurement simple.

SPECIFICATIONS	
Country of Origin:	USSR
Date:	1955
Calibre:	7.62mm (.3in) M1943
Operation:	Gas-operated, air-cooled
Weight:	4.76kg (10.5lb)
Overall Length:	1041mm (41in)
Barrel Length:	589mm (23.2in)
Muzzle Velocity:	732m/sec (2400ft/sec)
Feed/Magazine:	40-round box magazine or 75-round drum magazine
Cyclic Rate:	600rpm
Range:	800m (2625ft)

RPD

Developed late in World War II, the RPD was a highly influential weapon which was copied by China, under the designation Type 56, and North Korea, where it was called the Type 62.

SPECIFICATIONS	
Country of Origin:	USSR
Date:	1962
Calibre:	7.62mm (.3in) M1943
Operation:	Gas-operated, air-cooled
Weight:	7kg (15.43lb)
Overall Length:	1041mm (41in)
Barrel Length:	520mm (20.5in)
Muzzle Velocity:	735m/sec (2410ft/sec)
Feed/Magazine:	100-round belt contained in drum
Cyclic Rate:	700rpm
Range:	900m (2953ft)

TIMELINE  1955  1962

PKM

An upgraded version of the PK general-purpose machine gun, the PKM is a very simple weapon based on the Kalashnikov rifle. It can be most readily differentiated from earlier PK machine guns by its possession of an unfluted barrel.

SPECIFICATIONS	
Country of Origin:	USSR
Date:	1969
Calibre:	7.62mm (.3in) M1943
Operation:	Gas-operated, air-cooled
Weight:	9kg (19.84lb)
Overall Length:	1160mm (45.67in)
Barrel Length:	658mm (25.9in)
Muzzle Velocity:	800m/sec (2600ft/sec)
Feed/Magazine:	Belt-fed (belts contained in boxes)
Cyclic Rate:	710rpm
Range:	2000m (6560ft) +

Type 81

In the 1960s, China ceased to rely on Russian-made weapons and developed its own machine gun, designated Type 67. A process of evolution led to the Type 81, which is a support version of the Type 81 assault rifle.

SPECIFICATIONS	
Country of Origin:	China
Date:	1977
Calibre:	7.62mm (.3in)
Operation:	Gas-operated, rotating bolt
Weight:	3.4kg (7.5lb)
Overall Length:	955mm (37.6in)
Barrel Length:	445mm (17.5in)
Muzzle Velocity:	720m/sec (2362ft/sec)
Feed/Magazine:	30-round box or 75-round drum detachable magazine
Cyclical Rate:	c.650rpm
Range:	500m (1640ft)

1969   1977

Stoner 63 Medium Machine Gun

The Stoner Weapon System was a concept developed by Eugene Stoner, using a common receiver to create a range of weapons. With the correct choices of barrel, stock and feed system it was possible to create anything from a fully automatic carbine to a mounted machine gun. Spares and components were all common, thus simplifying logistics, and it was possible to dismantle weapons and rebuild them as another type, increasing the flexibility of a unit's weaponry.

RECEIVER
The Stoner family of weapons fire from an open bolt. This is beneficial for a machine gun as it improves cooling but is less desirable for the rifle configurations as accuracy may be impaired.

SPECIFICATIONS	
Country of Origin:	United States
Date:	1963
Calibre:	5.56mm (.219in)
Operation:	Gas-operated, air-cooled
Weight:	5.3kg (11.68lb)
Overall Length:	1022mm (40.25in) standard barrel
Barrel Length:	508mm (20in) standard
	399m (15.7in) short
Muzzle Velocity:	1000m/sec (3280ft/sec)
Feed/Magazine:	150-round disintegrating-link boxed belt or a detachable box magazine
Cyclic Rate:	700–1000rpm
Range:	1000m (3280ft)

There have been other variations on the weapon system theme, such as the MP5 submachine gun. The MP5 and similar weapons are more limited in scope than Stoner's system, however; while the MP5 can be configured in many ways, it is still a submachine gun and only capable of doing a submachine gun's job. Stoner's system wanted to be all things to all men, and was not quite up to the task.

BARREL
Two machine gun barrels were available for the Stoner Weapon System: a standard barrel for sustained fire and a shorter one for mobile use.

SIGHTS
Different configurations required different sights. The belt-fed light machine gun configuration was sighted out to 1000m (3280ft), though accurate fire at this distance was problematical.

The Stoner Weapon System was used with some success by elite US formations in the Vietnam War, but was prone to become unreliable as a result of exposure to dirt. The concept never caught on, and the Stoner system faded into history as an interesting novelty.

Aircraft and Vehicle Weapons

An aircraft weapon must have a very high rate of fire if it is to stand any chance of hitting a fast-moving target. The problem of delivering this immense rate of fire is usually solved by using multiple-barrel weapons.

M61/M168 Vulcan

A 20mm (.78in) rotary weapon delivering a much higher rate of fire than a single-barrel cannon or even a group of them, the M61 Vulcan was developed as an aircraft weapon but became the basis for the Phalanx air-defence system.

SPECIFICATIONS	
Country of Origin:	United States
Date:	1959
Calibre:	20mm (.78in)
Operation:	Hydraulically-driven Gatling
Weight:	136kg (300lb)
Overall Length:	1827mm (71.93in)
Barrel Length:	N/A
Muzzle Velocity:	670m/sec (2200ft/sec)
Feed/Magazine:	Belt-fed or linkless feed system
Cyclic Rate:	6000rpm
Range:	6000m (19,685ft)

M134 Minigun

The six-barrel Minigun uses electric power to move each barrel in turn to the firing position. The fired barrel is reloaded and cooled as the cycle continues. Spent cartridges are retained rather than being ejected from the aircraft.

SPECIFICATIONS	
Country of Origin:	United States
Date:	1963
Calibre:	7.62mm (.3in) NATO
Operation:	Electrically-driven Gatling
Weight:	15.9kg (35lb)
Overall Length:	800mm (31.5in)
Barrel Length:	559mm (22in)
Muzzle Velocity:	869m/sec (2850ft/sec)
Feed/Magazine:	Belt-fed or linkless feed system
Cyclic Rate:	Up to 6000rpm
Range:	3000m (9842ft) +

TIMELINE

 1959

 1963

 1964

M195 20mm Automatic Gun

A short-barrelled version of the M61 Vulcan, the M195 was developed for use aboard helicopter gunships. It was fed from two 950-round ammunition cans and had a rate of fire in the region of 750–800rpm depending on length of burst.

SPECIFICATIONS	
Country of Origin:	United States
Date:	1964
Calibre:	20mm (.78in)
Operation:	Hydraulically-driven Gatling
Weight:	112kg (248lb)
Overall Length:	Not known
Barrel Length:	N/A
Muzzle Velocity:	1050m/sec (3450ft/sec)
Feed/Magazine:	950-round cans
Cyclic Rate:	750–800rpm
Range:	2000m (6560ft) +

XM-214

A prototype weapon using the minigun principle, the XM-214 used 5.56mm (.219in) ammunition and a selectable rate of fire between 1000 and 6000rpm. It was fed from two 500-round cassettes mounted on either side of the weapon.

SPECIFICATIONS	
Country of Origin:	United States
Date:	1970
Calibre:	5.56mm (.219in) NATO
Operation:	Electrically-driven Gatling
Weight:	38.6kg (85lb)
Overall Length:	685mm (27in)
Barrel Length:	455mm (18in)
Muzzle Velocity:	990m/sec (3250ft/sec)
Feed/Magazine:	500-round cassettes
Cyclic Rate:	2000–10,000rpm
Range:	2000m (6560ft) +

GAU-8/A Avenger Rotary Cannon

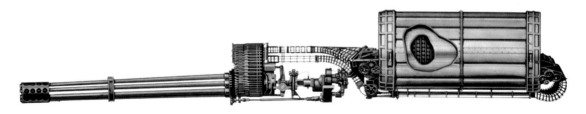

The General Electric GAU-8/A Avenger is a 30mm (1.18in) hydraulically driven seven-barrel Gatling-type rotary cannon. Designed specifically for the anti-tank role, it is mounted on the USAF's Fairchild A-10 Thunderbolt II ground attack aircraft. It is one of the largest, heaviest and most powerful aircraft cannons in the United States military inventory.

SPECIFICATIONS	
Country of Origin:	United States
Date:	1977
Calibre:	30mm (1.18in)
Operation:	Hydraulically-driven Gatling
Weight:	281kg (619.5lb)
Overall Length:	6060mm (238.5in)
Barrel Length:	2300m (90.5in)
Muzzle Velocity:	1070m/sec (3500ft/sec)
Feed/Magazine:	Linkless feed system
Cyclic Rate:	4200rpm
Range:	1220m (4003ft) +

1970

1977

Light Anti-Tank Weapons

While there is a limit to how big a weapon can be carried by infantry, and thus how effective an infantry anti-armour weapon can be, light anti-tank weapons give infantry at least some capability to fight tanks and armoured vehicles.

M2 Carl Gustav

The Carl Gustav took a different approach to many other light anti-armour weapons in that it had a reusable launcher and spin-stabilized projectiles rather than employing fins. Although no longer effective against modern tanks, it remains an effective anti-bunker weapon.

SPECIFICATIONS	
Country of Origin:	Sweden
Date:	1948
Calibre:	84mm (3.3in)
Operation:	Recoilless rifle
Weight:	8.5kg (18.73lb)
Overall Length:	1100mm (43.2in)
Barrel Length:	N/A
Muzzle Velocity:	230–255m/sec (754–836ft/sec)
Feed/Magazine:	Single shot, breech-loaded
Range:	c.1000m (3280ft)

M-72 LAW

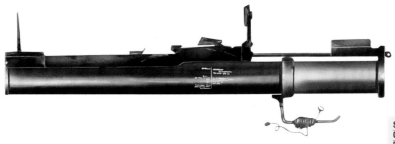

The M72 LAW (Light Anti-Tank Weapon) is a portable one-shot 66mm (2.6in) unguided anti-tank weapon. The weapon consists of a rocket packed inside of a launcher made up of two tubes, one inside the other. The outer tube contains the trigger, the arming handle, front and rear sights, and the rear cover.

SPECIFICATIONS	
Country of Origin:	United States
Date:	1963
Calibre:	66mm (2.6in)
Operation:	Rocket motor
Weight:	2.5kg (5.5lb)
Overall Length:	950mm (37.4in)
Barrel Length:	N/A
Muzzle Velocity:	145m/sec (475ft/sec)
Feed/Magazine:	Single-shot, muzzle-loaded
Range:	c.200m (650ft)

TIMELINE

 1948　　 1963　　 1980

B-300

An Israeli weapon developed from the RPG-7, the B-300 uses a reusable
launcher and a disposable tube containing the rocket-propelled projectile itself.
Accuracy is possible to about 400m (1312ft) using fin-stabilization.

SPECIFICATIONS	
Country of Origin:	Israel
Date:	1980
Calibre:	82mm (3.23in)
Operation:	Rocket motor
Weight:	3.65kg (8.04lb)
Overall Length:	1440mm (56.69in)
Barrel Length:	N/A
Muzzle Velocity:	c.270m/sec (886ft/sec)
Feed/Magazine:	Single shot
Range:	400m (1312ft)

SMAW

Developed from the B-300, the Shoulder-launched Multipurpose Assault
Weapon is primarily intended for 'bunker busting' against enemy infantry in
hard cover, but can launch an anti-armour rocket capable of disabling light
armoured vehicles.

SPECIFICATIONS	
Country of Origin:	United States
Date:	1984
Calibre:	83mm (3.27in)
Operation:	Rocket motor
Weight:	7.69kg (16.92lb)
Overall Length:	760mm (29.92in)
Barrel Length:	N/A
Muzzle Velocity:	220m/sec (721ft/sec)
Feed/Magazine:	Single shot, reloadable
Range:	500m (1640ft)

Panzerfaust 3

Using a reusable sighting unit/disposable launching tube system, the
Panzerfaust 3 employs a recoilless launching system, with the rocket motor
igniting when the projectile is safely clear of the weapon and its user. A range of
advanced warheads are available.

SPECIFICATIONS	
Country of Origin:	West Germany
Date:	1989
Calibre:	60mm (2.4in)
Operation:	Rocket motor
Weight:	12.9kg (28lb)
Overall Length:	950mm (37in)
Barrel Length:	N/A
Muzzle Velocity:	115m/sec (377ft/sec)
Feed/Magazine:	Single shot
Range:	920m (3018ft)

1984

1989

RPG-7D

Produced in enormous numbers, the RPG-7 uses a reusable launcher and a variety of rocket-propelled projectiles. These vary in diameter from 40mm (1.57in) to 105mm (4.1in), and have a theoretical maximum range of about 1000m (3280ft). Accuracy beyond 200m (656ft) is questionable, however. he ruggedness, simplicity, low cost and effectiveness of the RPG-7 has made it the most widely used anti-tank weapon in the world. Currently around 40 countries use the weapon, and it is manufactured in a number of variants.

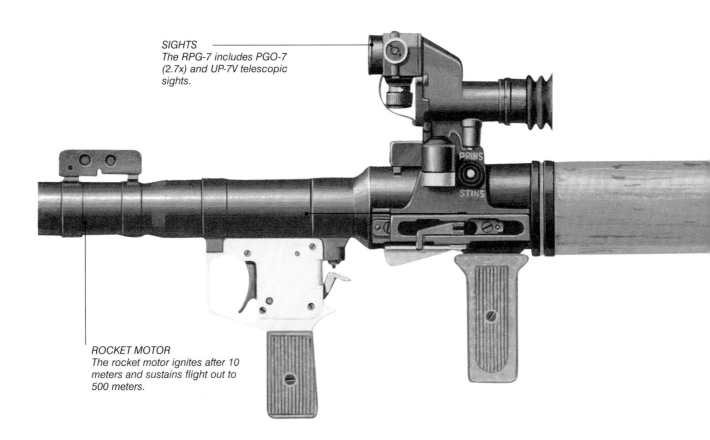

SIGHTS
The RPG-7 includes PGO-7 (2.7x) and UP-7V telescopic sights.

ROCKET MOTOR
The rocket motor ignites after 10 meters and sustains flight out to 500 meters.

SPECIFICATIONS

Country of Origin:	USSR
Date:	1961
Calibre:	40mm (1.57in)
Operation:	Rocket motor
Weight:	7kg (15lb)
Overall Length:	950mm (37.4in)
Barrel Length:	N/A
Muzzle Velocity:	115m/sec (377ft/sec)
Feed/Magazine:	Single-shot, muzzle-loaded
Range:	c.920m (3018ft)

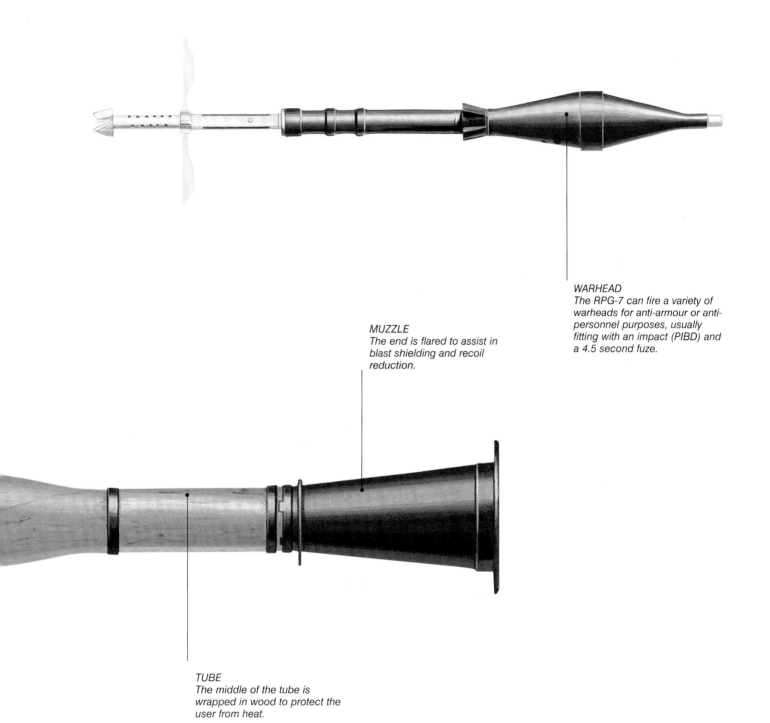

MUZZLE
The end is flared to assist in blast shielding and recoil reduction.

WARHEAD
The RPG-7 can fire a variety of warheads for anti-armour or anti-personnel purposes, usually fitting with an impact (PIBD) and a 4.5 second fuze.

TUBE
The middle of the tube is wrapped in wood to protect the user from heat.

The RPG-7 munition has 2 sections: a 'booster' and a 'warhead and sustainer motor' section. These must be assembled into the ready-to-use grenade. The booster consists of a small strip powder charge that propels the grenade out of the launcher; the sustainer motor ignites and propels the grenade for the next few seconds, reaching a speed of 294 meters per second.

Guided Anti-Tank Weapons for Infantry Support (MILAN)

The MILAN missile system is a Semi-Automatic to Command Line of Sight (SACLOS) system. This means that the missile is controlled from the firing post, by signals sent down a wire unreeling from the missile in flight. Guidance is provided by keeping the sight aimed at the target while the missile is in flight.

MILAN is a relatively expensive system, and requires a crew or vehicle to move the weapon and its ammunition around the battlefield. As such, when MILAN missiles were first used against enemy bunkers during the Falklands War, the practice attracted some criticism.

MUZZLE
Advanced payloads include a tandem warhead intended to defeat reactive armour by striking the same spot twice.

SPECIFICATIONS (rocket only)	
Country of Origin:	France/West Germany
Date:	1972
Calibre:	125mm (4.92in)
Operation:	Solid-fuel rocket, SACLOS wire guidance system
Weight:	7.1kg (15.56lb)
Length:	1200mm (47.2in)
Muzzle Velocity:	200m/sec (656ft/sec)
Feed/Magazine:	Shaped-charge warhead
Range:	400–2000m (1312–6560ft)

However, even leaving aside considerations of the value of lives risked in an infantry assault, the cost of training a soldier to the point where he can efficiently take part in such an assault makes the use of precisely guided weapons to eliminate bunkers economically attractive.

Today, it is common practice to use guided missiles against enemy bunkers or strongpoints. The ability to put the weapon where its warhead will be most effective does not come cheap, but then military efficiency never does.

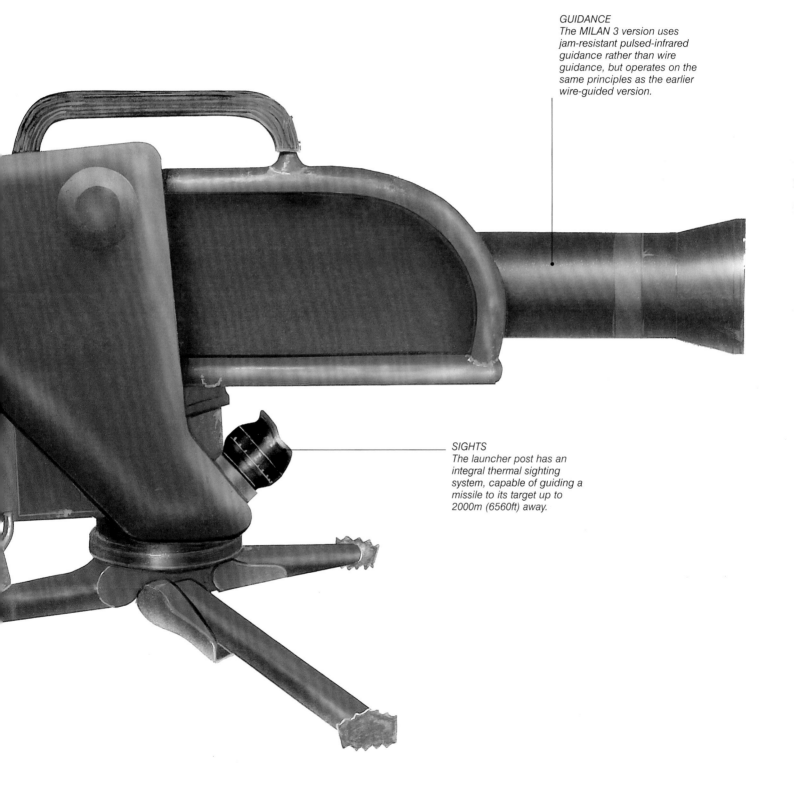

GUIDANCE
The MILAN 3 version uses jam-resistant pulsed-infrared guidance rather than wire guidance, but operates on the same principles as the earlier wire-guided version.

SIGHTS
The launcher post has an integral thermal sighting system, capable of guiding a missile to its target up to 2000m (6560ft) away.

Hand Grenades

The hand grenade has long been an important part of the infantry soldier's arsenal. Grenades can be used to attack hostiles located behind cover or inside a building, or to defend a position by being thrown out. The most basic type of grenade uses explosive blast or fragmentation to kill or injure anyone within its effective radius, but a vast array of specialist grenades also exist.

M26

The M26 grenade uses a coil of notched wire between the bursting charge and the outer casing to create a controlled fragmentation effect. It was replaced in US service by the M67 grenade during the 1970s.

SPECIFICATIONS	
Country of Origin:	United States
Date:	1950s
Type:	Fragmentation
Weight:	.454kg (1lb)
Height:	99mm (3.89in)
Diameter:	57mm (2.24in)
Detonation mechanism:	Timed friction fuse
Filling:	Composition B
Lethal radius:	15m (49ft)

L2A2

The L2A2 hand grenade was the standard British Army anti-personnel grenade until the early 2000s. An explosive bursting charge caused the casing to shatter, resulting in a combination of blast and fragmentation.

SPECIFICATIONS	
Country of Origin:	United Kingdom
Date:	1960
Type:	Fragmentation
Weight:	.395kg (.87lb)
Height:	84mm (3.25in)
Detonation Mechanism:	Timed friction fuse
Filling:	Composition B
Lethal Radius:	10m (32.8ft)

DM 51

With its jacket in place, the DM 51 grenade has a greater lethal radius and is normally used defensively, i.e. thrown out from a position of cover. Without the jacket it is well suited to offensive use as it has a smaller burst radius.

SPECIFICATIONS	
Country of Origin:	Germany
Date:	1960s
Type:	Fragmentation or concussion
Weight:	.44kg (.97lb) with jacket
	.15kg (.33lb) without jacket
Height:	107mm (4.25in)
Detonation Mechanism:	Not known
Filling:	Not known
Lethal radius:	35m (115ft)

OD82

The Italian OD82 grenade was withdrawn and redesigned after it began to display an alarming tendency to explode too soon. Most grenades use a pyrotechnic fuse with a reliable delay.

SPECIFICATIONS	
Country of Origin:	Italy
Date:	Not known
Type:	Fragmentation
Weight:	.286kg (.5lb)
Height:	83mm (3.26in)
Detonation mechanism:	Not known
Filling:	Composition B
Lethal radius:	15m (49ft)

NR20 C1

The Eurometaal NR20 C1 anti-personnel hand grenade was developed for the Royal Netherlands Army. It consists of a plastic body with an inner lining of steel balls and a high-explosive charge. During trials it was found that the grenade exploded into about 2100 fragments. This highly lethal weapon is effective up to a distance of 5m (16.4ft).

SPECIFICATIONS	
Country of Origin:	Netherlands
Date:	Not known
Type:	Fragmentation
Weight:	.39kg (.75lb)
Height:	104mm (4.1in)
Detonation mechanism:	Mechanical fuse with pyrotechnic delay
Filling:	Steel balls plus high-explosive charge
Lethal radius:	5m (16.4ft)

THE MODERN ERA

There have been some significant advances in weapon technology in recent years, but not all of them are particularly obvious. 'Human engineering' now plays a much greater part in design than ever before, with even fairly basic weapons being designed with ease of use, comfort and safety in mind.

Modern weapon designers have many different market niches to consider, and must tailor their product to one of them or else create a generally good weapon. In the military environment, the trend towards smaller, lighter weapons has continued, and most combat still takes place at short ranges.

Left: A British Army sniper team search for targets somewhere in Afghanistan, 2009. The sniper is armed with an L96 sniper rifle, wrapped in masking material to dull any reflection off the barrel and stock.

Modern Semi-Automatic Handguns

Recent years have seen a trend towards polymer construction and the creation of related 'families' of weapons that can be tailored to the user's requirements. Many advanced weapons are based around traditional mechanisms or design features.

Para P14-45

Para Ordnance (now called Para USA) made its name with M1911-type pistols updated to use high-capacity double-stacked magazines. These were offered in a range of calibres, and were followed by the LDA (Light Double Action) series, which added a double-action trigger.

SPECIFICATIONS	
Country of Origin:	United States
Date:	1989
Calibre:	11.4mm (.45in) .45 ACP
Operation:	Blowback
Weight:	1.1kg (2.5lb)
Overall Length:	215mm (8.5in)
Barrel Length:	127mm (5in)
Muzzle Velocity:	380m/sec (1250ft/sec)
Feed/Magazine:	13-round detachable box magazine
Range:	40m (131ft)

Star 30M

The Star 30M looks like a Browning clone but has some significant differences. The slide runs inside the frame rather than outside, improving stability and thus accuracy. A light-alloy 30K version is also marketed.

SPECIFICATIONS	
Country of Origin:	Spain
Date:	1990
Calibre:	9mm (.35in) Parabellum
Operation:	Blowback
Weight:	1.14kg (2.51lb)
Overall Length:	205mm (8.07in)
Barrel Length:	119mm (4.6in)
Muzzle Velocity:	380m/sec (1250ft/sec)
Feed/Magazine:	15-round detachable box magazine
Range:	40m (131ft)

TIMELINE

1989

1990

Smith & Wesson M&P series

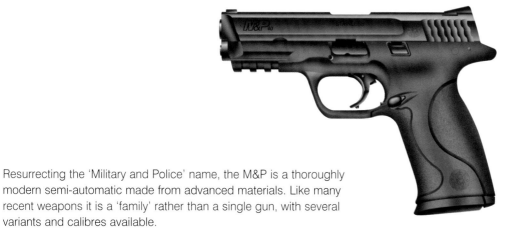

Resurrecting the 'Military and Police' name, the M&P is a thoroughly modern semi-automatic made from advanced materials. Like many recent weapons it is a 'family' rather than a single gun, with several variants and calibres available.

SPECIFICATIONS	
Country of Origin:	United States
Date:	2005
Calibre:	9mm (.35in) Parabellum
Operation:	Short recoil, locked-breech
Weight:	c. .68kg (1.5lb)
Overall Length:	190mm (7.5in)
Barrel Length:	108mm (4.25in)
Muzzle Velocity:	370m/sec (1214ft/sec)
Feed/Magazine:	10-round detachable box magazine
Range:	50m (164ft)

Taurus PT145

A sub-compact 'pocket pistol' chambered for 11.4mm/.45in (.45 ACP), the PT145 weighs very little due to its largely polymer construction. Controllability is assisted by a low bore-axis, which counteracts the tendency of the muzzle to flip up.

SPECIFICATIONS	
Country of Origin:	United States
Date:	2005
Calibre:	11.4mm (.45in) .45 ACP
Operation:	Recoil, autoloader
Weight:	.64kg (1.4lb)
Overall Length:	152mm (6in)
Barrel Length:	83mm (3.25in)
Muzzle Velocity:	305m/sec (100 ft/sec)
Feed/Magazine:	10-round detachable box magazine
Range:	40m (131ft)

Caracal Handguns

Manufactured from advanced materials in the United Arab Emirates, the Caracal series weapons are designed for ambidextrous use. In addition to the standard F model, smaller C and SC versions are available for concealed carry.

SPECIFICATIONS	
Country of Origin:	United Arab Emirates
Date:	2007
Calibre:	9mm (.35in) Parabellum
Operation:	Short recoil, locked-breech
Weight:	.75kg (1.65lb)
Overall Length:	178mm (7in)
Barrel Length:	104mm (4.1in)
Muzzle Velocity:	370m/sec (1214ft/sec)
Feed/Magazine:	18-round detachable box magazine
Range:	40m (131ft)

2005

2007

Eternal Classics

Some designs have survived the test of time and remain in service, little modified, decades after their introduction. This is more than nostalgia; these are designs that do their job reliably and well in any era.

Imbel M973/MD1

A straight M1911 copy, the M973 became available in 1973, chambered for 11.4mm/.45in (.45 ACP) or 9mm (.35in). The latter was adopted by the Brazilian Army as its service pistol. Additional calibres became available in the 1990s.

SPECIFICATIONS	
Country of Origin:	Brazil
Date:	1973
Calibre:	11.4mm (.45in) .45 ACP, 9.6mm (.38in) .38 Super Auto, 9mm (.35in) Parabellum
Operation:	Short recoil
Weight:	1.035kg (2.28lb)
Overall Length:	216mm (8.5in)
Barrel Length:	128mm (5.0in)
Muzzle Velocity:	338m/sec (1110ft/sec)
Feed/Magazine:	7-, 8- or 9-round detachable box magazine
Range:	50m (164ft)

AMT Hardballer

Other than being the first to be constructed from stainless steel, the Hardballer is a typical M1911 copy. Its name derives from the fact that it needs full metal jacket ('hardball') ammunition to feed properly.

SPECIFICATIONS	
Country of Origin:	United States
Date:	1977
Calibre:	11.4mm (.45in) .45 ACP
Operation:	Short recoil, locked-breech
Weight:	1.1kg (2.3lb)
Overall Length:	215mm (8.5in)
Barrel Length:	127mm (5in)
Muzzle Velocity:	338m/sec (1110ft/sec)
Feed/Magazine:	7-round detachable box magazine
Range:	50m (164ft)

TIMELINE

1973

1977

1983

Colt Mk IV Series 80

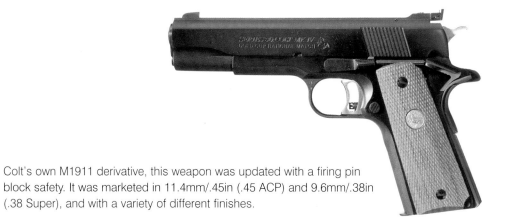

Colt's own M1911 derivative, this weapon was updated with a firing pin block safety. It was marketed in 11.4mm/.45in (.45 ACP) and 9.6mm/.38in (.38 Super), and with a variety of different finishes.

SPECIFICATIONS	
Country of Origin:	United States
Date:	1983
Calibre:	11.4mm (.45in) .45 ACP, 9.6mm (.38in) .38 Super, 9.6mm (.38in) .380 Auto
Operation:	Single-action
Weight:	.69kg (1.51lb)
Overall Length:	221mm (8.7in)
Barrel Length:	127mm (5 in)
Muzzle Velocity:	305m/sec (1001ft/sec)
Feed/Magazine:	8-, 9- or 7-round detachable box magazine
Range:	50m (164ft)

Colt Double Eagle

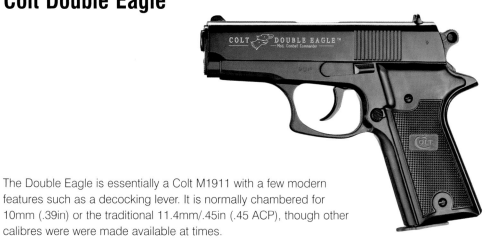

The Double Eagle is essentially a Colt M1911 with a few modern features such as a decocking lever. It is normally chambered for 10mm (.39in) or the traditional 11.4mm/.45in (.45 ACP), though other calibres were were made available at times.

SPECIFICATIONS	
Country of Origin:	United States
Date:	1989
Calibre:	11.4mm (.45in) .45 ACP, 10mm (.39in)
Operation:	DA/SA
Weight:	1.2kg (2.65lb)
Overall Length:	216mm (8.5in)
Barrel Length:	127mm (5in)
Muzzle Velocity:	338m/sec (1110ft/sec)
Feed/Magazine:	8-round detachable box magazine
Range:	50m (164ft)

Smith & Wesson 1911

The Smith & Wesson 1911 is virtually the same weapon as the original Colt model. The main exception is an external extractor, which was a feature of John Browning's later designs

SPECIFICATIONS	
Country of Origin:	United States
Date:	2003
Calibre:	11.4mm (.45in) .45 ACP
Operation:	Single Action Only
Weight:	1.13kg (2.4lb)
Overall Length:	221mm (8.7in)
Barrel Length:	127mm (5in)
Muzzle Velocity:	305m/sec (1001ft/sec)
Feed/Magazine:	9-round detachable box magazine
Range:	50m (164ft)

1989

2003

Advanced Semi-Automatics

A new generation of semi-automatic handguns has appeared in the past two decades, using advanced materials and, sometimes, innovative design to provide enhanced capabilities. These weapons are often beyond the budget of many potential users, however.

Jericho 941

Developed from the CZ 75, the Israeli Jericho 941 was originally marketed as the 'Baby Eagle'. It was built around the powerful 10.4mm/.41in (.41 Action Express) cartridge, but failed to achieve mainstream popularity.

SPECIFICATIONS	
Country of Origin:	Israel
Date:	1990
Calibre:	10.4mm (.41in) .41 Action Express
Operation:	Short recoil
Weight:	1.1kg (2.4lb)
Overall Length:	210mm (8.2in)
Barrel Length:	115mm (4.5in)
Muzzle Velocity:	370m/sec (1214ft/sec)
Feed/Magazine:	10-round detachable box magazine
Range:	50m (164ft)

Smith & Wesson Sigma

Primarily chambered for 10.16mm/.4in (.40 S&W), the Sigma is also available in other calibres. It is constructed largely from synthetic materials and uses a double-action trigger to cock and fire the weapon. There is no manual safety.

SPECIFICATIONS	
Country of Origin:	United States
Date:	1993
Calibre:	10.16mm (.4in) .40 S&W
Operation:	Short recoil
Weight:	.74kg (1.63lb)
Overall Length:	197mm (7.75in)
Barrel Length:	114mm (4.48in)
Muzzle Velocity:	305m/sec (1001ft/sec)
Feed/Magazine:	15-round box magazine
Range:	50–100m (164–328ft)

Walther P99

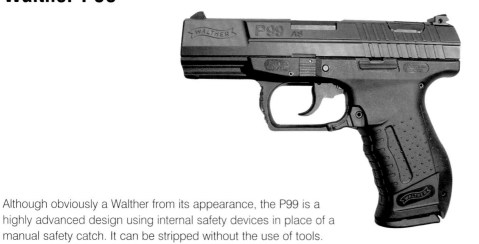

SPECIFICATIONS	
Country of Origin:	Germany
Date:	1996
Calibre:	10.16mm (.4in) .40 S&W, 9mm (.35in) Parabellum, 9mm (.35in) IMI
Operation:	Short recoil, locked-breech
Weight:	.65kg (1.44lb) .40 S&W; .63kg (1.38lb) Parabellum
Overall Length:	184mm (7.2in) .40 S&W; 180mm (7.1in) Parabellum
Barrel Length:	106mm (4.2in) .40 S&W; 102mm (4.in) Parabellum
Muzzle Velocity:	344m/sec (1129ft/sec) .40 S&W; 408m/sec (1339ft/sec) Parabellum
Feed/Magazine:	12-round (.40 S&W) or 15-round (Parabellum) detachable box magazine
Range::	60m (196ft)

Although obviously a Walther from its appearance, the P99 is a highly advanced design using internal safety devices in place of a manual safety catch. It can be stripped without the use of tools.

SOCOM Mk 23 Mod 0

SPECIFICATIONS	
Country of Origin:	United States
Date:	1996
Calibre:	11.4mm (.45in) .45 ACP
Operation:	Double-action
Weight:	1.1kg (2.4lb)
Overall Length:	245mm (9.6in)
Barrel Length:	150mm (5.9in)
Muzzle Velocity:	260m/sec (850ft/sec)
Feed/Magazine:	12-round detachable box magazine
Range:	25m (82ft)

Developed in response to a request from US Special Operations Command (SOCOM), the Mk 23 can take a quick-detach silencer and/or a laser pointer. It has dual recoil springs to reduce felt recoil and a polymer frame.

FN Five-Seven

SPECIFICATIONS	
Country of Origin:	Belgium
Date:	2000
Calibre:	5.7mm (.224in)
Operation:	Delayed blowback
Weight:	.62kg (1.36lb)
Overall Length:	208mm (8.2in)
Barrel Length:	122mm (4.8in)
Muzzle Velocity:	650m/sec (2133ft/sec)
Feed/Magazine:	10-round detachable box magazine
Range:	50m (164ft)

Using the same 5.7 x 28mm (.224 x 1.1in) round as the P90 Personal Defence Weapon, the Five-Seven is constructed of high-tech polymers. The felt recoil of the round is significantly less than for 9mm (.35in), and a very flat trajectory aids accurate shooting.

1996

2000

Different Users, Different Needs

Since no single handgun design can meet the needs of concealed carry and heavy-calibre hunting, home defence and military combat, a great variety of weapons are produced either as specialist designs or as families encompassing a range of options.

AMT On Duty

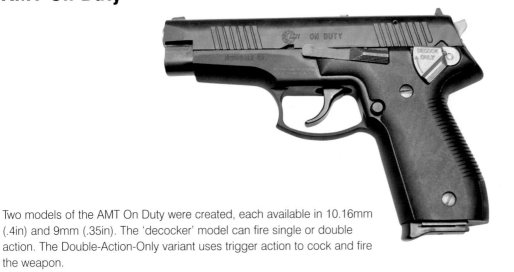

Two models of the AMT On Duty were created, each available in 10.16mm (.4in) and 9mm (.35in). The 'decocker' model can fire single or double action. The Double-Action-Only variant uses trigger action to cock and fire the weapon.

SPECIFICATIONS	
Country of Origin:	United States
Date:	1991
Calibre:	10.16mm (.4in) .40 S&W, 9mm (.35in) Parabellum
Operation:	DA/SA or DAO
Weight:	Not known
Overall Length:	Not known
Barrel Length:	Not known
Muzzle Velocity:	Not known
Feed/Magazine:	11-round (.40 S&W) or 15-round (Parabellum) magazine
Range:	50m (164ft)

Vektor SP1 &2

The Vektor SP is available as the SP1 in 9mm (.35in) or SP2 in 10.16mm/.4in (.40 S&W). It is derived from the Z88, which was a licensed Beretta 92F copy. It has been adopted by the South African military.

SPECIFICATIONS	
Country of Origin:	South Africa
Date:	1992
Calibre:	9mm (.35in), 10.16mm (.4in) .40 S&W
Operation:	DA/SA
Weight:	.96kg (2.19lb)
Overall Length:	210mm (8.26in)
Barrel Length:	118mm (4.64in)
Muzzle Velocity:	Not known
Feed/Magazine:	11-round (.40 S&W) or 15-round (9mm/.35in) magazine
Range:	50m (164ft)

TIMELINE			
	1991	1992	1995

Taurus Model 605

A 5-shot 9.1mm/.357in .357 Magnum revolver, the Model 605 is an ideal weapon for home defence. Revolvers are reassuringly simple to use, which can be important when grabbing for a gun in the middle of the night.

SPECIFICATIONS	
Country of Origin:	Brazil
Date:	1995
Calibre:	9.1mm (.357in) .357 Magnum
Operation:	DA/SA
Weight:	.68kg (1.4lb)
Overall Length:	165mm (6.5in)
Barrel Length:	51mm (2in)
Muzzle Velocity:	Not known
Feed/Magazine:	5-round cylinder
Range:	50m (164ft)

HS2000/Springfield XD (Extreme Duty)

Developed to arm the Croatian forces, these weapons are also now produced under licence in the United States and are popular with some police departments. A range of options and calibres are available.

SPECIFICATIONS	
Country of Origin:	Croatia
Date:	1999
Calibre:	Various, including 9mm (.35in) and 11.4mm (.45in) .45 ACP
Operation:	Short recoil
Weight:	.65kg (1.43lb)
Overall Length:	180mm (7.08in)
Barrel Length:	102mm (4in)
Muzzle Velocity:	Not known
Feed/Magazine:	13-round (.45 ACP) or 16-round (9mm/.35in) magazine
Range:	50m (164ft)

Taurus Model 856

A snub-nosed six-shot 9.6mm/.38in (.38 Special) revolver, the Model 856 is aimed at the self-defence market. A very short barrel makes accurate shooting at any real distance difficult, but this is not a problem when shooting in point-blank self-defence.

SPECIFICATIONS	
Country of Origin:	Brazil
Date:	2003
Calibre:	9.6mm (.38in) .38 Special
Operation:	DA/SA
Weight:	.374kg (.82lb)
Overall Length:	165mm (6.5in)
Barrel Length:	51mm (2in)
Muzzle Velocity:	Not known
Feed/Magazine:	5-round cylinder
Range:	50m (164ft)

1999

2003

Taurus Pistols

Brazilian firm Taurus has been producing handguns since the 1940s, and today markets a range of semi-automatic pistols for the self-defence, law enforcement and military markets. Some are derived from classic designs; others are entirely new.

Model 1911AL

The Model 1911 is, as the name suggests, a modern version of the Colt M1911. Predictably, most variants are chambered for 11.4mm/.45in (.45 ACP) but 9mm (.35in) and 9.6mm (.38in) versions are also available.

SPECIFICATIONS	
Country of Origin:	Brazil
Date:	2000s
Calibre:	11.4mm (.45in) .45 ACP
Operation:	Single-action
Weight:	.94kg (2.1lb)
Overall Length:	215.9mm (8.5in)
Barrel Length:	127mm (5in)
Muzzle Velocity:	Not known
Feed:	9-round detachable box magazine
Range:	50m (164ft)

24/7 Pro Compact

A compact semi-automatic intended as a backup gun or for concealed carry, the 24/7 has a double- or single-action trigger. Like many modern compact semi-automatics, it has a very respectable ammunition capacity.

SPECIFICATIONS	
Country of Origin:	Brazil
Date:	2004
Calibre:	11.4mm (.45in) .45 ACP
Operation:	Short recoil
Weight:	.77kg (1.69lb)
Overall Length:	180.9mm (7.12in)
Barrel Length:	102mm (4in)
Muzzle Velocity:	380m/sec (1250ft/sec)
Feed:	8-round detachable box magazine
Range:	25m (82ft)

TIMELINE

2004

Taurus PT100

When Taurus bought Beretta's Brazilian factory, they began producing a developed version of the Beretta 92. The Taurus 100 is the same gun rechambered for 10.16mm (.4in) ammunition.

SPECIFICATIONS	
Country of Origin:	Brazil
Date:	2000s
Calibre:	10.16mm (.4in) .40 S&W
Operation:	Double-action
Weight:	.96kg (2.1lb)
Overall Length:	216mm (8.5in)
Barrel Length:	5in (127mm)
Muzzle Velocity:	Not known
Feed:	10- or 15-round detachable box magazine
Range:	50m (164ft)

Taurus Millennium

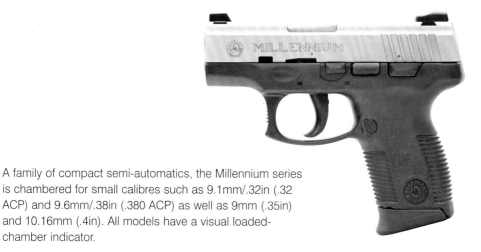

A family of compact semi-automatics, the Millennium series is chambered for small calibres such as 9.1mm/.32in (.32 ACP) and 9.6mm/.38in (.380 ACP) as well as 9mm (.35in) and 10.16mm (.4in). All models have a visual loaded-chamber indicator.

SPECIFICATIONS	
Country of Origin:	Brazil
Date:	2005
Calibre:	9mm (.35in)
Operation:	Short recoil, locked-breech
Weight:	.53kg (1.16lb)
Overall Length:	155mm (6.12in)
Barrel Length:	83mm (3.25in)
Muzzle Velocity:	Not known
Feed:	6- ,10,- or 12-9-detachable box magazine
Range:	25m (82ft)

Slim 708

Aimed specifically at the concealed-carry market, the Slim series is chambered for 9.6mm/.38in (.380 ACP) ammunition. The small dimensions of this round allow for a very narrow gun, permitting concealment under almost any clothing.

SPECIFICATIONS	
Country of Origin:	Brazil
Date:	2000s
Calibre:	9.6mm (.38in) .380 ACP
Operation:	Short recoil, locked-breech
Weight:	.54kg (1.18lb)
Overall Length:	158mm (6.24in)
Barrel Length:	81.3mm (3.2in)
Muzzle Velocity:	Not known
Feed/Magazine:	7-round detachable box magazine
Range:	40m (131ft)

2005

Taurus Revolvers

Taurus also produces a wide range of revolver designs, from concealed-carry weapons to specialist hunting designs. All incorporate a safety lock to render the weapon inoperable whilst it is stored.

Raging Bull 444 .44 Magnum

The original Raging Bull chambers the powerful 11.2mm/.44in (.44 Magnum) and 11.5mm/.454in (.454 Casull) rounds. The design comes in four distinct barrel lengths, with a crisp trigger break and smooth pull for accuracy, cushioned grips and factory porting to reduce felt recoil.

SPECIFICATIONS	
Country of Origin:	Brazil
Date:	c. 2000
Calibre:	11.5mm (.454in) .454 Casull; 11.2mm (.44in) .44 Magnum
Operation:	Revolver
Weight:	1.79kg (3.93lb)
Overall Length:	254–419mm (10–16.5in)
Barrel Length:	101–254mm (3.98–10in)
Muzzle Velocity:	Not known
Feed:	5- or 6-round cylinder
Range:	50m (164ft)

Raging Judge

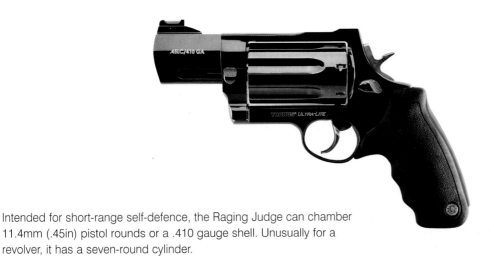

Intended for short-range self-defence, the Raging Judge can chamber 11.4mm (.45in) pistol rounds or a .410 gauge shell. Unusually for a revolver, it has a seven-round cylinder.

SPECIFICATIONS	
Country of Origin:	Brazil
Date:	c. 2000
Calibre:	11.4mm (.45in) .45 LC .410 GA
Operation:	Double action/single action
Weight:	1.17kg (2.57lb)
Overall Length:	Not known
Barrel Length:	76.2mm (3in)
Muzzle Velocity:	Not known
Feed:	7-round cylinder
Range:	30m (98ft)

TIMELINE

2000

CIA Model 650

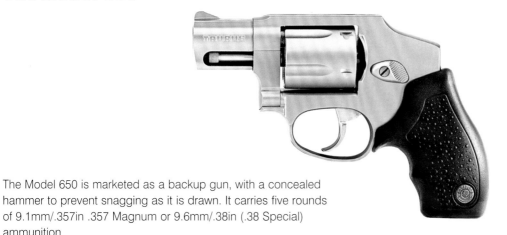

The Model 650 is marketed as a backup gun, with a concealed hammer to prevent snagging as it is drawn. It carries five rounds of 9.1mm/.357in .357 Magnum or 9.6mm/.38in (.38 Special) ammunition

SPECIFICATIONS	
Country of Origin:	Brazil
Date:	c. 2000
Calibre:	9.6mm (.38in) .38 Special, 9.1mm (.357in) .357 Magnum
Operation:	Revolver
Weight:	.68kg (1.4lb)
Overall Length:	165mm (6.5in)
Barrel Length:	51mm (2in)
Muzzle Velocity:	Not known
Feed:	5-round cylinder
Range:	25m (82ft)

Model 444 Ultralite

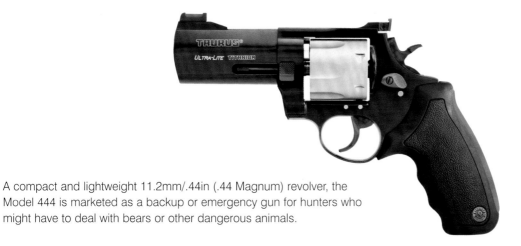

A compact and lightweight 11.2mm/.44in (.44 Magnum) revolver, the Model 444 is marketed as a backup or emergency gun for hunters who might have to deal with bears or other dangerous animals.

SPECIFICATIONS	
Country of Origin:	Brazil
Date:	c. 2000
Calibre:	11.2mm (.44in) .44 Remington Magnum
Operation:	revolver
Weight:	.8kg (1.76lb)
Overall Length:	249mm (9.8in)
Barrel Length:	102mm (4in)
Muzzle Velocity:	Not known
Feed:	6-round cylinder
Range:	30m (98ft)

991 Tracker .22 Magnum

A nine-shot revolver chambered for 5.6mm/.22in (.22 LR or .22 Magnum), the Tracker is primarily a 'plinking' gun intended for sport shooting. It is also suitable for vermin control, dealing with small nuisance animals and birds.

SPECIFICATIONS	
Country of Origin:	Brazil
Date:	c. 2000
Calibre:	5.6mm (.22in) .22 LR or Magnum
Operation:	Revolver
Weight:	1.24kg (2.73lb)
Overall Length:	273mm (10.75in)
Barrel Length:	165mm (6.5in)
Muzzle Velocity:	Not known
Feed:	9-round cylinder
Range:	50m (164ft)

Compact Handguns

Most users of compact handguns use them as a backup weapon or for concealed carry, but their small size and lightness can be attractive to users who do not want to carry or store anything bigger.

Smith & Wesson Model 2213/2214

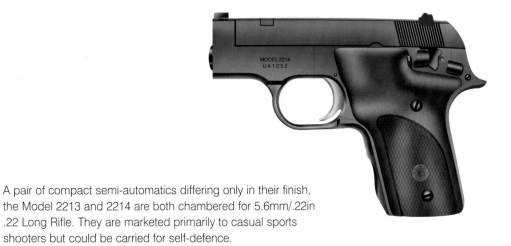

A pair of compact semi-automatics differing only in their finish, the Model 2213 and 2214 are both chambered for 5.6mm/.22in .22 Long Rifle. They are marketed primarily to casual sports shooters but could be carried for self-defence.

SPECIFICATIONS	
Country of Origin:	United States
Date:	c. 1990
Calibre:	5.6mm (.22in) .22 LR
Operation:	Recoil
Weight:	Not known
Overall Length:	82mm (3.25in)
Barrel Length:	76mm (2.99in)
Muzzle Velocity:	Not known
Feed/Magazine:	8-round detachable box magazine
Range:	30m (98ft)

SIG-Sauer P228/P229

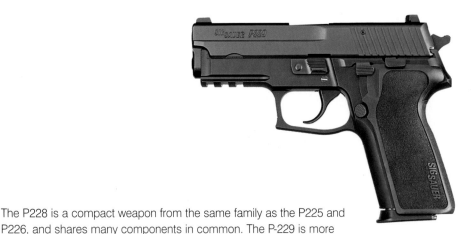

The P228 is a compact weapon from the same family as the P225 and P226, and shares many components in common. The P-229 is more or less the same gun, but chambered for 10.16mm/.4in .40 S&W.

SPECIFICATIONS	
Country of Origin:	Switzerland/Germany
Date:	c. 1990
Calibre:	Various, including 9mm (.35in) Luger (P228) and 10.16mm (.4in) .40 S&W (P229)
Operation:	Short recoil
Weight:	.825kg (1.81lb) P228 .905kg (1.99lb) P229
Overall Length:	180mm (7.08in)
Barrel Length:	99mm (3.89in)
Muzzle Velocity:	Not known
Feed/Magazine:	12- or 13-round detachable box magazine
Range:	30m (98ft)

Astra A-75

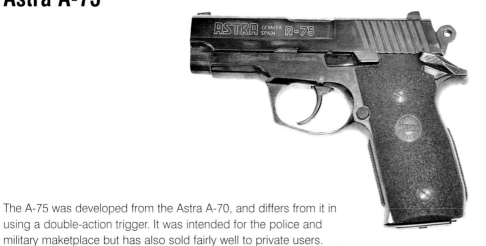

The A-75 was developed from the Astra A-70, and differs from it in using a double-action trigger. It was intended for the police and military maketplace but has also sold fairly well to private users.

SPECIFICATIONS	
Country of Origin:	Spain
Date:	1995
Calibre:	Various, including 9mm (.35in) Parabellum
Operation:	Recoil, double-action
Weight:	.82–1kg (1.8–2.2lb)
Overall Length:	166mm (6.5in)
Barrel Length:	89mm (3.5in)
Muzzle Velocity:	Not known
Feed/Magazine:	7- or 8-round detachable box magazine
Range:	30m (98ft)

SIG P232

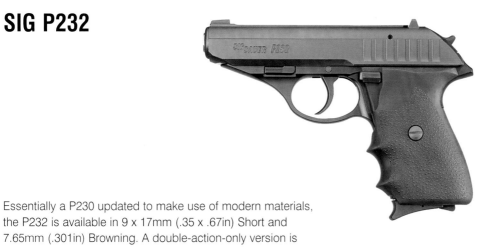

Essentially a P230 updated to make use of modern materials, the P232 is available in 9 x 17mm (.35 x .67in) Short and 7.65mm (.301in) Browning. A double-action-only version is also on offer.

SPECIFICATIONS	
Country of Origin:	Switzerland
Date:	1996
Calibre:	9mm (.35in), 7.65mm (.301in)
Operation:	DAO
Weight:	.5kg (1.1lb)
Overall Length:	168mm (6.61in)
Barrel Length:	92mm (3.62in)
Muzzle Velocity:	Not known
Feed/Magazine:	7-round (9mm/.35in) or 8-round (7.65mm/.301in) magazine
Range:	30m (98ft)

Kel-Tec PF-9

Marketed as the slimmest and lightest 9mm (.35in) handgun available, the PF-9 uses a single-stack magazine containing seven rounds. It is a double-action-only weapon and can be fired immediately upon being drawn.

SPECIFICATIONS	
Country of Origin:	United States
Date:	2006
Calibre:	9mm (.35in) Parabellum
Operation:	Short recoil
Weight:	.414kg (.91lb)
Overall Length:	149mm (5.85in)
Barrel Length:	79mm (3.1in)
Muzzle Velocity:	Not known
Feed/Magazine:	7-round detachable box magazine
Range:	30m (98ft)

1996

2006

New Concepts

Firearms technology continues to advance, with new concepts appearing and old ones being re-tried. Experimentation is not always successful, but those that do not try out new ideas risk being eclipsed by more innovative designers.

Ruger P90

The P90 is a double-action-only weapon designed primarily with safety in mind. A double-action weapon requires a much more deliberate trigger pull than a cocked semi-automatic, making accidental discharges and ill-considered shots less likely.

SPECIFICATIONS	
Country of Origin:	United States
Date:	1985
Calibre:	11.4mm (.45in) .45 ACP
Operation:	Short recoil
Weight:	.98kg (2.1lb)
Overall Length:	200mm (7.87in)
Barrel Length:	114mm (4.48in)
Muzzle Velocity:	380m/sec (1250ft/sec)
Feed/Magazine:	7- or 8-round detachable box magazine
Range:	50m (164ft)

Calico M-950

An innovative weapon that could be configured as a carbine, submachine gun or large handgun-like weapon, the M-950 used a helical feed magazine capable of holding 50 rounds. The US Assault Weapons Ban made civilian sales problematical.

SPECIFICATIONS	
Country of Origin:	United States
Date:	1990
Calibre:	9mm (.35in) Parabellum
Operation:	Delayed blowback
Weight:	1kg (2.2lb)
Overall Length:	365mm (14.3in)
Barrel Length:	152mm (6in)
Muzzle Velocity:	393m/sec (1290ft/sec)
Feed/Magazine:	50- or 100-round detachable helical magazine
Range:	60m (196ft)

TIMELINE

1985

1990

1994

Steyr SPP

The SPP, or Special Purpose Pistol, is a semi-automatic version of the firm's Tactical Machine Pistol (TMP) using more or less the same mechanism. The main difference is the lack of a foregrip.

SPECIFICATIONS	
Country of Origin:	Austria
Date:	1994
Calibre:	9mm (.35in)
Operation:	Short recoil, rotating barrel
Weight:	1.3kg (2.9lb)
Overall Length:	322mm (12.6in)
Barrel Length:	130mm (5.1in)
Muzzle Velocity:	380m/sec (1247ft/sec)
Feed/Magazine:	15- or 30-round detachable box magazine
Range:	100m (328ft)

Steyr M9/M40

Having been one of the first users of polymer construction (on their AUG rifle), Steyr used similar materials on their double-action semi-automatic. This weapon was the first pistol with an integrated key-lock to prevent unauthorized use.

SPECIFICATIONS (M9)	
Country of Origin:	Austria
Date:	1999
Calibre:	9mm (.35in)
Operation:	Short recoil, locked-breech
Weight:	.78kg (1.7lb)
Overall Length:	180mm (7.1in)
Barrel Length:	Not known
Muzzle Velocity:	Not known
Feed/Magazine:	14-round detachable box magazine
Range:	50m (164ft)

Steyr M-A1

In 2004, an improved version of the Steyr M series pistol went into production. The new Steyr M-A1 came with a redesigned grip, including some textured surfaces, and the ergonomics were slightly altered to improve handling.

SPECIFICATIONS	
Country of Origin:	Austria
Date:	2004
Calibre:	9mm (.35in) Parabellum
Operation:	Short recoil, locked-breech
Weight:	.851kg (1.87lb)
Overall Length:	176mm (6.9in)
Barrel Length:	102mm (4in)
Muzzle Velocity:	Not known
Feed/Magazine:	10- or 12-round detachable box magazine
Range:	50m (164ft)

1999

2004

Personal Defence Weapons

A relatively new concept, PDWs are intended, as the name suggests, for self-defensive use rather than infantry combat. They are optimized for high firepower at a modest range. Most use high-performance, small-calibre ammunition.

FN P90

Firing the same cartridge as the Five-Seven pistol, the P90 uses a novel loading system whereby rounds are carried in a clear plastic cartridge, lying at right angles to the barrel. Ejection is via the hollow grip.

SPECIFICATIONS	
Country of Origin:	Belgium
Date:	1990
Calibre:	5.7mm (.224in) FN
Operation:	Blowback
Weight:	2.8kg (6.17lb)
Overall Length:	400mm (15.75in)
Barrel Length:	263mm (7.75in)
Muzzle Velocity:	850m/sec (2800ft/sec)
Feed/Magazine:	50-round detachable box magazine
Range:	200m (656ft) +

H&K MP5K-PDW Personal Defence Weapon

A new incarnation of the excellent MP5K submachine gun, the MP5K-PDW can be concealed under a coat with the stock folded, or the stock can be removed and replaced by a buttcap if not needed. A suppressor can also be fitted.

SPECIFICATIONS	
Country of Origin:	Germany
Date:	1991
Calibre:	9mm (.35in) Parabellum
Operation:	Roller-delayed blowback, closed bolt
Weight:	2.1kg (4.63lb)
Overall Length:	325mm (12.8in)
Barrel Length:	115mm (4.53in)
Muzzle Velocity:	375m/sec (1230ft/sec)
Feed/Magazine:	15- or 30-round detachable box magazine
Range:	70m (230ft)

TIMELINE			
	 1990	1991	2001

H&K MP7

The MP7 uses the action of the G36 assault rifle, firing a high-velocity 4.6 x 30mm (.18 x 1.18in) cartridge with superior penetration qualities to the handgun-calibre rounds typically fired by submachine guns. The folding foregrip increases the user's options, which include one-handed automatic fire.

SPECIFICATIONS	
Country of Origin:	Germany
Date:	2001
Calibre:	4.6mm (.18in)
Operation:	Gas-operated, short-stroke piston, rotating bolt
Weight:	1.9kg (4.19lb) without magazine
Overall Length:	638mm (25.1in)
Barrel Length:	180mm (7.1in)
Muzzle Velocity:	c.725m/sec (2379ft/sec)
Feed/Magazine:	20-, 30-, 40-round box magazine
Range:	200m (656ft)

CZW 438 M9

Resembling a small assault rifle, the M9 is marketed as a PDW. It is effective at longer ranges than a typical submachine gun, but is lighter than an assault rifle and fires standard 9mm (.35in) Parabellum ammunition.

SPECIFICATIONS	
Country of Origin:	Czech Republic
Date:	2002
Calibre:	9mm (.35in)
Operation:	Lever-delayed blowback
Weight:	2.7kg (5.95lb)
Overall Length:	690mm (27.1in)
Barrel Length:	220mm (8.66in)
Muzzle Velocity:	Not known
Feed/Magazine:	15- or 30-round detachable box magazine
Range:	200m (656ft)

ST Kinetics CPW

A delayed-blowback weapon constructed of polymer and light alloys, the CPW is normally chambered for 9mm (.35in) but can be adapted by replacing the barrel and bolt if another calibre is desired.

SPECIFICATIONS	
Country of Origin:	Singapore
Date:	2007
Calibre:	9mm (.35in)
Operation:	Lever-delayed blowback
Weight:	1.5kg (3.31lb)
Overall Length:	500mm (19.7in)
Barrel Length:	180mm (7.1in)
Muzzle Velocity:	Not known
Feed/Magazine:	30-round plastic bdetachable box magazine
Range:	100m (328ft)

2002

2007

Smaller Personal Defence Weapons

Approaches to the PDW concept vary considerably; PDWs range from carbine-type weapons to overgrown handguns. The latter are effective only at short ranges but offer vastly more firepower than a handgun without weighing much more.

PM-63 (Wz63)

Long before the term 'Personal Defence Weapon' was coined, designers were trying to wring more firepower out of a handgun-sized package. The PM-63 is an overgrown pistol; it has a slide rather than an internal bolt.

SPECIFICATIONS	
Country of Origin:	Poland
Date:	1964
Calibre:	9mm (.35in) Makarov
Operation:	Straight blowback
Weight:	1.6kg (3.53lb)
Overall Length:	583mm (23in)
Barrel Length:	152mm (6in)
Muzzle Velocity:	320m/sec (1050ft/sec)
Feed/Magazine:	15- or 25-round detachable box magazine
Range:	100–150m (328–492ft)

Ruger MP-9

Designed by Uziel Gal, it is no surprise that the MP-9 uses a similar mechanism to the Uzi. It fires from a closed bolt, however, and is made from more modern materials.

SPECIFICATIONS	
Country of Origin:	United States
Date:	1995
Calibre:	9mm (.35in) Parabellum
Operation:	Blowback
Weight:	3kg (6.61lb)
Overall Length:	556mm (21.8in)
Barrel Length:	Not known
Muzzle Velocity:	Not known
Feed/Magazine:	32-round detachable box magazine
Range:	100m (328ft)

TIMELINE

 1964
 1995
 1999

H&K UMP

H&K's Universal Machine Pistol (UMP) is available chambered for 11.4mm/.45in .45 ACP, 10.16mm/.4in .40 S&W and 9mm (.35in) Parabellum. A range of accessories and configurations are available, including different configurations of the trigger group to give various burst and automatic fire options.

SPECIFICATIONS	
Country of Origin:	Germany
Date:	1999
Calibre:	11.4mm (.45in) .45 ACP, 10.16mm (.4in) .40 S&W, 9mm (.35in) Parabellum
Operation:	Blowback, closed bolt
Weight:	2.3kg (5lb)
Overall Length:	690mm (27.2in)
Barrel Length:	200mm (7.9in)
Muzzle Velocity:	Not known
Feed/Magazine:	25- or 30-round detachable box magazine
Range:	100m (328ft)

Steyr TMP

Steyr's Tactical Machine Pistol is simply a very small short-recoil-operated submachine gun. It is highly controllable under automatic fire, and thus capable of greater precision than many other small submachine gun designs.

SPECIFICATIONS	
Country of Origin:	Austria
Date:	2000
Calibre:	9mm (.35in) Parabellum
Operation:	Short recoil, rotating barrel
Weight:	1.3kg (2.9lb)
Overall Length:	282mm (11.1in)
Barrel Length:	130mm (5.1in)
Muzzle Velocity:	380m/sec (1247ft/sec)
Feed/Magazine:	15- or 30-round detachable box magazine
Range:	100m (328ft)

AGRAM 2000

Although based on a Beretta design rather than the Uzi, the Croatian AGRAM is compatible with Uzi magazines and is constructed from stamped sheet steel in a similar manner.

SPECIFICATIONS	
Country of Origin:	Croatia
Date:	2000
Calibre:	9mm (.35in) Parabellum
Operation:	Blowback
Weight:	1.8kg (3.96lb)
Overall Length:	482mm (18.9in)
Barrel Length:	200mm (7.8in)
Muzzle Velocity:	Not known
Feed/Magazine:	15-, 22-, 32-round detachable box magazine
Range:	100m (328ft)

Colt 9mm SMG

There is a fine line between an assault rifle and a submachine gun, and it is not always possible to differentiate simply by the ammunition type fired. As a general rule, a small automatic weapon firing pistol cartridges is a submachine gun and one that fires rifle-calibre rounds is an assault rifle.

STOCK
The already small dimensions of the M4 carbine are well suited to conversion to a submachine gun.

GRIP
The grip and controls remain unchanged, simplifying training for troops used to the M16/M4 family of weapons.

SPECIFICATIONS	
Country of Origin:	United States
Date:	late 1980s
Calibre:	9mm (.35in) Parabellum
Operation:	Blowback, closed bolt
Weight:	2.6kg (5.75lb)
Overall Length:	730mm (28.9in)
Barrel Length:	267mm (10.5in)
Muzzle Velocity:	396m/sec (1300ft/sec)
Feed/Magazine:	32-round detachable box magazine
Range:	300m (984ft)

However, some manufacturers muddy the waters by marketing rifle-calibre weapons as submachine guns, and the recent development of personal defence weapons has further confused the issue. Perhaps the only deciding factor is that a weapon is whatever the manufacturers say it is.

The Colt 9mm Submachine gun closely resembles the M16 rifle it is based upon, other than its short barrel and the curiously undersized appearance of its magazine. Adapting a rifle in this way results in a larger weapon than most custom-designed submachine guns, though it does have the advantage that troops trained to use an M16 have little difficulty converting to the 9mm (.35in) version.

BARREL
The main component of the conversion process is replacement of the barrel and chamber. Sights and foregrip remain unchanged.

HANDLE
The carrying handle is somewhat superfluous in a submachine gun, but as it houses the sights, it is simplest to leave it in place.

MAGAZINE
The magazine-well requires an internal conversion to ensure that the narrower 9mm (.35in) magazines are properly guided into position.

Assault Rifle Development

Many different approaches are possible in modern assault rifle design. Some introduce new features or a new take on an existing design; others are more conservative. The Bullpup-vs-traditional-layout debate continues; there are advantages and disadvantages to both.

LAPA FA-03

Produced in small numbers in the early 1980s, the FA-03 is chiefly notable for its double-action trigger which allows the weapon to be carried ready to fire but relatively safe. It is used by some Brazilian police units.

SPECIFICATIONS	
Country of Origin:	Brazil
Date:	1983
Calibre:	5.56mm (.219in)
Operation:	Gas-operated, rotating bolt
Weight:	3.5kg (7.72lb)
Overall Length:	738mm (29.1in)
Barrel Length:	490mm (19.3in)
Muzzle Velocity:	975m/sec (3200ft/sec)
Feed/Magazine:	20- or 30-round STANAG or 30-round proprietary clear plastic detachable box magazine
Range:	550m (1804ft)

SIG 550

Adopted by the Swiss Army as the StG90, the SIG 550 is in many ways a traditional design, but much careful thought went into its 'usability'. It has spawned a family of variants including short-barrelled carbine versions.

SPECIFICATIONS	
Country of Origin:	Switzerland
Date:	1986
Calibre:	5.56mm (.219in)
Operation:	Gas-operated, rotating bolt
Weight:	4.1kg (9.1lb)
Overall Length:	998mm (39.3in)
Barrel Length:	528mm (20.8in)
Muzzle Velocity:	911m/sec (2989ft/sec)
Feed/Magazine:	5-, 20-, or 30-round detachable box magazine
Range:	100–400m (328–1312ft)

TIMELINE

1983

1986

H&K G11

SPECIFICATIONS	
Country of Origin:	Germany
Date:	1990
Calibre:	4.7mm (.185in) DM11 caseless
Operation:	Gas-operated
Weight:	3.8kg (8.38lb)
Overall Length:	752.5mm (29.62in)
Barrel Length:	537.5mm (21.16in)
Muzzle Velocity:	930m/sec (3050ft/sec)
Feed/Magazine:	50-round detachable box magazine
Range:	500m (1640ft) +

An extremely advanced weapon, the G11 uses caseless ammunition, i.e. there is no cartridge case, just a formed block of propellant. This means there is nothing to eject. Despite extensive testing, the G11 has not been adopted for service.

Daewoo K1/K2

Seeking a replacement for its licence-built M16s, South Korea developed the K1 rifle and from it the K2, which is capable of semi- or full-automatic as well as burst fire. It can be fitted with a 40mm (1.57in) grenade launcher.

SPECIFICATIONS	
Country of Origin:	South Korea
Date:	1990
Calibre:	5.56mm (.219in) NATO
Operation:	Gas-operated, rotating bolt
Weight:	2.87kg (6.32lb)
Overall Length:	838mm (32.99in) K1; 980mm (38.58in) K2
Barrel Length:	263mm (10.35in) K1; 465mm (18.3in) K2
Muzzle Velocity:	820m/sec (2690ft/sec)
Feed/Magazine:	Various STANAG magazines
Range:	250m (820ft)

QBZ-03

SPECIFICATIONS	
Country of Origin:	China
Date:	2003
Calibre:	5.8mm (.228in) DBP87, 5.56mm (.219in) NATO
Operation:	Gas-operated, rotating bolt
Weight:	3.5kg (7.71lb)
Overall Length:	960mm (37.79in) stock extended; 710mm (27.95in) stock folded
Barrel Length:	Not known
Muzzle Velocity:	930m/sec (3050ft/sec)
Feed/Magazine:	30-round detachable box magazine
Range:	400m (1312ft)

Disappointed with the QBZ-95, the Chinese military requested a more traditional assault rifle which would still use the new 5.8 x 42mm (.228 x 1.65in) cartridge. The resulting QBZ-03 resembles the Type 87 rifle, a special project implemented to test the new ammunition.

1990

2003

Advanced Traditional Assault Rifles

Even though the bullpup configuration has its advantages, it has not been universally adopted. Many modern assault rifles retain the traditional magazine position, in front of the trigger group, though they do not always resemble the rifles of previous generations.

AK-103

An updated and modified AK-74, the AK-103 returns to the 7.62 x 39mm (.3 x 1.54in) cartridge used by the original AK-47. It is intended mainly for the export market but is also used by some Russian police agencies.

SPECIFICATIONS	
Country of Origin:	Russia
Date:	1994
Calibre:	7.62mm (.3in)
Operation:	Gas-operated
Weight:	3.4kg (7.49lb)
Overall Length:	943mm (37.1in)
Barrel Length:	415mm (16.3in)
Muzzle Velocity:	735m/sec (2411ft/sec)
Feed/Magazine:	30-round detachable box magazine
Range:	300m (984ft) +

AN-94

Designed as a successor to the Russian Army's AK-74s, the AN-94 is a complex weapon capable of firing two-round bursts at an extremely high rate of fire, or on full-automatic at a lower rate.

SPECIFICATIONS	
Country of Origin:	Russia
Date:	1994
Calibre:	5.45mm (.215in)
Operation:	Gas-operated
Weight:	3.85kg (8.49lb)
Overall Length:	943mm (37.1in)
Barrel Length:	405mm (15.in)
Muzzle Velocity:	900m/sec (2953ft/sec)
Feed/Magazine:	30- or 45-round AK-74-compatible box magazine; 60-round casket magazine
Range:	400m (1312ft)

TIMELINE

1994

1995

H&K G36

The G36 uses a gas-operated action rather than H&K's famous roller-locking system. It is available in assault rifle, carbine and light support weapon confgurations, and has been adopted by the German Army.

SPECIFICATIONS	
Country of Origin:	Germany
Date:	1995
Calibre:	5.56mm (.219in) NATO
Operation:	Gas-operated
Weight:	3.4kg (7.49lb)
Overall Length:	999mm (39.3in) stock extended; 758mm (29.8in) stock folded
Barrel Length:	480mm (18.9in)
Muzzle Velocity:	920m/sec (3018ft/sec)
Feed/Magazine:	30-round detachable box or 100-round C-Mag drum magazine
Range:	800m (2625ft)

INSAS Assault Rifle

Based on a developed version of the AK-47 action, the INSAS (Indian National Small Arms System) rifle is gas-operated and capable of semi- or full-automatic fire in addition to three-round bursts. An LMG version is also manufactured.

SPECIFICATIONS	
Country of Origin:	India
Date:	1999
Calibre:	5.56mm (.219in) NATO
Operation:	Gas-operated, self-loading
Weight:	3.2kg (7.05lb)
Overall Length:	990mm (38.97in)
Barrel Length:	464mm (18.26in)
Muzzle Velocity:	985m/sec (2903ft/sec)
Feed/Magazine:	20- or 30-round detachable box magazine
Range:	800m (2625ft)

FX-05 Xiuhcoatl

Although heavily influenced by the G36, the FX-05 is sufficiently different to escape a patent infringement suit from H&K. Three variants are available – a full-sized assault rifle, a carbine and a shorter carbine.

SPECIFICATIONS	
Country of Origin:	Mexico
Date:	2008
Calibre:	5.56 (.219in) NATO
Operation:	Gas-operated, rotating bolt
Weight:	3.89kg (8.6lb) assault rifle
Overall Length:	1087mm (42.8in) stock extended 887mm (34.9in) stock folded
Barrel Length:	Not known
Muzzle Velocity:	956m/sec (3136ft/sec)
Feed/Magazine:	30-round detachable box magazine
Range:	c.800m (2625ft)

1999   2008

Beretta SC70/90

The SC70/90 is the carbine form of the AR70/90 rifle. This weapon was developed in response to a request from the Italian Army for a new assault rifle to use 5.56mm (.219in) NATO ammunition and standard M16-type (STANAG) magazines. It was first produced in the mid-1980s but was not approved for service for some years. Once in service, it was followed by the SC70/90 carbine and its variants. The SC carbine differs from the AR rifle only in having a folding stock rather than a fixed one; barrel length is the same.

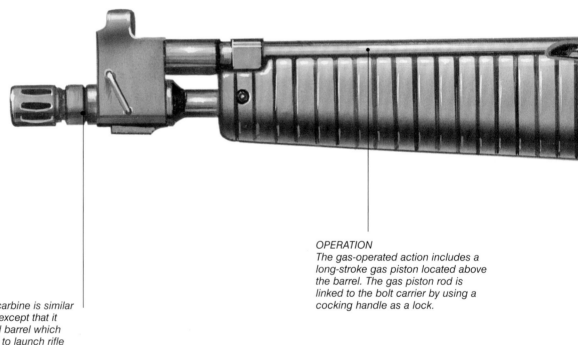

OPERATION
The gas-operated action includes a long-stroke gas piston located above the barrel. The gas piston rod is linked to the bolt carrier by using a cocking handle as a lock.

BARREL
The SCP70/90 carbine is similar to the SC70/90 except that it has a shortened barrel which cannot be used to launch rifle grenades directly.

SPECIFICATIONS	
Country of Origin:	Italy
Date:	1990
Calibre:	5.56mm (.219in) NATO
Operation:	Gas-operated
Weight:	3.79kg (8.36lb)
Overall Length:	876mm (34.49in)
Barrel Length:	369mm (14.5in)
Muzzle Velocity:	Not known
Feed:	30-round detachable box magazine
Range:	100m (328ft)

Variants of the SC70/90 include the SCS70/90 which can take an under-barrel grenade launcher, and the SCP70/90 which has a shorter barrel. Unlike other weapons in this family, the SCP cannot launch rifle grenades as it stands, but an adaptor is available to permit this if it seems desirable.

STOCK
All SC70/90 carbines use skeletonized folding stocks which are designed not to interfere with either right- or left-handed shooting when folded. Stocks are composed of plastic-coated metal.

MAGAZINE
Feeding is from the proprietary 30-round magazines, with the magazine release lever located between the magazine and the trigger guard.

Bullpup Assault Rifles

Many weapon designers choose to follow a bullpup configuration. The main disadvantage with this is that many weapons are impossible to use from the left shoulder, as spent cases are ejected into the side of the user's head.

QBZ-95

Built around a new 5.8 x 42mm (.228 x 1.65in) cartridge, the QBZ-95 is the assault rifle member of a family of weapons that also includes a carbine and a light support weapon. Its ejector position makes it impossible to use left-handed.

SPECIFICATIONS	
Country of Origin:	China
Date:	1997
Calibre:	5.8mm (.228in) DBP87
Operation:	Gas-operated, rotating bolt
Weight:	3.25kg (7.2lb)
Overall Length:	745mm (29.3in) rifle
Barrel Length:	463mm (18.2in)
Muzzle Velocity:	930m/sec (3050ft/sec)
Feed/Magazine:	30-round box or 75-round drum magazine
Range:	400m (1312ft)

SAR-21

The SAR-21 is a compact bullpup weapon which is equipped with a laser pointer as standard. It ejects spent cartridges to the right and cannot be converted to left-side extraction, which makes use by left-handed shooters problematical.

SPECIFICATIONS	
Country of Origin:	Singapore
Date:	1999
Calibre:	5.56mm (.219in) NATO
Operation:	Gas-operated, rotating bolt
Weight:	3.82kg (8.42lb)
Overall Length:	805mm (31.7in)
Barrel Length:	508mm (20in)
Muzzle Velocity:	970m/sec (3182ft/sec)
Feed/Magazine:	30-round box magazine; plastic or STANAG magazines
Range:	460m (1509ft)

TIMELINE   1997   1999

FN F2000

The F2000 was the first fully ambidextrous bullpup weapon. It is extremely compact and well balanced, and its modular construction allows accessories to be easily added. These include different sights, a grenade launcher or a less-lethal weapons launcher.

SPECIFICATIONS	
Country of Origin:	Belgium
Date:	2001
Calibre:	5.56mm (.219in) NATO
Operation:	Gas-operated, rotating bolt
Weight:	3.6kg (7.93lb)
Overall Length:	694mm (27.3in)
Barrel Length:	400mm (15.7in)
Muzzle Velocity:	900m/sec (2953ft/sec)
Feed/Magazine:	30-round detachable box magazine
Range:	500m (1640ft)

IMI Tavor TAR 21

Developed as the Israeli Army's new service weapon, the TAR 21 does not use a separate receiver. Instead, all its parts are contained within the plastic housing and accessed by swinging the hinged buttplate down.

SPECIFICATIONS	
Country of Origin:	Israel
Date:	2001
Calibre:	5.56mm (.219in) NATO
Operation:	Gas-operated, rotating bolt
Weight:	3.27kg (7.21lb)
Overall Length:	720mm (28.3in)
Barrel Length:	460mm (18.1in)
Muzzle Velocity:	910m/sec (2986ft/sec)
Feed/Magazine:	Various STANAG magazines
Range:	550m (1804ft)

Khaybar KH 2002

The KH 2002 was developed by converting the Iranian S-5.56 rifle, itself a copy of the Chinese CQ rifle, to a bullpup configuration. It is available as a carbine, assault rifle, or with a longer barrel for use by designated marksmen.

SPECIFICATIONS	
Country of Origin:	Iran
Date:	2004
Calibre:	5.56mm (.219in)
Operation:	Gas-operated, rotating bolt
Weight:	3.7kg (8.15lb)
Overall Length:	730mm (28.7in)
Barrel Length:	Not known
Muzzle Velocity:	900–950m/sec (2952–3116ft/sec)
Feed/Magazine:	Various STANAG magazines
Range:	450m (1476ft)

2001

2004

Multi- and Larger-Calibre Assault Rifles

Recent years have seen renewed interest in larger-calibre assault rifles, and in combination weapons that use more than one calibre in order to give the rifleman additional capabilities. The technical challenges are significant, however.

XM29/Objective Infantry Combat Weapon

The XM29 OICW combines a semi-automatic grenade launcher, originally 20mm (.78in) and later 25mm (.98in), with a 5.56mm (.219in) assault rifle. Problems with weight and bulk have yet to be overcome, and the project has been diverged into its rifle and launcher components.

SPECIFICATIONS	
Country of Origin:	United States
Date:	2003
Calibre:	5.56mm (.219in) NATO plus 20mm (.78in) or 25mm (.98in)
Operation:	Gas-operated, rotating bolt
Weight:	5.5kg (12.12lb)
Overall Length:	890mm (35.03in)
Barrel Length:	460mm (18.11in)
Muzzle Velocity:	Not known
Feed/Magazine:	Various STANAG magazines
Range:	1000m (3280ft)

Advanced Infantry Combat Weapon

The AICW project combines the Australian F88 rifle with a Metal Storm 40mm (1.57in) grenade launcher. As with the OICW project, the weapon is very promising but faces significant technical problems before it is ready for widespread use.

SPECIFICATIONS	
Country of Origin:	Australia
Date:	2005
Calibre:	5.56mm (.219in) NATO plus 40mm (1.57in)
Operation:	Gas-operated, rotating bolt, plus electronic fire control and grenade firing
Weight:	6.48kg (14.28lb)
Overall Length:	738mm (29.05in)
Barrel Length:	508mm (20in)
Muzzle Velocity:	950m/sec (3116ft/sec)
Feed/Magazine:	30-round detachable magazine plus Metal Storm patented stacked projectile system with 3 grenades
Range:	500m (1640ft)

TIMELINE

2003

2005

2009

FN SCAR

SPECIFICATIONS	
Country of Origin:	United States
Date:	2009
Calibre:	7.62mm (.3in) SCAR-H,
	5.56mm (.219in) SCAR-L
Operation:	Gas-operated, rotating bolt
Weight:	3.58kg (7.9lb) SCAR-H;
	3.29kg (7.3lb) SCAR-L
Overall Length:	Various, depending on variant
Barrel Length:	400mm (16in) SCAR-H;
	351mm (13.8in) SCAR-L
Muzzle Velocity:	870m/sec (2870ft/sec)
Feed/Magazine:	20-round box magazine (SCAR-H)
	or STANAG box magazine (SCAR-L)
Range:	600m (1968ft)

The SCAR (Special Forces Combat Assault Rifle) is a family of weapons chambered for 5.56mm/.219in (SCAR-L) and 7.62mm/.3in (SCAR-H) ammunition. A common receiver can be assembled into a variety of configurations. These include sniper, close combat and general-purpose variants.

SIG 716

SPECIFICATIONS	
Country of Origin:	Switzerland
Date:	2011
Calibre:	7.62mm (.3in)
Operation:	Gas-operated, rotating bolt
Weight:	3.58kg (7.9lb)
Overall Length:	Not known
Barrel Length:	504mm (20in)
Muzzle Velocity:	Not known
Feed/Magazine:	10- or 20-round detachable box
	magazine
Range:	600m (1968ft)

The SIG 716 is based on the M16 family of weapons, but is chambered for 7.62mm (.3in) instead. The 'patrol' configuration uses a fairly short barrel, with a 'precision' version available with a longer barrel.

XM25

SPECIFICATIONS	
Country of Origin:	United States
Date:	2011
Calibre:	25mm (.98in)
Operation:	Gas-operated
Weight:	6.35kg (14lb)
Overall Length:	737mm (29in)
Barrel Length:	460mm (18.11in)
Muzzle Velocity:	210m/sec (690ft/sec)
Feed/Magazine:	N/A
Range:	500m (1640ft)

Essentially the grenade launcher component of the XM29, the XM25 is designed to deliver 25mm (.98in) grenades of various types. Range is computed with the help of a laser rangefinder, allowing an accurate airburst over an enemy using frontal cover.

2011

Metal Storm

The Metal Storm technology offers new possibilities for support weapons. Rather than storing ammunition in a magazine or belt, Metal Storm uses projectiles 'stacked' in the weapon barrel and fired by an electrically initiated primer.

GRENADE
Grenades are stacked one atop another in the launcher tube, which serves as muzzle and magazine in one.

LAUNCHER MUZZLE
Metal Storm technology is used for the launcher component of the Australian Advanced Infantry Combat Weapon project.

RIFLE
The assault rifle component of the weapon uses conventional ammunition.

SPECIFICATIONS	
Country of Origin:	Australia
Date:	2005
Calibre:	5.56mm (.219in) NATO plus 40mm (1.57in)
Operation:	Gas-operated, rotating bolt, plus electronic fire control and grenade firing
Weight:	6.48kg (14.28lb)
Overall Length:	738mm (29.05in)
Barrel Length:	508mm (20in)
Muzzle Velocity:	950m/sec (3116ft/sec)
Feed/Magazine:	30-round detachable magazine plus Metal Storm patented stacked projectile system with 3 grenades
Range:	500m (1640ft)

Electrically controlled operation grants some options that are not available with conventional weapons. It is possible to set up a fire pattern with several support weapons and launchers, and to deliver a saturation attack at a single keystroke on the controlling laptop. However, in a small-arms context the most important advantage is the ability to carry several grenades in a launcher, ready to fire, without needing a bulky feed device or separately carried grenades.

A Metal Storm weapon is not, correctly speaking, a 'machine gun' as it operates in a quite different manner. Extremely high rates of fire are possible from small-calibre support weapons and grenade launchers using this technology, which permits several grenades to be fired in very rapid succession by an infantryman, without having to reload the launcher.

BASE OF GRENADES
Grenades are initiated electrically rather than by a traditional primer, so do not need to be moved to a firing chamber before launch.

LAUNCHER
The Metal Storm launcher gives the user considerably more firepower than a single-shot grenade launcher, and is always ready to fire.

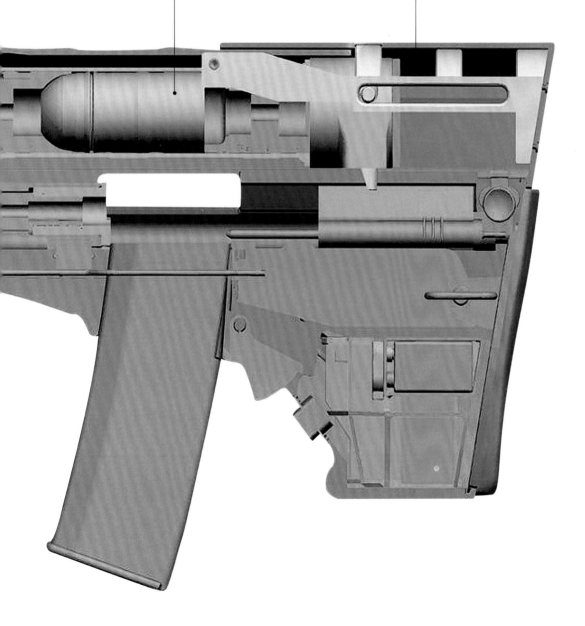

Modern Sniper Rifles

Modern sniper rifles are, on the whole, vastly more expensive than standard infantry weapons. It is possible to put together an effective sniping rifle at a fraction of the cost, though top-end capability will not be achieved.

Heckler & Koch G3SG/1

One of many variants on the G3, the G3SG/1 is modified with an improved trigger group and a carefully selected barrel. Adding a bipod and telescopic sight creates a rugged sniping weapon which has been adopted for police service.

SPECIFICATIONS	
Country of Origin:	Germany
Date:	1990
Calibre:	7.62mm (.3in) NATO
Operation:	Delayed blowback
Weight:	4.4kg (9.7lb)
Overall Length:	1025mm (40.35in)
Barrel Length:	450mm (17.71in)
Muzzle Velocity:	800m/sec (2625ft/sec)
Feed/Magazine:	20-round detachable box magazine
Range:	500m (1640ft) +

Stoner SR-25

Although it looks like a converted assault rifle, the SR-25 was designed from the outset as a sniper weapon. It is extremely accurate but requires careful maintenance to avoid reliability issues.

SPECIFICATIONS	
Country of Origin:	United States
Date:	1990
Calibre:	7.62mm (.3in) NATO
Operation:	Gas-operated, rotating bolt
Weight:	4.88kg (10.75lb)
Overall Length:	1118mm (44in)
Barrel Length:	610mm (24in)
Muzzle Velocity:	780m/sec (2559ft/sec)
Feed/Magazine:	10- or 20-round detachable box magazine
Range:	500m (1640ft) +

TIMELINE

1990

1996

SIG SSG550 Sniper

Developed in conjunction with various law enforcement agencies, the SSG550 differs considerably from military sniper rifles. It is chambered for the relatively light 5.56mm/.219in .223 Remington round and has a very precise trigger pull, even by the standards of sniping weapons.

SPECIFICATIONS	
Country of Origin:	Switzerland
Date:	1996
Calibre:	5.56mm (.219in) .223 Remington
Operation:	Gas-operated, semi-automatic
Weight:	7.02kg (15.47lb)
Overall Length:	1130mm (44.48in)
Barrel Length:	650mm (25.59in)
Muzzle Velocity:	911m/sec (2989ft/sec)
Feed/Magazine:	5-, 20- or 30-round detachable box magazine
Range:	100–400m (328–1312ft)

M39 Marksman Rifle

Descended from the venerable M14, the M39 is intended for use by marksmen (not necessarily snipers) who may need to shoot out to 800m (2625ft) or more. It can also function as a battle rifle at closer ranges if necessary.

SPECIFICATIONS	
Country of Origin:	United States
Date:	2008
Calibre:	7.62mm (.3in) NATO
Operation:	Gas-operated, rotating bolt
Weight:	7.5kg (16.5lb)
Overall Length:	1120mm (44.2in)
Barrel Length:	560mm (22in)
Muzzle Velocity:	865m/sec (2837ft/sec)
Feed/Magazine:	20-round detachable box magazine
Range:	780m (2559ft)

M110 Semi-Automatic Sniper System

Although light by the standards of sniper rifles, the M110 proved itself in Afghanistan. Semi-automatic weapons offer an advantage over bolt-action rifles, in that they possess the ability to engage groups of targets rapidly.

SPECIFICATIONS	
Country of Origin:	United States
Date:	2008
Calibre:	7.62mm (.3in) NATO
Operation:	Gas-operated, rotating bolt
Weight:	6.94kg (15.3lb)
Overall Length:	1029mm (40.5in)
Barrel Length:	508mm (20in)
Muzzle Velocity:	783m/sec (2570ft/sec)
Feed/Magazine:	10- or 20-round detachable box magazine
Range:	800m (2625ft)

2008

Changing Needs, New Developments

Sniper rifles continue to develop in order to use new technology or to fit new requirements. Longer accurate range is usually desirable, though other factors such as the capability for a fast follow-up shot may influence a design.

Accuracy International L96A1

In service with the British Army since the 1980s, the L96A1 is normally chambered for 7.62 x 51mm (.3 x 2in) but is available in other calibres. A silenced version and a single-shot long-range variant have both been fielded.

SPECIFICATIONS	
Country of Origin:	United Kingdom
Date:	1985
Calibre:	7.62mm (.3in) NATO and others
Operation:	Bolt action
Weight:	6.2kg (13.68lb)
Overall Length:	1163mm (45in)
Barrel Length:	654mm (26in)
Muzzle Velocity:	840m/sec (2830ft/sec)
Feed/Magazine:	10-round detachable box magazine
Range:	1000m (3280ft)

L115A3/AWM

The L115A3, or Arctic Warfare Magnum, can be chambered for 7.62mm/.3in (.300 Winchester Magnum) or the specialist long-range 8.58mm/.338in (.338 Lapua Magnum) round. The current record for a long-range sniper shot was set in 2009 with this weapon.

SPECIFICATIONS	
Country of Origin:	United Kingdom
Date:	1997
Calibre:	7.62mm (.3in) .300 Winchester Magnum, 8.58mm (.338in) .338 Lapua Magnum
Operation:	Bolt action
Weight:	6.8kg (15lb)
Overall Length:	1300mm (51in)
Barrel Length:	686mm (27in)
Muzzle Velocity:	c.850m/sec (2788ft/sec)
Feed/Magazine:	5-round detachable box magazine
Range:	1100m (3609ft) .300 Winchester; 1500m (4921ft) .338 Lapua

TIMELINE

1985   1997   1999

Sako TRG 22

A bolt-action weapon chambered for 7.62mm (.3in) .308 Winchester ammunition, the TRG 22 is fully adjustable in terms of trigger pull, stock and even the height of the optional bipod. The rifle can be precisely fitted to its user.

SPECIFICATIONS	
Country of Origin:	Finland
Date:	1999
Calibre:	7.62mm (.3in) .308 Winchester
Operation:	Bolt action
Weight:	4.9kg (10.8lb)
Overall Length:	1150mm (45.28in)
Barrel Length:	660mm (25.98in)
Muzzle Velocity:	c.850m/sec (2788ft/sec)
Feed/Magazine:	5-, 7- or 10-round detachable box magazine
Range:	1100m (3609ft)

SIG SSG3000

The SSG3000 uses a modified Mauser-type bolt and is offered with the choice of a one-stage or two-stage trigger. Its modular construction enables conversion to other calibres, for example to 5.6mm/.22in (.22 Rimfire) for training purposes.

SPECIFICATIONS	
Country of Origin:	Switzerland
Date:	2005
Calibre:	7.62mm (.3in) NATO
Operation:	Bolt action
Weight:	5.4kg (11.9lb)
Overall Length:	1180mm (45.5in)
Barrel Length:	610mm (24in)
Muzzle Velocity:	830m/sec (2723ft/sec)
Feed/Magazine:	5-round box magazine
Range:	1000m (3280ft)

L129A1 Sharpshooter Rifle

The L129A1 was adopted for use by British Army sharpshooters in response to experience in Afghanistan. Although not trained to the same standards as snipers, these personnel can engage distant targets beyond the capabilities of ordinary infantry with assault rifles.

SPECIFICATIONS	
Country of Origin:	United Kingdom
Date:	2010
Calibre:	7.62mm (.3in) NATO
Operation:	Gas-operated, semi-automatic
Weight:	4.5kg (9.92lb)
Overall Length:	990mm (38.9in)
Barrel Length:	406mm (16in)
Muzzle Velocity:	Not known
Feed/Magazine:	20-round detachable box magazine
Range:	800m (2625ft)

2005

2010

Heavy Sniper Rifles

Very large-calibre sniper weapons are usually referred to as Anti-Materiel Rifles since their normal use is to attack targets such as vehicles and communications equipment. However, they can also be used for long-range sniping against personnel.

Barrett M82A1 'Light Fifty'

The first large-calibre sniper weapon to achieve widespread popularity, the M82A1 uses a short-recoil system and has a large muzzle brake to reduce recoil. It uses a 12.7 x 99mm (.5 x 3.9in) cartridge originally developed for the Browning M2HB machine gun.

SPECIFICATIONS	
Country of Origin:	United States
Date:	1983
Calibre:	12.7mm (.5in) .50 BMG
Operation:	Short recoil, semi-automatic
Weight:	14.7kg (32.41lb)
Overall Length:	1549mm (60.98in)
Barrel Length:	838mm (33in)
Muzzle Velocity:	843m/sec (2800ft/sec)
Feed/Magazine:	11-round detachable box magazine
Range:	1000m (3280ft) +

Harris (McMillan) M87R

The M87R is a magazine-fed version of the earlier McMillan M87. The firm was bought out by Harris Gunworks in 1995, hence the change of name. The weapons themselves remained in production; no design changes were made.

SPECIFICATIONS	
Country of Origin:	United States
Date:	1987
Calibre:	12.7mm (.5in)
Operation:	Bolt action
Weight:	9.53kg (21lb)
Overall Length:	1346mm (53in)
Barrel Length:	736mm (29in)
Muzzle Velocity:	853m/sec (2800ft/sec)
Feed/Magazine:	5-round detachable box magazine
Range:	1000m (3280ft) +

TIMELINE			
	1983	1987	1993

PGM Hecate II

Used by the French Army since the 1990s, the Hecate II uses a skeleton-type construction. The barrel has vents to protect the user if a cartridge ruptures during firing, and a very large muzzle brake to reduce felt recoil.

SPECIFICATIONS	
Country of Origin:	France
Date:	1993
Calibre:	12.7mm (.5in) .50 BMG
Operation:	Bolt action
Weight:	13.8kg (30.42lb)
Overall Length:	1380mm (54.3in)
Barrel Length:	700mm (27.6in)
Muzzle Velocity:	825m/sec (2707ft/sec)
Feed/Magazine:	7-round detachable box magazine
Range:	2000m (6560ft) +

McMillan TAC-50

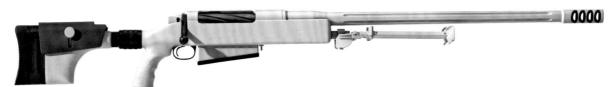

The standard long-range sniping weapon of the Canadian armed forces, the TAC-50 was used in 2003 to make what was at the time the longest-range sniper kill on record. This record was broken by the same rifle shortly afterwards.

SPECIFICATIONS	
Country of Origin:	United States
Date:	2000
Calibre:	12.7mm (.5in)
Operation:	Manually operated rotary bolt action
Weight:	11.8kg (26lb)
Overall Length:	1448mm (57in)
Barrel Length:	736mm (29in)
Muzzle Velocity:	823m/sec (2700ft/sec)
Feed/Magazine:	5-round detachable box magazine
Range:	1600m (5249ft)

Accuracy International AS50

A semi-automatic 12.7mm (.5in) rifle, the AS50 uses a muzzle brake and cushioned buttpad to absorb some of the weapon's recoil and thus permit a rapid follow-up shot if necessary.

SPECIFICATIONS	
Country of Origin:	United Kingdom
Date:	2006
Calibre:	12.7mm (.5in)
Operation:	Gas-operated (direct impingement)
Weight:	12.2kg (27lb)
Overall Length:	1369mm (53.9in)
Barrel Length:	692mm (27.2in)
Muzzle Velocity:	Not known
Feed/Magazine:	5- or 10-round detachable box magazine
Range:	1500m (4921ft)

Anti-Materiel Rifles

Anti-Materiel Rifles have obvious military applications but are also used in law enforcement to disable the engine of a suspect vehicle or boat. A 12.7mm (.5in) bullet will smash an engine block with ease.

RAI Model 500

The Model 500 was one of the first 12.7mm (.5in) sniper weapons, and its design was purchased by various manufacturers, none of whom produced very large numbers. Favourable results in the field nevertheless prompted interest in large-bore sniper weapons.

SPECIFICATIONS	
Country of Origin:	United States
Date:	1983
Calibre:	12.7mm (.5in)
Operation:	Bolt action
Weight:	5.7kg (12.56lb)
Overall Length:	1384mm (54.4in)
Barrel Length:	813mm (32in)
Muzzle Velocity:	Not known
Feed/Magazine:	4- or 5-round detachable box magazine
Range:	1500m (4921ft)

Gepard M1

The single-shot Gepard M1 can quickly be converted from firing NATO 12.7 x 99mm (.5 x 3.9in) to Russian 12.7 x 107mm (.5 x 4.2in) ammunition. It uses an artillery-style recoil system, the barrel and firing mechanism recoiling together.

SPECIFICATIONS	
Country of Origin:	Hungary
Date:	1990
Calibre:	12.7mm (.5in) NATO and Russian
Operation:	Bolt action
Weight:	17.5kg (38.6lb)
Overall Length:	1570mm (61.8in)
Barrel Length:	1100mm (43.3in)
Muzzle Velocity:	860m/sec (2821ft/sec)
Feed/Magazine:	Single shot
Range:	2000m (6560ft)

TIMELINE

1983

1990

Gepard M3

SPECIFICATIONS	
Country of Origin:	Hungary
Date:	1990
Calibre:	14.5mm (.57in)
Operation:	Semi-automatic
Weight:	17.5kg (38.6lb)
Overall Length:	1570mm (61.8in)
Barrel Length:	1100mm (43.3in)
Muzzle Velocity:	860m/sec (2821ft/sec)
Feed/Magazine:	5-round magazine
Range:	2000m (6560ft)

A semi-automatic version of the Gepard rifle, the M3 is chambered for 14.5mm (.57in) ammunition. Other variants exist, including a short-barrel version for use by airmobile troops and the bullpup-configuration M5.

Gepard M6

SPECIFICATIONS	
Country of Origin:	Hungary
Date:	1995
Calibre:	14.5mm (.57in)
Operation:	Semi-automatic
Weight:	11.4kg (25.1lb)
Overall Length:	1125mm (44.29in)
Barrel Length:	730mm (28.7in)
Muzzle Velocity:	780m/sec (2559ft/sec)
Feed/Magazine:	5-round magazine
Range:	600–1000m (1968–3280ft)

The M6 is the final member of the Gepard family of rifles. It uses the 14.5mm (.57in) round, like the M3, but features stronger parts and an improved scope. The M6 is strictly an Anti-Materiel Rifle (used for attacking helicopters, APCs and bunkers), because the accuracy of the otherwise extremely powerful 14.5mm (.57in) round degrades rapidly at ranges beyond 1000m (3280ft).

Steyr HS .50

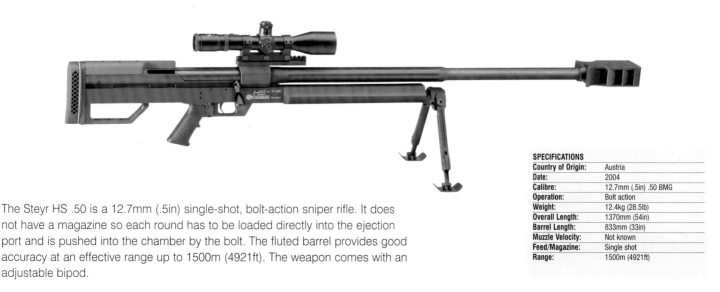

SPECIFICATIONS	
Country of Origin:	Austria
Date:	2004
Calibre:	12.7mm (.5in) .50 BMG
Operation:	Bolt action
Weight:	12.4kg (28.5lb)
Overall Length:	1370mm (54in)
Barrel Length:	833mm (33in)
Muzzle Velocity:	Not known
Feed/Magazine:	Single shot
Range:	1500m (4921ft)

The Steyr HS .50 is a 12.7mm (.5in) single-shot, bolt-action sniper rifle. It does not have a magazine so each round has to be loaded directly into the ejection port and is pushed into the chamber by the bolt. The fluted barrel provides good accuracy at an effective range up to 1500m (4921ft). The weapon comes with an adjustable bipod.

1995   2004

Light Support Weapons

It is not uncommon for modern weapons to be designed as a family, with an assault rifle, carbine and light support weapon based on the same receiver. Dedicated support weapons do continue to appear, however.

Galil ARM

The Galil AR (Assault Rifle) is converted into the ARM (Assault Rifle/Machine gun) version by the addition of a bipod and a 50-round magazine. The operation of the weapon remains unchanged, allowing any rifleman to take over the support gunner's role.

SPECIFICATIONS	
Country of Origin:	Israel
Date:	1972
Calibre:	5.56mm (.219in) NATO
Operation:	Gas-operated, self-loading
Weight:	4.35kg (9.59lb)
Overall Length:	979mm (38.54in)
Barrel Length:	460mm (18.11in)
Muzzle Velocity:	990m/sec (3250ft/sec)
Feed/Magazine:	35- or 50-round detachable box magazine
Range:	800m (2625ft) +

Beretta AS70/90

The support version of the AR70/90 rifle, the AS70/90 suffered from reliability problems. The intended user, the Italian Army, wanted greater ammunition capacity than a magazine-fed weapon could offer, and the project was not a success.

SPECIFICATIONS	
Country of Origin:	Italy
Date:	1990
Calibre:	5.56mm (.219in) NATO
Operation:	Gas-operated
Weight:	5.34kg (11.77lb)
Overall Length:	1000mm (39.37in)
Barrel Length:	465mm (18.3in)
Muzzle Velocity:	980m/sec (3215ft/sec)
Feed/Magazine:	30-round detachable box magazine
Range:	500m (1640ft) +

TIMELINE			
	1972	1990	1997

H&K MG36

The MG36 was simply the G36 rifle fitted with a heavy barrel and a bipod, and using a 100-round drum magazine. It was intended to complement the G36 in German Army service, but was not adopted.

SPECIFICATIONS

Country of Origin:	Germany
Date:	1997
Calibre:	5.56mm (.219in) NATO
Operation:	Gas-operated, rotating bolt
Weight:	3.83kg (8.4lb)
Overall Length:	999mm (39.3in)
Barrel Length:	480mm (18.3in)
Muzzle Velocity:	920m/sec (3018ft/sec)
Feed/Magazine:	30-round detachable box magazine or 100-round C-Mag drum magazine
Range:	800m (2625ft)

INSAS

The support version of the INSAS assault rifle differs mainly in its heavier barrel, which has different rifling to improve long-range performance. It is also chromed to help resist wear and heating.

SPECIFICATIONS

Country of Origin:	India
Date:	1998
Calibre:	5.56mm (.219in) NATO
Operation:	Gas-operated, rotating bolt
Weight:	4.25kg (9.4lb)
Overall Length:	960mm (37.8in)
Barrel Length:	464mm (18.3in)
Muzzle Velocity:	900m/sec (2953ft/sec)
Feed/Magazine:	20- or 30-round detachable box magazine
Range:	450m (1476ft)

H&K MG4

Developed as a replacement for the MG3, the MG4 is chambered for 5.56mm (.219in) rather than 7.62mm (.3in) ammunition. The project was designated MG43 by H&K, and is often referred to by that designation.

SPECIFICATIONS

Country of Origin:	Germany
Date:	2005
Calibre:	5.56mm (.219in) NATO
Operation:	Gas-operated, rotating bolt
Weight:	8.15kg (17.97lb)
Overall Length:	1030mm (40.6in)
Barrel Length:	482mm (19in)
Muzzle Velocity:	920m/sec (3018ft/sec)
Feed/Magazine:	Disintegrating link belt
Range:	c.1000m (3280ft)

1998   2005

Pump-Action Shotguns

Although their effective range is limited, shotguns offer excellent knockdown power and their projectiles are unlikely to overpenetrate, making them ideal for security operations and home defence. The spread of shot also increases the chance of a hit.

Ithaca Model 37 M and P

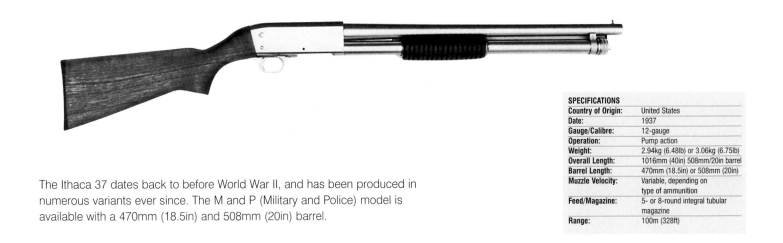

The Ithaca 37 dates back to before World War II, and has been produced in numerous variants ever since. The M and P (Military and Police) model is available with a 470mm (18.5in) and 508mm (20in) barrel.

SPECIFICATIONS	
Country of Origin:	United States
Date:	1937
Gauge/Calibre:	12-gauge
Operation:	Pump action
Weight:	2.94kg (6.48lb) or 3.06kg (6.75lb)
Overall Length:	1016mm (40in) 508mm/20in barrel
Barrel Length:	470mm (18.5in) or 508mm (20in)
Muzzle Velocity:	Variable, depending on type of ammunition
Feed/Magazine:	5- or 8-round integral tubular magazine
Range:	100m (328ft)

Mossberg ATPS 500

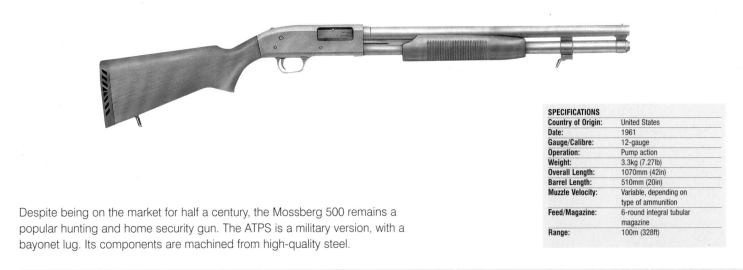

Despite being on the market for half a century, the Mossberg 500 remains a popular hunting and home security gun. The ATPS is a military version, with a bayonet lug. Its components are machined from high-quality steel.

SPECIFICATIONS	
Country of Origin:	United States
Date:	1961
Gauge/Calibre:	12-gauge
Operation:	Pump action
Weight:	3.3kg (7.27lb)
Overall Length:	1070mm (42in)
Barrel Length:	510mm (20in)
Muzzle Velocity:	Variable, depending on type of ammunition
Feed/Magazine:	6-round integral tubular magazine
Range:	100m (328ft)

TIMELINE   1937   1961   1966

Remington M870

The M870 series of shotguns has seen extensive military and police service worldwide. The reliability of a pump-action gun as opposed to a semi-automatic weapon prompted the US Marine Corps to adopt the M870 for a variety of applications.

SPECIFICATIONS
Country of Origin:	United States
Date:	1966
Gauge/Calibre:	12-gauge
Operation:	Pump action
Weight:	3.6kg (7.94lb)
Overall Length:	1060mm (41.73in)
Barrel Length:	533mm (21in)
Muzzle Velocity:	Variable, depending on type of ammunition
Feed/Magazine:	7-round integral tubular magazine
Range:	100m (328ft)

Ithaca Stakeout

Produced for the police market, the Stakeout has a pistol grip in place of a rifle-style butt. The basic action is based on that patented by John Moses Browning in 1915.

SPECIFICATIONS
Country of Origin:	United States
Date:	1970
Gauge/Calibre:	12-, 16-, 20- or 28-gauge
Operation:	Pump action
Weight:	Variable
Overall Length:	Variable
Barrel Length:	330–762mm (13–30in)
Muzzle Velocity:	Variable, depending on type of ammunition
Feed/Magazine:	4-round integral tubular magazine
Range:	100m (328ft)

Beretta RS200

The RS200 is a police and military weapon, capable of delivering a range of specialist loads including tear gas and solid slugs as well as various sizes of shot.

SPECIFICATIONS
Country of Origin:	Italy
Date:	1970
Gauge/Calibre:	12-gauge
Operation:	Pump action
Weight:	3.26kg (7.2lb)
Overall Length:	Not known
Barrel Length:	520mm (20.47in)
Muzzle Velocity:	Variable
Feed/Magazine:	6-round tubular ma

1970

Winchester Model 12 Defender

The Model 12 entered service during World War II and has progressed through several versions. The Model 12 is a classic, still used today for both police and military work. The basic specifications include a six- or seven-round under-barrel tubular magazine, with various configurations for firing shots or slugs.

STOCK
The Defender is available with a conventional stock or stockless, with a pistol grip.

SPECIFICATIONS	
Country of Origin:	United States
Date:	1990
Gauge/Calibre:	12-, 16- or 20-gauge
Operation:	Pump action
Weight:	2.9kg (6.5lb)
Overall Length:	1003–1245mm (39.5–49in)
Barrel Length:	457–711mm (18–28in)
Muzzle Velocity:	Variable
Feed/Magazine:	2–6-round integral tubular magazine
Range:	100m (328ft)

The Defender is a classic 'combat shotgun' and is still used in military, law enforcement and self-defence applications. Deterrence is generally considered a better option than having to shoot, and shotguns of this sort are very intimidating, meaning that often the user will not have to fire.

The Defender has a fixed choke and a very robust pump action; there is little to go wrong with this weapon. Winchester 1200s intended for sporting applications are available with a variable choke but are hardly less reliable.

FORE-END/PUMP
The original Defender was used as the basis for a range of 12- and 20-gauge shotguns, all of which use the same basic mechanism.

MAGAZINE
Various magazine sizes are available, with four or six rounds being commonest.

BARREL/MUZZLE
Civilian and law enforcement versions of the Defender were not built with bayonet lugs or sling swivels, but were otherwise similar.

Combat Shotguns

Pump-action shotguns are prized for their reliability and robust construction, but they have a low rate of fire and limited ammunition capacity. Various attempts have been made to address these drawbacks, but the pump-action gun remains a staple security weapon.

Browning Automatic Shotgun/Auto 5

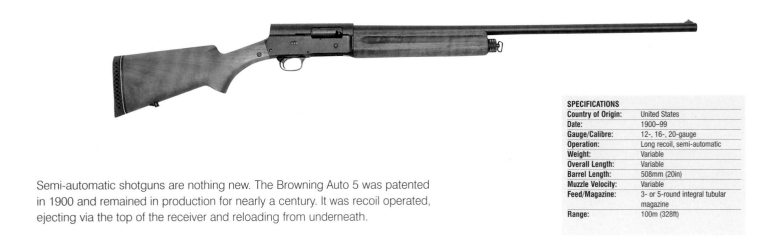

Semi-automatic shotguns are nothing new. The Browning Auto 5 was patented in 1900 and remained in production for nearly a century. It was recoil operated, ejecting via the top of the receiver and reloading from underneath.

SPECIFICATIONS	
Country of Origin:	United States
Date:	1900–99
Gauge/Calibre:	12-, 16-, 20-gauge
Operation:	Long recoil, semi-automatic
Weight:	Variable
Overall Length:	Variable
Barrel Length:	508mm (20in)
Muzzle Velocity:	Variable
Feed/Magazine:	3- or 5-round integral tubular magazine
Range:	100m (328ft)

Beretta RS202-MI

Based on the RS200, the RS202-MI is the folding stock version of the successful RS202P 12-guage shotgun. With a folding stock, it is much easier to store this weapon in a confined space, such as the back of a vehicle.

SPECIFICATIONS	
Country of Origin:	Italy
Date:	1973
Gauge/Calibre:	12-gauge
Operation:	Pump action
Weight:	3.20kg (7lb)
Overall Length:	1020mm (40.1in)
Barrel Length:	520mm (20.47in)
Muzzle Velocity:	Variable
Feed/Magazine:	6-round integral tubular magazine
Range:	100m (328ft)

TIMELINE   1900   1973   1979

Franchi SPAS 12

The SPAS 12 can be switched between pump-action and semi-automatic mode at will, allowing specialist ammunition to be loaded when the need arises. The shoulder stock can act as an elbow hook for one-handed shooting.

SPECIFICATIONS	
Country of Origin:	Italy
Date:	1979
Gauge/Calibre:	12-gauge
Operation:	Pump action/gas-operated
Weight:	4.2kg (9.26lb)
Overall Length:	930mm (36.6in)
Barrel Length:	460mm (18.11in)
Muzzle Velocity:	Variable
Feed/Magazine:	7-round integral tubular magazine
Range:	100m (328ft)

Striker

The Striker shotgun uses a 12-round drum rather than the more customary tubular under-barrel magazine. The result is a somewhat bulky but reliable weapon, offering twice the firepower of a conventional shotgun.

SPECIFICATIONS	
Country of Origin:	South Africa
Date:	1985
Gauge/Calibre:	12-gauge
Operation:	Rotary cylinder
Weight:	4.2kg (9.25lb)
Overall Length:	792mm (31.18in)
Barrel Length:	304mm (12in) or 457mm (18in)
Muzzle Velocity:	Variable
Feed/Magazine:	12- or 20-round revolving magazine
Range:	100m (328ft)

Benelli M4/M1014

A military shotgun capable of firing a range of ammunition including less-lethal rubber rounds, the M4 is available with a conventional stock, a pistol grip or a telescoping stock. It was taken into US Marine Corps service as the M1014.

SPECIFICATIONS	
Country of Origin:	Italy
Date:	1998
Gauge/Calibre:	12-gauge
Operation:	Gas-operated, semi-automatic
Weight:	3.8kg (8.37lb)
Overall Length:	1010mm (39.76in)
Barrel Length:	470mm (18.50in)
Muzzle Velocity:	Variable
Feed/Magazine:	6-round under-barrel integral tubular magazine
Range:	100m (328ft)

1985   1998

Pump-Action Security Shotguns

While some weapons are aimed at a single market, many shotguns are equally suited to sport shooting or home defence. The simple and robust mechanism of a pump-action shotgun is attractive to many non-professional shooters.

Winchester Model 1300

An advanced pump-action design, the Model 1300 uses recoil to assist the operation of the action, allowing very rapid fire. A number of variants and developed models have been produced, including the Winchester Defender.

SPECIFICATIONS	
Country of Origin:	United States
Date:	1978
Gauge/Calibre:	12-gauge
Operation:	Pump action
Weight:	3.06–3.18kg (6.7–7lb)
Overall Length:	1003–1245mm (39.5–49in)
Barrel Length:	457–711mm (18–28in)
Muzzle Velocity:	Variable
Feed/Magazine:	4-, 5- or 7-round integral tubular magazine
Range:	100m (328ft)

Armscor M30R6

Armscor's M30 range includes a number of variants. The M30R6 is specifically designed for security users. It has an extended magazine and makes extensive use of polymer construction rather than the wooden furniture of the sporting models.

SPECIFICATIONS	
Country of Origin:	United States
Date:	2000
Gauge/Calibre:	12-gauge
Operation:	Pump action
Weight:	3.22kg (7.1lb)
Overall Length:	1009mm (39.75in)
Barrel Length:	508mm (20in)
Muzzle Velocity:	Variable
Feed/Magazine:	5-round integral tubular magazine
Range:	100m (328ft)

TIMELINE

1978

2000

Armscor M30DI

Intended primarily for sports shooters, the DI is part of the M30 range and has obvious defensive applications. Its magazine can hold four 76.2mm (3in) or five 63.5mm (2.5in) 12-gauge shells, plus one in the breech.

SPECIFICATIONS	
Country of Origin:	Philippines
Date:	2000
Gauge/Calibre:	12-gauge
Operation:	Pump action
Weight:	3.51–3.63kg (7.75–8lb)
Overall Length:	1159mm–1210mm (45.625–47.525in)
Barrel Length:	660–710mm (26–28in)
Muzzle Velocity:	Variable
Feed/Magazine:	4- or 5-round integral tubular magazine
Range:	150m (492ft)

Mossberg 835 Ulti-Mag

Mossberg's Ulti-Mag was built around 88.9mm/3.5in (3.5in Magnum) 12-gauge ammunition. These longer, more powerful shells require a very robust weapon to fire them. The barrel is ported to reduce felt recoil.

SPECIFICATIONS	
Country of Origin:	United States
Date:	2004
Gauge/Calibre:	12-gauge
Operation:	Pump action
Weight:	Up to 3.5kg (7.75lb)
Overall Length:	Variable
Barrel Length:	Up to 710mm (28in)
Muzzle Velocity:	Variable
Feed/Magazine:	4 + 1-round integral tubular magazine
Range:	150m (492ft)

Mossberg 535 All Terrain Shotgun

Designed to tackle a range of targets, the 535 can use 69.85mm (2.75in), 76.2mm (3in) or 88.9mm/3.5in (3.5in Magnum) 12-gauge shells, enabling the user to select ammunition appropriate to the task at hand.

SPECIFICATIONS	
Country of Origin:	United States
Date:	2005
Gauge/Calibre:	12-gauge
Operation:	Pump action
Weight:	Up to 3.2kg (7lb)
Overall Length:	Variable
Barrel Length:	Up to 710mm (28in)
Muzzle Velocity:	Variable
Feed/Magazine:	4 + 1 or 5 + 1-round integral tubular magazine
Range:	150m (492ft)

2004

2005

Automatic Shotguns

A fully automatic shotgun represents fearsome firepower, but the large size of 12-gauge shells means that such a weapon needs a bulky magazine or will suffer from limited ammunition capacity. Automatic shotguns also have heavy recoil.

Atchisson Assault Shotgun

A gas-operated, fully automatic 12-gauge shotgun using either a seven-round box magazine or a bulky 20-round drum, the Atchisson Assault Shotgun was designed for military applications. It was able to launch rifle grenades and had a bayonet mounting.

SPECIFICATIONS	
Country of Origin:	United States
Date:	1972
Gauge/Calibre:	12-gauge
Operation:	Forced gas blowback, selective fire
Weight:	7.3kg (16.09lb)
Overall Length:	991mm (39.01in)
Barrel Length:	457mm (17.99in)
Muzzle Velocity:	350m/sec (1100 ft/sec)
Feed/Magazine:	7-round detachable box or 20-round drum magazine
Range:	100m (328ft)

Pancor Jackhammer

The Jackhammer was a fully automatic bullpup weapon. It was fed from a 10-round drum magazine, and retained spent cases rather than ejecting them. Although apparently workable, the idea failed to attract sales and remained a curiosity only.

SPECIFICATIONS	
Country of Origin:	United States
Date:	1985
Gauge/Calibre:	12-gauge
Operation:	Gas-operated
Weight:	4.57kg (10lb) loaded
Overall Length:	762mm (30in)
Barrel Length:	457mm (18in)
Muzzle Velocity:	Variable, depending on type of ammunition
Feed/Magazine:	10-round detachable pre-loaded rotary cassette
Range:	200m (656ft) +

TIMELINE   1972   1985

Franchi SPAS 15

Developed from the SPAS 12, the SPAS 15 is capable of semi-automatic or pump-action operation. There were plans to make it capable of full-automatic fire, but this proved impractical. A magazine change is much quicker than reloading a conventional shotgun.

SPECIFICATIONS	
Country of Origin:	Italy
Date:	1985
Gauge/Calibre:	12-gauge
Operation:	Pump action/gas-operated
Weight:	3.9kg (8.5lb) or 4.1kg (9lb)
Overall Length:	980mm (38.58in) or 1000mm (39.3in)
Barrel Length:	450mm (17.71in)
Muzzle Velocity:	Variable, depending on type of ammunition
Feed/Magazine:	10-round detachable box magazine
Range:	100m (328ft)

USAS-12 Auto Shotgun

Broadly similar to the earlier Atchisson Assault Shotgun, the USAS-12 used more modern materials and went into production in the 1990s. The full-automatic military version was bought by several nations, though the semi-automatic civilian variant was less successful.

SPECIFICATIONS	
Country of Origin:	South Korea
Date:	1992
Gauge/Calibre:	12-gauge
Operation:	Gas-operated
Weight:	5.5kg (12.12lb)
Overall Length:	960mm (37.79in)
Barrel Length:	460mm (18.11in)
Muzzle Velocity:	400m/sec (1300ft/sec)
Feed/Magazine:	10-round box or 20-round drum detachable magazine
Range:	200m (656ft)

AA-12/Auto Assault 12

SPECIFICATIONS	
Country of Origin:	United States
Date:	2005
Gauge/Calibre:	12-gauge
Operation:	Forced gas blowback, selective fire
Weight:	5.7kg (12.6lb)
Overall Length:	966mm (38in)
Barrel Length:	330mm (13in)
Muzzle Velocity:	350m/sec (1100ft/sec)
Feed/Magazine:	8-round box or 20- or 32-round drum magazine
Range:	200m (656ft) FRAG-12 ammunition

Developed over many years from the Atchisson Assault Shotgun, the AA-12 is capable of firing a range of ammunition including airburst rounds. It can take an eight-round box magazine or a 20- or 32-round drum.

1992

2005

Riot Control Weapons

Wherever possible, less-lethal weapons are used to bring a riot under control. The term 'less-lethal' is used instead of 'non-lethal' since any weapon can cause a fatality under the right circumstances.

Federal Riot Gun

A break-open single-shot weapon, the Federal Riot Gun is a basic but effective weapon which is used by police, military and security forces worldwide. Various updated models have appeared over the years but all are basically similar in operation.

SPECIFICATIONS	
Country of Origin:	United States
Date:	1960
Calibre:	37mm (1.45in)
Operation:	Breech-loaded, single shot
Weight:	N/A
Overall Length:	737mm (29in)
Barrel Length:	Not known
Muzzle Velocity:	Not known
Feed/Magazine:	Baton rounds, smoke, flares, CS gas rounds
Range:	100m (328ft) baton rounds

Smith & Wesson No 210 Shoulder Gas Gun

Based on a revolver frame, the No 210 is a break-open single-shot weapon capable of firing a range of projectiles. Its recoil is very significant, and accuracy is not good, but at close range it is an effective weapon.

SPECIFICATIONS	
Country of Origin:	United States
Date:	1960s
Calibre:	37mm (1.45in)
Operation:	Breech-loaded, single shot
Weight:	2.7kg (5.95lb)
Overall Length:	736mm (29in)
Barrel Length:	Not known
Muzzle Velocity:	Not known
Feed/Magazine:	Baton rounds, smoke grenades, CS gas rounds
Range:	135m (443ft)

TIMELINE

 1960    1960s

Smith & Wesson No 209 Gas Pistol

Very similar to the No 210, but using a short barrel and pistol grip, the No 209 is, like the larger version, intended primarily to deliver tear gas rounds. Accuracy is not a major issue in this role.

SPECIFICATIONS	
Country of Origin:	United States
Date:	1960s
Calibre:	37mm (1.45in)
Operation:	Breech-loaded, single shot
Weight:	N/A
Overall Length:	N/A
Barrel Length:	N/A
Muzzle Velocity:	N/A
Feed/Magazine:	Baton rounds, tear gas rounds
Range:	9–30m (29–98ft)

ARWEN

The Anti-Riot Weapon, Enfield (ARWEN) was developed to give riot control troops or police the capability to make repeated shots without reloading. Variants include a stockless short version and one permanently mounted on a vehicle.

SPECIFICATIONS	
Country of Origin:	United Kingdom
Date:	1970
Gauge/Calibre:	37mm (1.45in) and 12-gauge
Operation:	Breech-loaded, rotary drum
Weight:	3.8kg (8.36lb) loaded
Overall Length:	840mm (33in)
Barrel Length:	760mm (29.9in)
Muzzle Velocity:	N/A
Feed/Magazine:	5-round rotary magazine
Range:	100m (328ft) baton rounds

Schermuly Anti-Riot gun

For military or police personnel attempting to deal with a riot, there are many factors to be balanced. Personnel and innocent bystanders must be protected, but wherever possible the level of force used must be kept low. Weapons that allow a flexible response are a good choice for such a situation.

SPECIFICATIONS	
Country of Origin:	United Kingdom
Date:	1970s
Gauge/Calibre:	37mm (1.45in) and 12-gauge
Operation:	Breech-loaded, single shot
Weight:	3.18kg (7lb)
Overall Length:	828mm (32.6in)
Barrel Length:	Not known
Muzzle Velocity:	N/A
Feed/Magazine:	Baton rounds, smoke grenades, CS gas rounds, irritant agents
Range:	150m (492ft)

1970

1970s

FN303

Capable of being used independently or fixed to a rifle, the FN303 fires a 12-gauge-sized projectile using compressed air. It can launch gas rounds, marking agents or other projectiles as well as illumination shells. It has also been designed to fit onto assault rifles, such as the M16.

STOCK
The stock can be removed for mounting the weapon under a conventional rifle.

MAGAZINE
The drum magazine contains 15 rounds, giving a huge firepower advantage over traditional single-shot weapons.

SPECIFICATIONS	
Country of Origin:	Belgium
Date:	2003
Calibre:	18mm (.71in)
Operation:	Compressed air
Weight:	2.3kg (5.07lb)
Overall Length:	740mm (29.1in)
Barrel Length:	250mm (9.8in)
Muzzle Velocity:	85m/sec (279ft/sec)
Feed/Magazine:	15-round detachable drum magazine
Range:	70m (230ft)

The FN303 addresses a major problem with many riot-control weapons, which usually lack repeat-fire capability. This weapon allows multiple fast shots when necessary, enabling riot-control personnel to disperse a group or defend themselves from a mob.

The FN303 also has the advantage of being able to use a range of ammunition types, granting additional flexibility to security personnel without requiring the issue of a range of different weapons.

TOP RAIL
A rail allows the mounting of a range of accessories, including tactical lights and laser pointers.

GAS CYLINDER
The gas cylinder allows about 110 shots before requiring refilling. It has a lifetime of hundreds of refills.

UNDER-BARREL MOUNTED
Mounted under a rifle, the FN303 uses the rifle's magazine as a handgrip in the same manner as many grenade launchers.

Man-Portable Grenade Launchers

Grenade launchers enable infantry units to carry their own light artillery support. A well-trained grenadier can lob a projectile through a window or over cover, eliminating hostiles who are well protected against direct small-arms fire.

M79 Grenade Launcher

Sometimes referred to as the 'Thump Gun', the M79 was developed in the Vietnam War era to increase infantry capabilities. Its weight and bulk made it impossible for the grenadier to also carry a rifle.

SPECIFICATIONS	
Country of Origin:	United States
Date:	1961
Calibre:	40mm (1.57in)
Operation:	Breech-loaded
Weight:	2.95kg (6.5lb) loaded
Overall Length:	783mm (29in)
Barrel Length:	Not known
Muzzle Velocity:	75m/sec (245ft/sec)
Feed/Magazine:	Single shot
Range:	150m (492ft)

HK69A1 Grenatpistole

Originally developed as an under-barrel rifle-mounted weapon, the HK69 became a weapon in its own right. It is a manually cocked single-action weapon capable of launching illumination and signal flares in addition to offensive grenades.

SPECIFICATIONS	
Country of Origin:	West Germany
Date:	1969
Calibre:	40mm (1.57in)
Operation:	Breech-loaded
Weight:	2.3kg (5lb)
Overall Length:	683mm (27in)
Barrel Length:	Not known
Muzzle Velocity:	75m/sec (245ft/sec)
Feed/Magazine:	Single shot
Range:	350m (1148ft)

TIMELINE

1961

1969

M203 Grenade Launcher

Fitting under the barrel of an assault rifle, the M203 does not need the bulk of its own stock and thus enables a grenadier to also be a rifleman. It is slower to reload than the M79.

SPECIFICATIONS	
Country of Origin:	United States
Date:	1969
Calibre:	40mm (1.57in)
Operation:	Breech-loaded
Weight:	1.63kg (3.5lb) loaded
Overall Length:	380mm (15in)
Barrel Length:	305mm (12in)
Muzzle Velocity:	75m/sec (245ft/sec)
Feed/Magazine:	Single shot
Range:	400m (1312ft)

CIS 40GL

Marketed by Chartered Industries of Singapore (now ST Kinetics), the CIS 40GL can be fitted to a variety of rifles or used independently with a stock fitted. It has sold to police and military forces worldwide.

SPECIFICATIONS	
Country of Origin:	Singapore
Date:	1989
Calibre:	40mm (1.57in)
Operation:	Breech-loaded
Weight:	2.05kg (4.52lb)
Overall Length:	655mm (25.8in) with stock
Barrel Length:	305mm (12in)
Muzzle Velocity:	76m/sec (249ft/sec)
Feed/Magazine:	Single shot
Range:	400m (1312ft)

AG36 Grenade Launcher

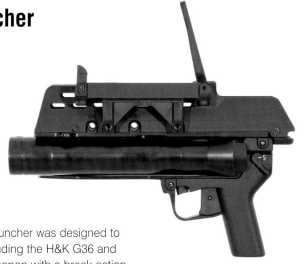

The Heckler & Koch AG36 grenade launcher was designed to fit a range of NATO assault rifles, including the H&K G36 and the British SA 80. It is a single-shot weapon with a break-action steel barrel.

SPECIFICATIONS	
Country of Origin:	Germany
Date:	2003
Calibre:	40mm (1.8in)
Operation:	Semi-auto
Weight:	1.5kg (3.31lb)
Overall Length:	350mm (13.8in)
Barrel Length:	280mm (11in)
Muzzle Velocity:	76 m/sec (249ft/sec)
Feed/Magazine:	Manually loaded
Range:	200m (650ft)

1989

2003

Grenade Launchers

Heavier grenade launchers, often belt-fed, can be used from a tripod or vehicle mount for infantry support. They are imprecise weapons, best used for area fire or suppression of enemy troops. Many launchers use the same grenades as rifle-mounted launchers.

Mk 19

Developed in the 1960s by the US Navy, the Mk 19 was originally intended to arm riverine patrol craft but was soon adopted for a range of other uses including helicopter and vehicle armament.

SPECIFICATIONS	
Country of Origin:	United States
Date:	1966
Calibre:	40mm (1.57in)
Operation:	Advanced Primer Ignition/ blowback
Weight:	32.9kg (72.5lb)
Overall Length:	1090mm (43.1in)
Barrel Length:	413mm (16.25in)
Muzzle Velocity:	185m/sec (606ft/sec)
Feed/Magazine:	Belt-fed
Range:	1400m (4593ft)

AGS-17

The Russian AGS-17 or Plamya ('Flame') uses boxed 30-round belts of grenades. Operation is similar to a machine gun, using blowback to chamber the next round.

SPECIFICATIONS	
Country of Origin:	USSR
Date:	1970
Calibre:	30mm (1.18in)
Operation:	Blowback
Weight:	31kg (68.34lb)
Overall Length:	840mm (33.1in)
Barrel Length:	Not known
Muzzle Velocity:	185m/sec (606ft/sec)
Feed/Magazine:	30-round boxed belt
Range:	1700m (5577ft)

TIMELINE

 1966
 1970
 1977

Brunswick RAW

The Rifleman's Assault Weapon (RAW) is an alternative take on the concept of a rifle grenade. It will travel up to 2000m (6560ft) but is only accurate to 200–300m (656–984ft). Its primary role is to demolish hard cover used by hostiles.

SPECIFICATIONS	
Country of Origin:	United States
Date:	1977
Calibre:	140mm (5.5in)
Operation:	Rifle-fired
Weight:	3.8kg (8.36lb)
Overall Length:	305mm (12in)
Barrel Length:	N/A
Muzzle Velocity:	180m/sec (590ft/sec)
Feed/Magazine:	Single round
Range:	200m (656ft) +

Milcor MGL

The Milcor Multiple Grenade Launcher (MGL) uses a non-detachable six-round revolver-style cylinder to provide rapid firepower. The cylinder revolves using a spring mechanism and must be wound against the spring before being reloaded.

SPECIFICATIONS	
Country of Origin:	South Africa
Date:	1983
Calibre:	40mm (1.57in)
Operation:	Double-action
Weight:	5.3kg (11.68lb)
Overall Length:	778mm (30.6in)
Barrel Length:	300mm (11.8in)
Muzzle Velocity:	76m/sec (249ft/sec)
Feed/Magazine:	6-round rotating swing-out-type cylinder
Range:	400m (1312ft)

H&K GMG

H&K's Grenade Machine Gun was developed as a private venture and was adopted by the German Army in the 1990s. Using blowback operation, the GMG reduces felt recoil by using an advanced primer initiation system.

SPECIFICATIONS	
Country of Origin:	Germany
Date:	1995
Calibre:	40mm (1.57in)
Operation:	Recoil-operated blowback
Weight:	28.8kg (63.49lb)
Overall Length:	1090mm (42.91in)
Barrel Length:	415mm (16.33in)
Muzzle Velocity:	241m/sec (790ft/sec)
Feed/Magazine:	32-round disintegrating, closed-link belt
Range:	1500m (4921ft)

1983

1995

SPORTING GUNS

The term 'sporting guns' is applied to a range of firearms used for recreational or competitive target shooting or hunting. A hunter typically makes one or two precise shots, and does not need a large-capacity semi-automatic weapon.

Sporting guns rarely encounter the abuse inflicted upon military weapons, but they do still get knocked about. A sporting gun must be able to retain its accuracy whilst being transported or being hauled up a hillside during a hunting expedition, so a degree of robustness is vital.

Left: A hunter aims his Winchester Model 1300. The Model 1300 is famed for the extraordinary speed of its pump action.

Double-Barrelled Sporting Shotguns

Double-barrelled shotguns come in two types: over-under or side-by-side. Both are breech-loading weapons but they have different characteristics, with over-under shotguns better suited to rapid shooting.

Browning B125

First produced in the 1920s, the B125 has a single trigger, with the order the barrels fire in chosen using the combined safety/selector switch. The basic weapon spawned a series of variants and upgraded models.

SPECIFICATIONS	
Country of Origin:	United States
Gauge/Calibre:	12-gauge
Operation:	Breech-loading
Weight:	3.2kg (7.14lb)
Barrel Length:	760mm (30in)
Ejector Type:	Automatic ejectors

Browning B425

A modern development of the B125, several variants of the B425 are available. Each is optimized to a particular application, such as clay shooting or waterfowl hunting. It is available in 12-gauge and 20-gauge.

SPECIFICATIONS	
Country of Origin:	United States
Gauge/Calibre:	12- or 20-gauge
Operation:	Breech-loading
Weight:	3.5kg (7.75lb)
Barrel Length:	710mm (28in)
Ejector Type:	Automatic ejectors

Fabarm Beta

A modern take on the more traditional side-by-side shotgun, the Beta series includes several variants. All are aimed primarily at the rough-game market, which demands a very tough and reliable gun.

SPECIFICATIONS	
Country of Origin:	Italy
Gauge/Calibre:	12-gauge
Operation:	Breech-loading
Weight:	3.3kg (7.2lb)
Barrel Length:	660mm (26in), 710mm (28in)
Ejector Type:	Automatic ejectors

Miroku MK70 Sporter Grade 1

Miroku produce a range of good-quality but relatively inexpensive guns based on the Browning B125 mechanism. The Game variant has a fixed choke; the Sporter version is available with a variable choke.

SPECIFICATIONS	
Country of Origin:	Japan
Gauge/Calibre:	12-, 20- or 28-gauge
Operation:	Breech-loading
Weight:	3.5kg (7.7lb)
Barrel Length:	710mm (28in), 760mm (30in), 810mm (32in)
Ejector Type:	Automatic ejectors

Fausti Style ST

Available in calibres from 12- to 32-gauge and .410, the Style ST is an entry-level weapon intended to appeal to a wide range of users. Most versions use 69.85mm (2.75in) shells but 76.2mm (3in) and 88.9mm (3.5in) versions are available.

SPECIFICATIONS	
Country of Origin:	Italy
Gauge/Calibre:	12-, 16-, 20-, 24-, 28- or 32-gauge; .410
Operation:	Breech-loading
Weight:	3.4kg (7.5lb)
Barrel Length:	600mm (24in), 630mm (25in), 650mm (25.5in), 680mm (27in), 710mm (28in), 770mm (30in)
Ejector Type:	Automatic ejectors

Marocchi Model 99

The commonest calibre for shotguns is 12-gauge (or 12-bore). This measurement is derived from the weight of a solid lead sphere with the same diameter as the weapon's barrel. Twelve-gauge means that 12 such balls would weigh one pound (.454kg); 20-gauge indicates that each ball weighs $\frac{1}{20}$ (.05) of a pound (.023kg), and so forth.

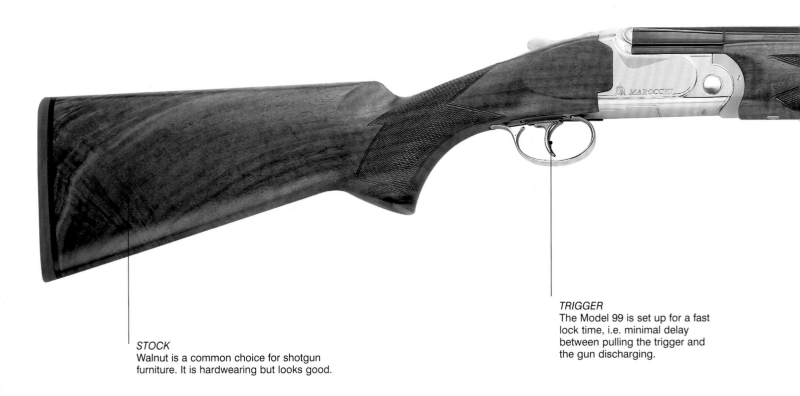

STOCK
Walnut is a common choice for shotgun furniture. It is hardwearing but looks good.

TRIGGER
The Model 99 is set up for a fast lock time, i.e. minimal delay between pulling the trigger and the gun discharging.

Twelve-gauge is widely considered the best all-round calibre for shotgun shooting, offering a good balance of power, manageability and the ability to use different types of ammunition to suit a range of applications.

CONFIGURATION
Over-under configuration is widely considered to give more consistent sighting than side-by-side arrangement.

BARRELS
Like many modern shotguns, the Model 99 is able to use non-toxic steel shot in addition to the more traditional lead.

SPECIFICATIONS

Country of Origin:	Italy
Gauge/Calibre:	12-gauge
Operation:	Breech-loading
Weight:	3.5kg (7.7lb)
Barrel Length:	710mm (28in), 760mm (30in), 810mm (32in)
Ejector Type:	Automatic ejectors

Over-Under Shotguns

Over-under shotguns offer a slightly different sighting picture to side-by-side weapons. Rather than a bead foresight between the barrels, the shooter aims along the strengthening rib above the barrels. Although the difference may seem marginal, many shooters prefer this setup.

FAIR Jubilee Prestige

As the name suggests, this weapon is aimed at the quality end of the market, and uses high-quality materials throughout its construction. As with many sporting guns, a range of calibres and barrel lengths are available.

SPECIFICATIONS	
Country of Origin:	Italy
Gauge/Calibre:	12-, 16-, 20-, 28- or 36-gauge
Operation:	Breech-loading
Weight:	3.2kg (7lb)
Barrel Length:	660mm (26in), 710mm (28in), 760mm (30in)
Ejector Type:	Automatic ejectors

FAIR Premier

At the 'budget' end of the FAIR catalogue, the Premier is aimed at the sporting market and comes with a range of multichokes to adapt the spread of shot to the user's requirements.

SPECIFICATIONS	
Country of Origin:	Italy
Gauge/Calibre:	12-, 16-, 20- or 28-gauge; .410
Operation:	Breech-loading
Weight:	3.4kg (7.4lb)
Barrel Length:	710mm (28in)
Ejector Type:	Automatic ejectors

Baikal IZH-27/Remington SPR-310

A tough Russian budget gun produced under licence by Remington, the SPR-310 is available in a range of calibres from .410 to 12-gauge. It is well suited to rough shooting or vermin control, both of which are hard on guns.

SPECIFICATIONS	
Country of Origin:	United States/Russia
Gauge/Calibre:	12-, 16-, 20- or 28-gauge; .410
Operation:	Breech-loading
Weight:	3.4kg (7.5lb)
Barrel Length:	660mm (26in), 710mm (28in)
Ejector Type:	Automatic ejectors

Ruger Red Label

Like many sporting shotguns, the Ruger Red Label is available in barrel lengths from 660mm (26in) to 760mm (30in) to suit different users and applications. It is intended as a general-purpose hunting and sporting gun.

SPECIFICATIONS	
Country of Origin:	United States
Gauge/Calibre:	12-, 20- or 28-gauge
Operation:	Breech-loading
Weight:	3.6kg (8lb)
Barrel Length:	660mm (26in), 710mm (28in), 760mm (30in)
Ejector Type:	Automatic ejectors

Lanber Deluxe Sporter

Another budget gun, this weapon is very conventional in design but offers good quality for the price. It is aimed at the sporting and field shooting market and comes with a set of multichokes.

SPECIFICATIONS	
Country of Origin:	Spain
Gauge/Calibre:	12-gauge
Operation:	Breech-loading
Weight:	3.5kg (7.7lb)
Barrel Length:	710mm (28in), 760mm (30in)
Ejector Type:	Automatic ejectors

Fabarm Axis 20M

Twenty-gauge shotguns are significantly lighter than 12-gauges, which appeals to many shooters. The trade-off is that they cannot throw shot as far, or as much of it, as a heavier gun. However, this does not prevent 20-gauge shotguns from being very good field guns if set up correctly.

As a general rule, a gun intended for field shooting will have a somewhat shorter barrel than one meant for clay pigeon shooting. Combined with the lighter gauge, this makes a short 20-gauge shotgun rather more agreeable to carry around all day.

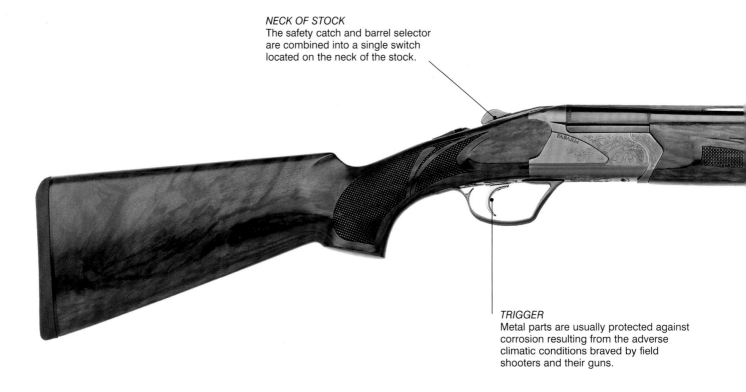

NECK OF STOCK
The safety catch and barrel selector are combined into a single switch located on the neck of the stock.

TRIGGER
Metal parts are usually protected against corrosion resulting from the adverse climatic conditions braved by field shooters and their guns.

SPECIFICATIONS	
Country of Origin:	Italy
Gauge/Calibre:	20-gauge
Operation:	Breech-loading
Weight:	3.6kg (8lb)
Barrel Length:	610mm (24in), 660mm (26in), 710mm (28in), 760mm (30in)
Ejector Type:	Automatic ejectors

Field guns, as a rule, have a fixed choke whereas sporting guns are often variable to allow the user to fine-tune the weapon to conditions. The 'choke' is part of the barrel which narrows, altering the spread of shot. Weapons like the Axis 20M, which have a variable choke, allow the user to insert a tube into the barrel to alter the choke.

Altering the choke only matters if the shooter is reasonably competent in the first place, and it is possible to become overly concerned with spread of shot. Variable chokes are also somewhat more vulnerable to corrosion and propellant fouling, but do allow an expert user to optimize the performance of a weapon.

BARRELS
An adjustable choke allows the user to tailor the spread of shot to his or her own preferences. Ribs above and between the barrels add strength. They are ventilated to improve barrel cooling.

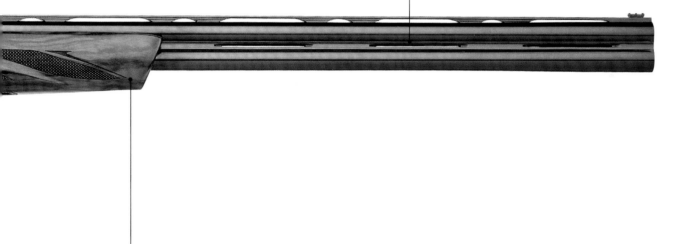

FOREARM
The Axis 20M is a fairly short and light gun, well suited to field shooting. Clay shooters often prefer a heavier gun for a more stable swing.

Specialist Shotguns

Whilst many guns are aimed at the general user, some are optimized for a particular function or feature. Some users are willing to pay a high price for enhanced accuracy, reduced weight or excellence in a specific field.

FALCO SO27A

The SO27A is a very light weapon, largely due to its small calibre. By using a very tight choke, it is possible to achieve good results at range with a .410 shotgun, but this requires accurate shooting.

SPECIFICATIONS	
Country of Origin:	Italy
Gauge/Calibre:	.410
Operation:	Breech-loading
Weight:	2.7kg (6lb)
Barrel Length:	700mm (27.5in)
Ejector Type:	Extractors

Beretta 682

Developed specifically for the clay pigeon shooting market, the 682 is adjustable in many dimensions to fit its user perfectly. Variants optimized for trap and skeet shooting are available.

SPECIFICATIONS	
Country of Origin:	Italy
Gauge/Calibre:	12-gauge
Operation:	Breech-loading
Weight:	3.45kg (7.6lb)
Barrel Length:	710mm (28in), 760mm (30in), 810mm (32in)
Ejector Type:	Automatic ejectors

Beretta Ultralight

The Beretta Ultralight pushes the limit of how light a 12-gauge shotgun can be made. A certain amount of barrel weight is necessary to a steady swing while tracking a moving target.

SPECIFICATIONS	
Country of Origin:	Italy
Gauge/Calibre:	12-gauge
Operation:	Breech-loading
Weight:	2.7kg (5.9lb)
Barrel Length:	710mm (28in)
Ejector Type:	Automatic ejectors

Salvinelli L1

The L1 is one of several models available in Salvinelli's sporting range. It uses a combination of multichokes and long forcing cones (the stage between the chamber and the barrel) to create a very consistent shot pattern.

SPECIFICATIONS	
Country of Origin:	Italy
Gauge/Calibre:	12-gauge
Operation:	Breech-loading
Weight:	3.5kg (7.7lb)
Barrel Length:	700mm (27.6in), 720mm (28.3in), 760mm (30in)
Ejector Type:	Automatic ejectors

Weatherby SBS Athena Deluxe

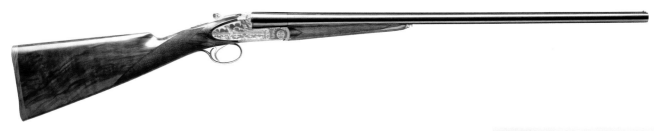

Although a classic design, this weapon benefits from modern thinking. It uses long forcing cones to reduce shot deformation, which in turn results in a more predictable and even shot pattern, and better range.

SPECIFICATIONS	
Country of Origin:	Italy
Gauge/Calibre:	12- or 20-gauge
Operation:	Breech-loading
Weight:	Up to 3.3kg (7.25lb) 12-gauge
Barrel Length:	660mm (26in), 710mm (28in)
Ejector Type:	Automatic ejectors

Browning Cynergy

While the basic action of the breech-loading shotgun is fairly simple, the construction of the weapon is what makes the difference between a mediocre gun and an excellent one. Modern materials and techniques, applied to a classic configuration like the over-under shotgun, can further refine its capabilities.

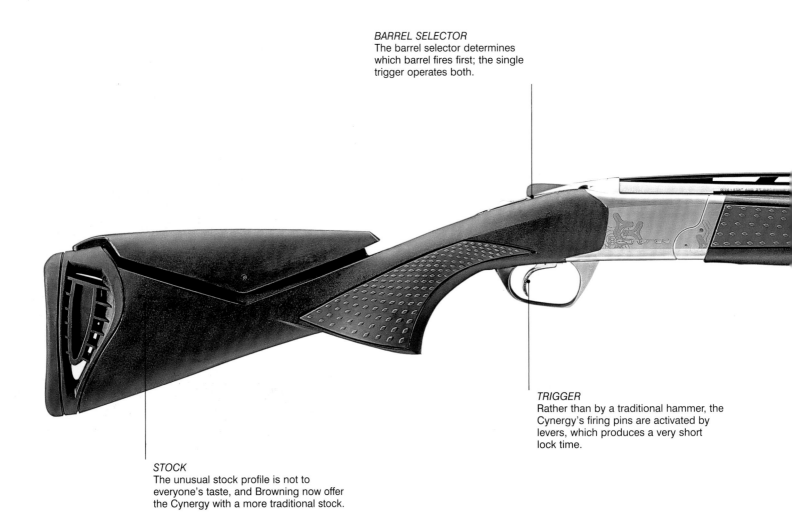

BARREL SELECTOR
The barrel selector determines which barrel fires first; the single trigger operates both.

TRIGGER
Rather than by a traditional hammer, the Cynergy's firing pins are activated by levers, which produces a very short lock time.

STOCK
The unusual stock profile is not to everyone's taste, and Browning now offer the Cynergy with a more traditional stock.

SPECIFICATIONS	
Country of Origin:	United States
Gauge/Calibre:	12-gauge
Operation:	Breech-loading
Weight:	3.4kg (7.48lb)
Barrel Length:	710mm (28in), 760mm (30in), 810mm (32in)
Ejector Type:	Automatic ejectors

The Browning Cynergy uses a ported barrel, venting off propellant gas to counteract muzzle flip. The barrel is also back-bored. This is a fairly modern technique, whereby the barrel is bored out to a larger diameter than is usual for the calibre in use. Back-boring reduces the proportion of shot that deforms on the way out of the barrel, creating more consistent shot spread and better performance at longer ranges.

Other innovations in this weapon include a new striker system which gives a crisp trigger pull and minimizes the delay between the shooter's decision to fire and the shot leaving the muzzle. The shorter this time, the more likely it is that the shot will go where the shooter expected it to. This is not a matter of increased accuracy as such; it is more about reducing the effects of human error on the shot.

BARRELS
The barrel interiors are chromed to resist corrosion and can handle steel shot.

MUZZLE
The choke tubes protrude slightly from the barrel. A colour-coding system allows easy identification of the choke that has been selected.

Pump-Action vs Semi-Automatic Sporting Shotguns

A pump-action or semi-automatic shotgun offers the capability for fast follow-up shots in the event of a miss or multiple targets. This is equally useful for clay pigeon shooting or when hunting.

Browning BPS

The BPS is a family of weapons, offered in several barrel lengths and various calibres. The 28-gauge version uses 69.85mm (2.75in) shells while the other gauges can use this or 76.2mm (3in) and even 88.9mm (3.5in) ammunition. A rifled version, firing heavy slugs, is also available.

SPECIFICATIONS	
Country of Origin:	United States
Gauge/Calibre:	12-, 20- or 28-gauge; .410
Operation:	Pump action
Weight:	Up to 3.7kg (8.3lb)
Barrel Length:	560mm (22in) to 710mm (28in), depending on model
Ejector Type:	Bottom ejector

Benelli Nova Pump

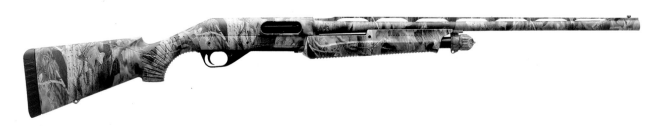

The Nova Pump uses modern polymer construction and has a magazine cutoff switch. This allows the chambered round to be ejected without chambering the next. It is available in 12-gauge or 20-gauge.

SPECIFICATIONS	
Country of Origin:	Italy
Gauge/Calibre:	12- or 20-gauge
Operation:	Pump action
Weight:	Up to 3.68kg (8.1lb)
Barrel Length:	610mm (24in), 660mm (26in), 710mm (28in)
Ejector Type:	Bottom ejector

Benelli Super Black Eagle II

The Black Eagle relies on force transmitted by the bolt to an inertia spring to reload the weapon. It uses advanced construction to reduce the recoil from heavy 88.9mm (3.5in) ammunition. It can also use shorter, lighter cartridges.

SPECIFICATIONS	
Country of Origin:	Italy
Gauge/Calibre:	12-gauge
Operation:	Inertia-operated
Weight:	3.3kg (7.3lb) 710mm/28in barrel
Barrel Length:	610mm (24in), 660mm (26in), 710mm (28in)
Ejector Type:	Side ejector

Benelli SuperSport

Another inertia-operated Benelli weapon, the SuperSport is intended for competition clay pigeon shooting rather than hunting. The barrel is ported to reduce muzzle flip, which is important when tracking multiple targets.

SPECIFICATIONS	
Country of Origin:	Italy
Gauge/Calibre:	12-gauge
Operation:	Inertia-operated
Weight:	3.3kg (7.3lb) 760mm/30in barrel
Barrel Length:	710mm (28in), 760mm (30in)
Ejector Type:	Side ejector

Franchi I-12

Where a pump-action user has to manually work the action, inevitably taking the weapon off target and requiring time to re-acquire it, an inertia-operated weapon such as the Franchi I-12 can continue to track while the weapon reloads itself.

SPECIFICATIONS	
Country of Origin:	Italy
Gauge/Calibre:	12-gauge
Operation:	Inertia-operated
Weight:	Up to 3.5kg (7.7lb)
Barrel Length:	610mm (24in), 660mm (26in), 710mm (28in)
Ejector Type:	Side ejector

Beretta SO9

Some weapons go beyond being merely hunting or sporting tools, and acquire a greater value almost as works of art. This applies mainly to shotguns, possibly as a result of a long tradition of hunting among the ruling classes. High-quality, decorated guns have been a prestigious gift item for centuries, and that tradition still exists today.

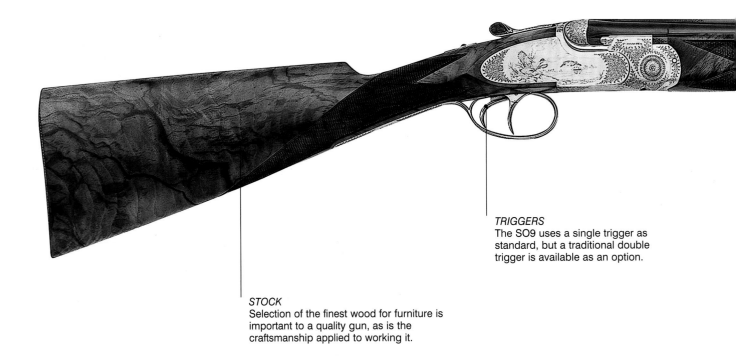

TRIGGERS
The SO9 uses a single trigger as standard, but a traditional double trigger is available as an option.

STOCK
Selection of the finest wood for furniture is important to a quality gun, as is the craftsmanship applied to working it.

SPECIFICATIONS

Country of Origin:	Italy
Gauge/Calibre:	12-, 20- or 28-gauge; .410
Operation:	Breech-loading
Weight:	3.25kg (7.16lb) 12-gauge
Barrel Length:	660mm (26in), 710mm (28in), 760mm (30in)
Ejector Type:	Automatic ejectors

Beretta's SO series are 'prestige' weapons in their own right, having been used by Olympic and World champion shooters, and would command a high price purely for their worth as excellent weapons. However, their aesthetics increase their value beyond that of a tool.

Manufactured from extremely high-quality materials and featuring sideplates hand-engraved by master craftsmen, these guns transcend the boundaries of what is necessary to create an effective shotgun for sport or hunting. This might be questionable were it not for the fact that these beautiful guns are still capable of doing their job, and doing it very well indeed.

SIDEPLATES
Sideplates on this shotgun are hand-engraved, adding decorative value to its worth as an excellent sporting gun.

BARRELS
The SO9's light barrels move its centre of gravity back somewhat, allowing a faster swing which is complemented by excellent balance.

Gas-Operated Semi-Automatic Shotguns

Gas-operated semi-automatic shotguns have to be wider than inertia-operated models, to accommodate the gas piston. Gas operation is, however, a robust and well-proven technology which has been popular with users over many years.

Browning Gold Hunter

The Browning Gold is a family of weapons which includes a rifled variant for use with heavy slugs and a small-calibre, reduced-dimensions model aimed at young users. Its gas system can be regulated to accommodate different kinds of ammunition.

SPECIFICATIONS	
Country of Origin:	United States
Gauge/Calibre:	12- or 20-gauge
Operation:	Gas-operated
Weight:	Up to 3.5kg (7.6lb)
Barrel Length:	660mm (26in), 710mm (28in)

Fabarm H35 Azur

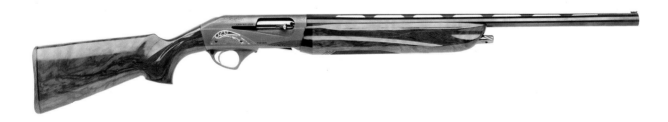

Although it is a general-purpose gun, the Azur has luminous sights intended to improve low-light shooting. This is important to wildfowl hunters, who often shoot at dawn or dusk. It is one of the lightest semi-automatic shotguns available.

SPECIFICATIONS	
Country of Origin:	Italy
Gauge/Calibre:	12-gauge
Operation:	Gas-operated
Weight:	Up to 3kg (6.6lb)
Barrel Length:	610mm (24in), 660mm (26in), 710mm (28in), 760mm (30in)

Fabarm Lion H38 Hunter

Using an advanced gas-operation system, Fabarm's Lion series does not require adjustment to handle different loads, and cycles somewhat faster than a typical gas-operated shotgun. The amount of felt recoil is much the same whatever ammunition is being used.

SPECIFICATIONS	
Country of Origin:	Italy
Gauge/Calibre:	12-gauge
Operation:	Gas-operated
Weight:	2.8kg (6.2lb), 3.05kg (6.7lb)
Barrel Length:	610mm (24in), 660mm (26in), 710mm (28in), 760mm (30in)

Beretta AL391 Teknys

An advanced gas-operated semi-automatic, the Teknys is capable of handling 88.9mm/3.5in 3.5in Magnum loads. The semi-automatic mechanism helps absorb some of the weapon's recoil, and a recoil-reduction unit (essentially a mass on a spring) can be fitted internally if desired.

SPECIFICATIONS	
Country of Origin:	Italy
Gauge/Calibre:	12- or 20-gauge
Operation:	Gas-operated
Weight:	3kg (6.6lb)
Barrel Length:	610mm (24in), 660mm (26in), 710mm (28in), 760mm (30in) 12-gauge

Beretta AL391 Urika

The Urika is essentially a lightweight version of the Teknys, with a recoil reducer fitted as standard. It is intended as a general-purpose weapon, but cannot chamber 88.9mm (3.5in) cartridges.

SPECIFICATIONS	
Country of Origin:	Italy
Gauge/Calibre:	12- or 20-gauge
Operation:	Gas-operated
Weight:	Up to 3.3kg (7.28lb)
Barrel Length:	560mm (22in), 610mm (24in), 660mm (26in), 710mm (28in), 760mm (30in)

BRNO 800 Series

Double-barrelled weapons which use one smoothbore (shotgun) barrel and one rifled barrel are uncommon compared with true rifles and shotguns, but they are useful to rough hunters who do not know what their next target will be. Effectively having both a loaded rifle and a shotgun in hand at all times grants great versatility to a hunter.

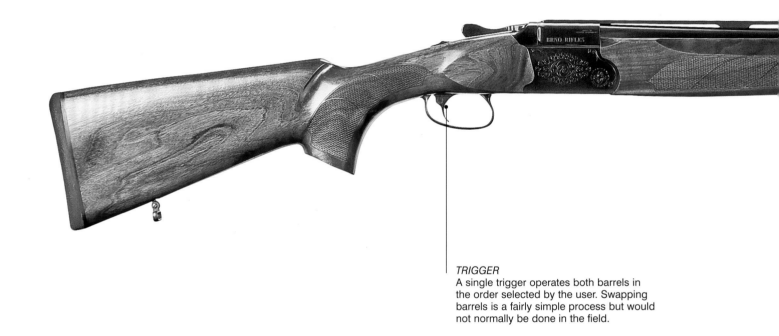

TRIGGER
A single trigger operates both barrels in the order selected by the user. Swapping barrels is a fairly simple process but would not normally be done in the field.

SPECIFICATIONS	
Country of Origin:	Czech Republic
Gauge/Calibre:	12-gauge and/or 9.3mm (.366in), 8mm (.314in) JRS, 7.62mm (.3in) .308 Winchester or .30-06, 7mm (.275in) R
Operation:	Breech-loading
Weight:	3.65kg (8lb)
Barrel Length:	600mm (24in)
Ejector Type:	Automatic ejectors

The BRNO 800 takes the combination concept further. By selecting different barrels, it can be configured as a double-barrelled rifle or shotgun, or a combination rifle/shotgun. The shotgun barrels use a fixed choke in any given barrel, but different choke configurations can be ordered when the barrel is purchased.

Thus the BRNO 800 can be set up for anything from competitive clay pigeon shooting to rough hunting. It is, however, rather heavy, and the use of a sling is probably necessary during an extended hunt.

BARRELS
It is not really feasible to carry a huge array of guns on a shoot. A combination rifle/shotgun allows the user to engage a range of targets without swapping weapons.

SELECTOR
The barrel selector allows the user to choose between the available loads in the short time a target may be visible.

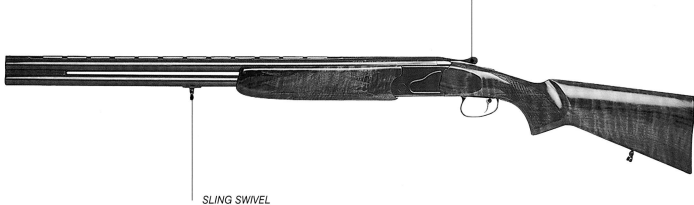

SLING SWIVEL
Sling swivels are a sign of a field, rather than competition, gun. Carrying a heavy gun all day without a sling is unnecessarily tiring.

Bolt-Action Sporting Rifles

While the bolt-action rifle was supplanted decades ago for military use, it remains a favourite of sports shooters and hunters. Firearms regulations make it much easier to obtain a bolt-action weapon than a semi-automatic rifle.

CZ 527 Varmint Kevlar

The term 'varmint gun' refers to a weapon intended for hunting small nuisance animals and birds. The CZ 527 family includes the Varmint Kevlar, a small-calibre weapon with a Kevlar composite stock.

SPECIFICATIONS	
Country of Origin:	Czech Republic
Calibre:	5.2mm (.204in) .204 Ruger, 5.66mm (.223in) .223 Rem
Operation:	Bolt action
Weight:	Up to 3.4kg (7.5lb)
Barrel Length:	610mm (24in)
Mechanism:	Magazine-fed
Sights:	Provision for scope

Dakota Model 76

Available in calibres ranging from 5.6mm (.22in) all the way up to heavy rounds such as 10.36mm/.416in .416 Remington Magnum, the Model 76 is intended to appeal to hunters of all kinds of game.

SPECIFICATIONS	
Country of Origin:	United States
Calibre:	More than 20 calibres from 5.6mm (.22in) .22-250 to 10.36mm (.416in) .416 Rem
Operation:	Bolt action
Weight:	3.4kg (7.5lb) average
Barrel Length:	533–584mm (21–23in)
Mechanism:	Magazine-fed
Sights:	Provision for scope

Accuracy International Varmint

Varmint guns normally use a small calibre, but the Accuracy International Varmint is available in 7.8mm (.308in) as well as the more usual 5.66mm (.223in) calibre. It also uses an eight-round magazine, larger than is typical for weapons of this type.

SPECIFICATIONS	
Country of Origin:	United Kingdom
Calibre:	5.66mm (.223in) to 7.8mm (.308in)
Operation:	Bolt action
Weight:	Up to 6kg (13.2lb)
Barrel Length:	660mm (26in)
Mechanism:	Magazine-fed
Sights:	Provision for scope

Mannlicher Pro Hunter

Chambered for a range of calibres, the Pro Hunter is constructed from rugged synthetic materials. Warping of the furniture due to environmental conditions can affect the accuracy of any rifle; synthetics are less prone to this than traditional wood.

SPECIFICATIONS	
Country of Origin:	Austria
Calibre:	14 calibres from 5.6mm (.22in) .222 Rem to 7.62mm (.3in) .300 Win Mag
Operation:	Bolt action
Weight:	Up to 3.7kg (8.2lb)
Barrel Length:	600mm (23.6in), 650mm (25.6in)
Mechanism:	Magazine-fed
Sights:	Provision for scope

Walther KK300

A precision sporting tool, the KK300 is available with an aluminium stock or one of (slightly) more traditional-looking beech. Both versions are adjustable in many dimensions to create the perfect target weapon for any given shooter.

SPECIFICATIONS	
Country of Origin:	Germany
Calibre:	5.6mm (.22in) .22 LR
Operation:	Bolt action
Weight:	5.9kg (13lb)
Barrel Length:	650mm (25.5in)
Mechanism:	Single shot
Sights:	Aperture rear site and front post

Larger-Calibre Rifles

Larger calibres are generally used to shoot at longer ranges or against large animals. A one-shot kill is important in long-range hunting, as a wounded animal may run a significant distance and be lost, suffering needlessly before dying.

Mauser 98

The venerable Mauser 98 is available chambered for a vast range of ammunition from 5.6mm (.22in) to large big-game hunting calibres. Despite over a century in service it remains an excellent hunting or target rifle.

SPECIFICATIONS	
Country of Origin:	Germany
Calibre:	Multiple calibres from 5.6mm (.22in) .22-250 Rem to 9.3mm (.366in)
Operation:	Bolt action
Weight:	3.5kg (7.75lb)
Barrel Length:	600mm (23.6in)
Mechanism:	Magazine-fed
Sights:	Drilled for scope mounting

Browning Eurobolt

Named for the 'European' styling of its stock, the Eurobolt is intended for deer hunting or similar applications. The 7.62mm/.3in (.30-06) version can hold four rounds in the magazine (plus one in the chamber); the 6.2mm/.243in variant holds three plus one.

SPECIFICATIONS	
Country of Origin:	United States
Calibre:	Several calibres, including 6.2mm (.243in) .243 WSSM, 6.85mm (.27in) .270 WSM, 7.62mm (.3in) .300 WSM and .30-06
Operation:	Bolt action
Weight:	c.3kg (6.6lb)
Barrel Length:	560mm (22in)
Mechanism:	Magazine-fed
Sights:	Drilled for scope mounting

Henry Big Boy

Lever-action rifles have a distinctive 'Old West' look about them that appeals to many shooters, but the Big Boy is also a serious short-range hunting weapon. It is chambered for a range of powerful pistol cartridges.

SPECIFICATIONS	
Country of Origin:	United States
Calibre:	9.1mm (.357in) .357 Magnum, 11.2mm (.44in) .44 Magnum, 11.4mm (.45in) .45 Colt
Operation:	Lever action
Weight:	3.9kg (8.68lb)
Barrel Length:	510mm (20in)
Mechanism:	Magazine-fed
Sights:	Open

Robar Precision Hunter

A custom-built weapon available in almost any calibre, the Precision Hunter can be fitted with a muzzle brake to allow it to handle extremely large cartridges such as 12.7mm/.5in (.50 BMG).

SPECIFICATIONS	
Country of Origin:	United States
Calibre:	To order
Operation:	Bolt action
Weight:	Dependent upon order
Barrel Length:	Dependent upon order
Mechanism:	Single shot
Sights:	Provision for scope

Weatherby Mk V

Chambered for a variety of Magnum cartridges, the Mk V is based on an action proven in half a century of use. Many variants are available, including a stockless two-handed pistol which is usually chambered for lighter rounds.

SPECIFICATIONS	
Country of Origin:	United States
Calibre:	Eight Magnum calibres from 6.5mm (.257in) .257 Wby Mag to 11.7mm (.46in) .460 Wby Mag
Operation:	Bolt action
Weight:	3.8–4.5kg (8.5–10lb)
Barrel Length:	660mm (26in), 710mm (28in)
Mechanism:	Magazine-fed
Sights:	Provision for scope

Small-Calibre Rifles

Smaller calibres are popular with target shooters and hunters of smaller game. A 5.66mm (.223) round can take down a small deer, but anything larger requires a more potent round, and a heavier gun to fire it.

Remington XR-100 Rangemaster

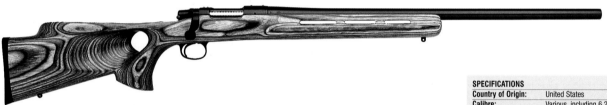

Remington's XR-100 Rangemaster is intended for target shooting or hunting small, fast game. The mechanism is based on that of Remington's XP-100 target pistol rather than being a traditional rifle action.

SPECIFICATIONS	
Country of Origin:	United States
Calibre:	Various, including 6.2mm (.243in) .243 Win, 6.85mm (.27in) .270 Win, 7mm (.275in) Rem Mag, 9.5mm (.375in) .375 H&H Mag, 11.6mm (.458in) .458 Win Mag
Operation:	Bolt action
Weight:	3.18kg (7lb) average
Barrel Length:	560mm (22in), 610mm (24in), 660mm (26in)
Mechanism:	Magazine-fed
Sights:	Receiver drilled and tapped for scope mounts

Armscor M1700

The Armscor M1700 is a conventional bolt-action rifle firing 4.5mm/.17in .17 Hornady Magnum Rimfire cartridges. It is suitable for target shooting or dealing with small pests out to a range of 100m (328ft) or more.

SPECIFICATIONS	
Country of Origin:	South Africa
Calibre:	4.5mm (.17in) .17 HMR
Operation:	Bolt action
Weight:	2.7kg (6lb)
Barrel Length:	560mm (22in)
Mechanism:	Magazine-fed
Sights:	Adjustable rear and front fibre optic

Sako Quad

The Sako Quad is named for the fact that it can use four of the most popular small-bore Rimfire cartridges, all of which have the same case head diameter. Calibre can thus be altered by swapping the quick-change barrel.

SPECIFICATIONS	
Country of Origin:	Finland
Calibre:	4.5mm (.17in) .17 HMR or .17 Mach 2; 5.6mm (.22in) .22 LR or .22 WMR
Operation:	Bolt action
Weight:	2.6kg (5.75lb)
Barrel Length:	560mm (22in)
Mechanism:	Magazine-fed
Sights:	Provision for scope

Browning BL-22

A short lever-action weapon firing very light rounds, the BL-22 is suitable for young shooters, or as a light hunting weapon. Its magazine can hold 15–22 rounds, depending on the ammunition it is chambered for.

SPECIFICATIONS	
Country of Origin:	United States
Calibre:	5.6mm (.22in) .22 S, .22 L, .22 LR
Operation:	Lever action
Weight:	Up to 2.27kg (5lb)
Barrel Length:	510mm (20in)
Mechanism:	Magazine-fed
Sights:	Folding leaf rear, bead front

Sauer S90

Available in various calibres from 6.35mm/.25in (.25-06) up to 9.5mm/.375in (.375 H&H Magnum), the S90 is designed around a minimal-rotation bolt, better enabling the user to keep his weapon on target.

SPECIFICATIONS	
Country of Origin:	Germany
Calibre:	17 calibres from 6.35mm (.25in) .25-06 Rem to 9.5mm (.375in) .375 H&H Mag
Operation:	Bolt action
Weight:	Up to 3.9kg (8.85lb)
Barrel Length:	600mm (23.5in), 650mm (26in)
Mechanism:	Magazine-fed
Sights:	Adjustable rear and front scope mounting

Military Influences

Many match rifles or top-end hunting guns are adapted to – or from – military sniping rifles. Other military weapons may remain in use, converted to sporting or 'fun' guns, long after they cease to serve with the armed forces.

Tikka T3 Hunter

The Tikka T3 is available in many variants including a military sniper rifle, and chambered for various calibres. It has an optional single set trigger, whereby the trigger is pushed forward to set it for a very light pull.

SPECIFICATIONS	
Country of Origin:	Finland
Calibre:	19 different calibres from 5.6mm (.22in) .222 Rem to 8.58mm (.338in) .338 Win Mag
Operation:	Bolt action
Weight:	Up to 3.2kg (7lb)
Barrel Length:	520mm (20.5in), 620mm (24.4in)
Mechanism:	Magazine-fed
Sights:	Adjustable, open

CZ 511

A version of the CZ 511 is available with a threaded muzzle (for a suppressor) and is capable of using very quiet subsonic ammunition. This is useful for hunting small game without frightening off additional targets.

SPECIFICATIONS	
Country of Origin:	Czech Republic
Calibre:	5.6mm (.22in) .22 LR
Operation:	Blowback
Weight:	2.6kg (5.9lb)
Barrel Length:	530mm (21in)
Mechanism:	Magazine-fed
Sights:	Adjustable, open

Benelli R1

Benelli's R1 rifle uses a self-regulating gas-operation system which was proven in the M1014 semi-automatic shotgun. This helps reduce the recoil from powerful loads such as the 8.58mm/.338in .338 Winchester Magnum.

SPECIFICATIONS	
Country of Origin:	Italy
Calibre:	6.85mm (.27in) .270 WSM; 7.62mm (.3in) .30-06 Springfield, .300 WSM, .300 Win Mag; 7.8mm (.308in) .308 Win
Operation:	Gas-operated
Weight:	Up to 3.3kg (7.3lb)
Barrel Length:	510mm (20in), 560mm (22in), 610mm (24in)
Mechanism:	Magazine fed
Sights:	Receiver drilled and tapped for scope mount

Colt Match Target HBAR

The military pedigree of the HBAR (Heavy Barrel AR-15) is obvious at a glance, but it is a sporting gun intended for competition shooting. An M4 version, with a shorter barrel and military-style stock, is also available.

SPECIFICATIONS	
Country of Origin:	United States
Gauge/Calibre:	5.66mm (.223in) .223 Rem
Operation:	Gas-operated
Weight:	3.6kg (8lb)
Barrel Length:	510mm (20in)
Mechanism:	Magazine-fed
Sights:	Flat receiver for scope mount

Remington M750

The M750 is available in several large and powerful calibres. Its gas-operated semi-automatic action helps absorb recoil whilst reloading the weapon, allowing rapid accurate shooting when necessary.

SPECIFICATIONS	
Country of Origin:	United States
Calibre:	6.2mm (.243in) .243 Win, 6.85mm (.27in) .270 Win, 7.62mm (.3in) .30-06 Springfield (and carbine), 7.8mm (.308in) .308 Win (and carbine), 9mm (.35in) .35 Whelen (and carbine)
Operation:	Gas-operated
Weight:	Up to 3.4kg (7.5lb)
Barrel Length:	560mm (22in)
Mechanism:	Magazine-fed
Sights:	Receiver drilled and tapped for scope mount

Browning BAR

Traditionally, hunters have tended to use bolt-action rifles, but there is no reason why a semi-automatic cannot be an effective hunting weapon. While a semi-automatic action does involve internal movement, which can possibly disturb the aim point while the round is travelling down the barrel, working the action of a bolt-action weapon inevitably causes the weapon to move and imposes a delay in acquiring a new target or re-engaging the same one.

RECEIVER
The BAR is an accurate rifle, made more so by advanced recoil-compensation technology which reduces the amount the aim point is disturbed by as the round travels down the barrel.

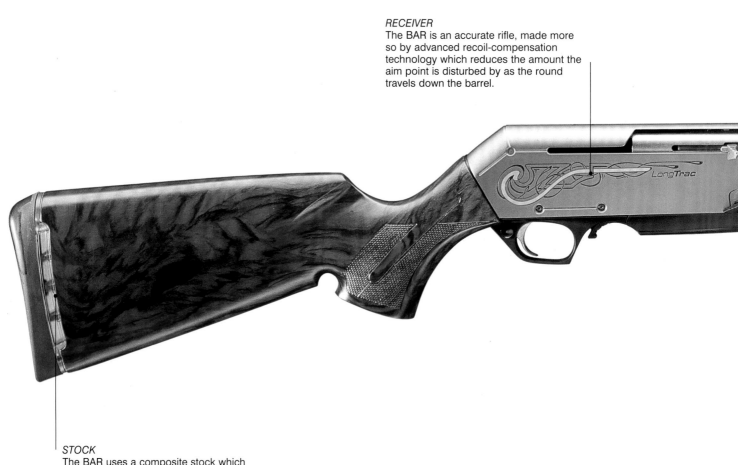

STOCK
The BAR uses a composite stock which is highly resistant to warping caused by damp conditions or changes in temperature.

SPECIFICATIONS	
Country of Origin:	United States
Calibre:	6.85mm (.27in) .270 Win, 7mm (.275in) Rem Mag, 7.62mm (.3in) .30-06 Springfield, 7.62mm (.3in) .300 Win Mag
Operation:	Gas-operated
Weight:	Up to 3.4kg (7.5lb)
Barrel Length:	560mm (22in), 610mm (24in)
Mechanism:	Magazine-fed
Sights:	Receiver drilled and tapped for scope

The question of whether bolt or semi-automatic operation is better is largely a matter of personal preference, but unquestionably there are times when the ability to take a rapid second shot can be useful. This can be important in the event of a miss or a non-fatal wound when hunting dangerous game such as boar.

Well-respected in the hunting community, the BAR is not related to the M1918 Browning Automatic Rifle, even though it shares a name. It is not a military conversion but was developed specifically for hunting large game such as deer or moose. It is available with a long or short action, and the Safari version uses a recoil control system called BOSS (Ballistic Optimized Shooting System) consisting of a muzzle brake and weights to help reduce felt recoil.

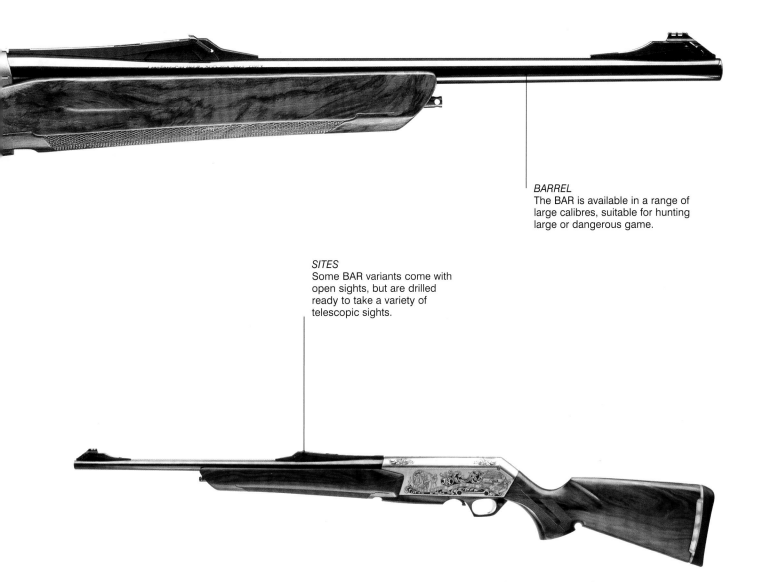

BARREL
The BAR is available in a range of large calibres, suitable for hunting large or dangerous game.

SITES
Some BAR variants come with open sights, but are drilled ready to take a variety of telescopic sights.

Glossary

Bolt The part of a firearm which usually contains the firing pin or striker and which closes the breech ready for firing.

Blowback Operating system in which the bolt is not locked to the breech, thus it is consequently pushed back by breech pressure on firing and cycles the gun.

Breech The rear of the gun barrel.

Breech-block Another method of closing the breech which generally involves a substantial rectangular block rather than a cylindrical bolt.

Bullpup Term for when the receiver of a gun is actually set in the butt behind the trigger group, thus allowing for a full length barrel.

Carbine A shortened rifle for specific assault roles.

Chamber The section at the end of the barrel which receives and seats the cartridge ready for firing.

Closed bolt A mechanical system in which the bolt is closed up to the cartridge before the trigger is pulled. This allows greater stability through reducing the forward motion of parts on firing.

Compensator A muzzle attachment which controls the direction of gas expanding from the weapon and thus helps to resist muzzle climb or swing during automatic fire.

Delayed blowback A delay mechanically imposed on a blowback system to allow pressures in the breech to drop to safe levels before breech opening.

Double action Relates to pistols which can be fired both by cocking the hammer and then pulling the trigger, and by a single long pull on the trigger which performs both cocking and firing actions.

Flechette An bolt-like projectile which is smaller than the gun's calibre and requires a sabot to fit it to the barrel. Flechette rounds achieve very high velocities.

Gas operation Operating system in which a gun is cycled by gas being bled off from the barrel and used against a piston or the bolt to drive the bolt backwards and cycle the gun for the next round.

GPMG Abbreviation for General Purpose Machine Gun. A versatile light machine gun intended to perform a range of different roles.

LMG Abbreviation for Light Machine Gun.

Locking Describes the various methods by which the bolt or breech block is locked behind the chamber ready for firing.

Long recoil A method of recoil operation in which the barrel and bolt recoil for a length greater than that of the entire cartridge, during which extraction and loading are performed.

Muzzle brake A muzzle attachment which diverts muzzle blast sideways and thus reduces overall recoil.

Open bolt A mechanical system in which the bolt is kept at a distance from the cartridge before the trigger is pulled. This allows for better cooling of the weapon between shots.

PDW Abbreviation for Personal Defence Weapon. A compact firearm, smaller than a regular assault rifle but more powerful than a pistol, intended as a defensive weapon for personnel whose duties do not normally include small arms combat.

Receiver The body of the weapon which contains the gun's main operating parts.

Recoil The rearward force generated by the explosive power of a projectile being fired.

Recoil operated Operating system in which the gun is cycled by the recoil-propelled force of both barrel and bolt when the weapon is fired. Both components recoil together for a certain distance before the barrel stops and the bolt continues backwards to perform reloading and rechambering.

SAW Abbreviation for Squad Automatic Weapon.

Self-loading Operating system in which one pull of the trigger allows the gun to fires and reload in a single action.

Shaped charge An anti-armour charge designed to concentrate the effect of an explosive warhead by focusing a cone of superheated gas on a critical point on the target.

Short recoil A compressed version of recoil operation in which the barrel and bolt move back less than the length of the cartridge before the bolt detaches and continues backwards to perform reloading and rechambering.

Index

Picture Credits

Accuracy International: 427t; **Amber Books:** 11, 22/23, 27t, 56t, 57t&b, 63c&b, 64/65, 66t, 82t, 141c, 143, 154/155, 164t, 172t, 173c, 187b, 207t, 214b, 233b, 251c, 252t, 261, 277c&b, 283c&b, 285b, 295c, 296b, 297b, 299b, 312c, 323c, 331t, 345c&b, 354t, 359c, 364t, 365b, 366b, 367b, 370-371 all, 372b, 372t&c, 377c&b, 378b, 378c, 380b, 381b, 383b, 385c&b, 394t, 395b; **AMT Hardball:** 344b (Creative Commons Licence); **Antique Military Rifles:** 20t (Creative Commons Licence); **Armscor:** 392b, 393t, 430b; **Art-Tech/MARS:** 6, 70, 74/75, 128/129, 212/213; **Atirador:** 221c (Creative Commons Licence); **Baikal:** 411t; **Benelli:** 418b, 419t&c, 433t; **Beretta:** 414b, 415t, 420/421, 423c&b; **Bridgeman Art Library:** 28 (Peter Newark); **BRNO:** 424/425; **Browning:** 406 both, 416/417, 418t, 422t, 428b, 431c, 434/435, 435; **Teri Bryant:** 88b, 111t, 138b; **Caracal:** 343b; **China-defense.com:** 327b; **Cody Images:** 69c, 240/241; **Colt:** 215c, 248t, 433c; **Corbis:** 8/9 (Bettmann); **CZ:** 426t, 432b; **Dakota:** 426b;**Keith Doyon/militaryrifles.com:** 57c; **Dreamstime:** 21c (McCool), 160t (Freakazoit), 197c (McCool); **Mary Evans Picture Library:** 25c; **Fabarm:** 407t, 412/413, 422b, 423t; **Fabrykabroni:** 360t; **Fair:** 410 both; **Falco:** 414t; **Fausti:** 407b; **Franchi:** 419b;

GMK.co.uk: 369 both; **Martin Godio:** 62t; **Heckler & Koch:** 287b, 347c, 359t, 361t, 401b, 403b; **Henry:** 429t; **Imbel:** 344t; **Knightarmco.com:** 376b; **Lanber:** 411b; **LEI:** 379b; **Library of Congress:** 30/31, 150/151; **Littlegun.be:** 50t; **Marocchi:** 408/409; Mauser: 428t; **McMillan:** 381c; **Metal Storm:** 374/375; Miroku: 407c; **Mossberg:** 393c&b; **Para USA:** 432t; **Pgmprecision.com:** 381t; **Photos.com:** 24t, 41t, 46, 54t, 55t, 59t, 76t, 86, 109b, 175, 254t, 311, 313t; **Max Popenker/world.guns.ru:** 83c, 94b, 123t, 130t, 153t, 166t, 177b, 215t, 220t, 221b, 253c, 263b, 264t, 265b, 267t&b, 278b, 281, 286/287, 313b; **Rarewinchesters.com:** 62b; **Recoilless Technologies International:** 382b, 383t&c; **Remington:** 430t, 433b; Robar: 429c; Sako: 431t; **Salvinelli:** 415c; **Shotgunlee:** 365c (Creative Commons Licence); **SIG-Sauer:** 354b, 355c, 431b; **Steyr Mannlicher:** 307b, 316t, 357 all, 361c, 427c; **ST Kinetics:** 359b, 401c; **Sturm, Ruger:** 360b, 411c; **Taurus:** 343c, 349t&b, 350-353 all; **Tikka:** 432t; **U.S. Department of Defense:** 7, 340/341, 372t; **Walther:** 427b; **Weaponspecialists.com:** 233c; **Weatherby:** 415b, 429b; **Winchester:** 392t, 404/405; **Steve Z:** 253b (Creative Commons Licence)

All other illustrations **Art-Tech Ltd**.